IMPORTANT BIRDS IN ZAMBIA

Priority sites for conservation

Peter Leonard

Sponsored by the WildiZe Foundation®

with additional support from The Norwegian Ornithological Society (NOF)
through a grant from the Norwegian Agency for Development Cooperation
(NORAD).

Published by:
The Zambian Ornithological Society
P.O. Box 33944, Lusaka, Zambia
zos@zamnet.zm

ISBN 9982-811-01-0

Printed in Singapore under the supervision of MRM Graphics Ltd

Cover photo: Chaplin's Barbet *Lybius chaplini* by Claire Spottiswoode

Photographs by: Neil Baker, Rich Beilfuss, Woody Cotterill, Tim Dodman, Edmund Farmer, Johann Grobbelaar, Lizet Grobbelaar, Mike Harrison mike.harrison@harrisonclear.co.uk, Andrea Leonard, Peter Leonard, Chris McIntyre/Sunvil Africa www.sunvil.co.uk, Bob Medland, Wouter Peters, Peter Ryan, Claire Spottiswoode, Warwick Tarboton, Heather Tyrrell/Sunvil Africa, Elsabe van der Westhuizen, Louise Warburton

Illustrations by Peter Leonard

Maps by Kenna Kelly

The WildiZe Foundation® is dedicated to the sustainable conservation and protection of our Earth's diminishing wildlife, habitats, and cultures. Our philosophy is grounded in the belief that humanity be in balance as one with, and not separate from, nature. Addressing human needs and linking them with the needs of wildlife and the wilds is critical to the long-term conservation of our Earth's diversity and resources. Toward this goal, WildiZe Foundation® programs are focused toward on-the-ground grass-roots projects supporting local communities in finding joint solutions to complex problems.

www.wildize.org

Contents

Foreword vii

1. Summary & overview..1

2. Acknowledgements 4

3. Introduction...5
   3.1 About Zambia...5
       Geography...5
       Biomes, habitats and bird communities....................5
       Population and economics 11
   3.2 Conservation infrastructure..............................15
       Institutional structures.................................15
       Conservation legislation.................................17
       Protected area systems 18
       International conventions and agreements.................18
   3.3 Conservation issues 21
   3.4 The IBA programme..23
       What is the IBA programme?...............................23
       Biological rationale.....................................23
       Categories and criteria 24
       Zambia's ornithological Importance.......................27
       Selection of sites 30
       The Zambian IBA network - coverage and gaps..............30
   3.5 The next steps 33
       What needs to be done....................................33
       Prioritising action.....................................33
       Limitations of this book 34

4. Site Accounts 36
   4.1 Presentation of data 36
   4.2 Site accounts...39

Contents

1 Hillwood 40

2 Source of the Zambezi 42

3 Chitunta Plain..45

4 Jimbe Drainage 47

5 West Lunga NP & Lukwakwa GMA 49

6 Minyanya Plain 53

7 Mbulo Forest..56

8 Liuwa Plain NP..57

9 Barotse Floodplains 62

10 Sioma Ngwezi NP..65

11 Simungoma 68

12 Machile 70

13 Mosi-Oa-Tunya NP & Batoka Gorge 74

14 Kafue NP...78

15 Kafue Flats (inc. Lochinvar & Blue Lagoon NPs)........83

16 Nkanga River Conservation Area..................................90

17 Mutulanganga 93

18 Lower Zambezi NP...96

19 Chisamba..100

20 Lukanga Swamp...103

21 Imanda..107

22 Chimfunshi Wildlife Orphanage....................................109

23 North Swaka...112

24 Wonder Gorge 115

25 Kasanka NP...118

26 Lavushi Manda NP 122

27 Mutinondo Wilderness..124

28 Bangweulu Swamps (inc. Isangano NP) 127

29 North Luangwa NP 132

30 Shiwa Ng'andu...136

31 Luapula Mouth...140

32 Lusenga Plain NP...143

33 Kalungwishi 145

34 Mweru Wantipa NP 148

35 Sumbu NP & Tondwa GMA 152

36 Saise River 154

37 Uningi Pans 157

38 Nyika NP...159

39 Mafinga Mountains 163

40 South Luangwa NP 165
41 Lukususi NP...171
42 Nyanje Hills 173

5. References..177

6. Appendices...183
1 IBA checklists...183
2 Biome-restricted species 212
3 Globally important congregations - qualifying sites 214
4 Taxonomic notes..215

7. Useful Information....................................217
Travel tips 217
The Zambian Ornithological Society...............................218
BirdLife International 218

Foreword

When you consider some of the problems that face Africa today, such as poverty, debt, disease and civil conflict, you may wonder what is so important about conserving birds.

In truth, there is no point in conserving birds alone. However, they represent a component in every ecosystem upon which we, as humans, ultimately depend. When we look after these ecosystems, we are looking after ourselves.

Birds have simply been used as indicator species in the conservation of IBAs. Not only are birds beautiful, engaging and popular, they are also well-known, well-studied and widespread. Compared with many other types of animals and plants, more is known about Zambian birds. This makes them an ideal indicator for the start of habitat conservation. Furthermore, if an area is important for bird conservation it is almost certainly important for conservation in general.

A huge trade-off exists between conservation and development initiatives to combat the desperate levels of poverty, inequality and injustice throughout Africa. Wise use of scarce and dwindling resources is imperative. This book aims to support decision-makers at all levels of society. It is a tool designed for practical use. It presents the first ever attempt to identify the country's most important sites for sustainable conservation, in every region and in every biome, using internationally agreed, objective criteria and the most up-to-date information. It also makes suggestions for what should happen next.

As such, this book is a milestone in Zambian conservation. However, a milestone does not mark the end of a journey, simply a point along the way and there is still a long journey ahead.

That this book is the result of a partnership between the Zambian Ornithological Society and BirdLife International highlights the important role played by non-governmental organisations in conservation. The enormous task of data-collection has long been the realm of the dedicated amateur and now ZOS has taken the next steps towards raising awareness and suggesting action. With the support of a respected and influential organisation such as BirdLife International and in the context of the global IBA Programme, Zambia now has the opportunity to make enormous progress in its conservation strategy.

Zambia is very fortunate to have large tracts of wilderness still intact and to support tremendous biodiversity. This book outlines a set of clear goals to ensure that this remains so.

I strongly recommend this book to those working in all fields of conservation.

Hapenga M. Kabeta
Director General - Zambia Wildlife Authority

1. Summary & overview

This book is a contribution to identifying Zambia's conservation priorities.

Although protected areas may be found in countries throughout the world, few attempts have ever been made to assess, on a global scale, whether or not these areas are sufficient to conserve global biodiversity. In many cases, protected areas have been identified for reasons other than biodiversity conservation (e.g. large mammal populations, scenic beauty, protection of watersheds or timber resources). The aim of BirdLife International's Important Bird Areas (IBA) Programme is to identify and protect a global network of sites that are critical for the long-term survival of all bird species and their habitats.

But why birds? In short, birds are well-known, well-studied, widespread and popular. Birds are prone to endemism and they are excellent indicators of biodiversity in general. If an area holds rare or endemic birds or a particularly diverse range of birds, it is likely to hold a comparable array of other organisms. So, birds provide the scientific baseline data but the underlying aim is the conservation of all living things.

Of course, birds are not faultless surrogates for biodiversity in general. Some sites with, for example, rare plants, endemic amphibians or unusual bacteria will not be identified by the process. (The need to collect information on a range of little-known organisms remains pressing.) Conversely, a few sites may be important only for their rare birds, and not for other wildlife. However, no other group of organisms lends itself to the process in the same way and the identification and protection of sites that are important for birds is undoubtedly a giant step in the right direction for biodiversity conservation.

Throughout the world, IBAs have been selected using 4 categories of internationally agreed, objective ornithological criteria:
- Globally threatened species (22 species in Zambia)
- Restricted-range species (8 species in Zambia)
- Biome-restricted Assemblages (138 species in Zambia)
- Globally important congregations (12 qualifying sites in Zambia)

The initial phase of the project in Zambia identified 31 IBAs (Leonard 2001b). After much revision, the current inventory now comprises 42 IBAs. Map 1 shows their locations in Zambia. Table 1 lists the IBAs and indicates the criteria used to select them, the area of each site and its current protected status. Together, the 42 IBAs cover approximately 14% of Zambia's total land surface. At present, about 82% of the area covered by IBAs receives some form of protection, although when this takes the form of Game Management Areas or forest reserves, enforced protection may be minimal.

Detailed information on each site (location, area, altitude, status, description, birds, other flora and fauna, conservation issues) is given in the site accounts that form the bulk of this book (section 4). In addition, full bird checklists for each IBA are given in Appendix 1.

Some important findings include:
- several areas are not adequately covered by the current protected area network: northern Mwinilunga District (IBAs 1-4), the deciduous thickets of the Zambezi Valley (IBA 17) and the papyrus swamps of the Lower Luapula River (IBA 31)
- IBA 15 Kafue Flats is an extremely important area which faces a large number of severe threats
- the most important sections of the Bangweulu Swamps (IBA 28) would benefit greatly from better protection
- plateau habitats in northern Zambia are poorly represented in the current protected area network, so those that do already exist are extremely valuable, despite a paucity of large mammals (IBAs 5, 25, 26, 32, 41) whilst others would benefit greatly from better protection (IBAs 23, 33)

Many sites require more fieldwork and the programme as a whole requires constant evaluation and revision if it is to succeed.

This book is aimed at conservationists, governmental and non-governmental agencies, policy-makers, donors, land-owners and managers, researchers, consultants, planners, ornithologists and bird-watchers. It is designed as a tool and a basic database to help the IBA programme as it moves onto the next crucial phase.

MAP 1: Important Bird Areas

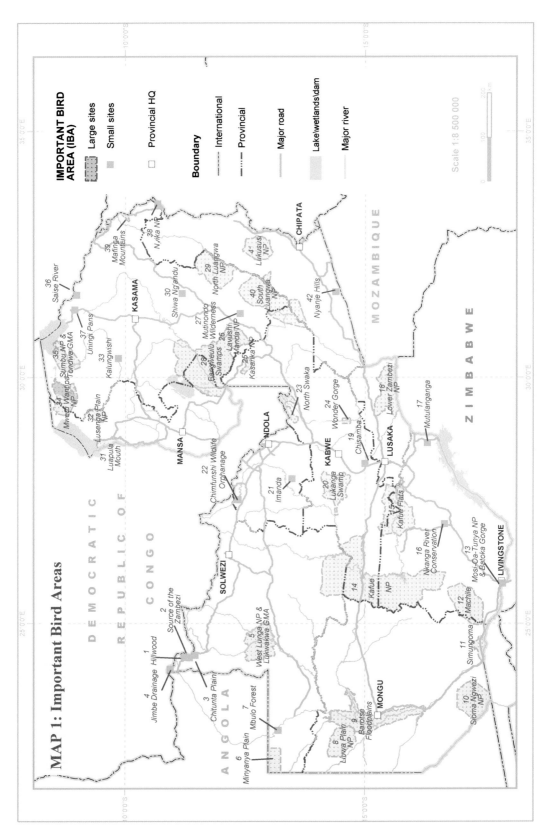

Table 1: IBAs in Zambia - selection criteria, area and protected status.

Important Bird Area		Criteria used to select site				IBA area	Protected Status				
site no.	site name	GT	RR	BR	GIC	hectares	NP	GMA	N/LF	PO	U
1	Hillwood	●		●		3200				●	
2	Source of the Zambezi			●		250		●			
3	Chitunta Plain	●		●		10000					●
4	Jimbe Drainage	●		●		15600			●		●
5	West Lunga NP & Lukwakwa GMA	●		●		445000	●	●			
6	Minyanya Plain	●		●		50000					●
7	Mbulo Forest	●		●		500					●
8	Liuwa Plain NP	●		●	●	366000	●				
9	Barotse Floodplains	●		●		730000		●			●
10	Sioma Ngwezi NP	●		●		527600	●				
11	Simungoma	●		●		100000			●		●
12	Machile	●	●	●	●	477000		●			●
13	Mosi-Oa-Tunya NP & Batoka Gorge	●		●		8600	●				
14	Kafue NP	●	●	●	●	2240000	●				
15	Kafue Flats	●		●	●	650500	●	●		●	
16	Nkanga River Conservation Area	●		●		9700				●	
17	Mutulanganga	●		●		28000			●		●
18	Lower Zambezi NP	●		●		440000	●				
19	Chisamba	●		●		52000			●	●	●
20	Lukanga Swamp	●		●	●	330000					●
21	Imanda			●		1000					●
22	Chimfunshi Wildlife Orphanage	●		●		9300				●	
23	North Swaka			●		108000			●		
24	Wonder Gorge	●		●		10000					●
25	Kasanka NP	●		●		39000	●				
26	Lavushi Manda NP	●		●		150000	●				
27	Mutinondo Wilderness	●		●		10000				●	
28	Bangweulu Swamps	●		●	●	1284000	●	●			●
29	North Luangwa NP	●		●		463600	●				
30	Shiwa Ng'andu	●		●		9000				●	
31	Luapula Mouth	●		●	●	90000					●
32	Lusenga Plain NP	●		●		88000	●				
33	Kalungwishi	●		●		15000					●
34	Mweru Wantipa NP	●		●	●	313400	●				
35	Sumbu NP & Tondwa GMA	●		●	●	256000	●	●			
36	Saise River	●	●	●		4000					●
37	Uningi Pans	●		●	●	1000					●
38	Nyika NP	●	●	●		8000	●				
39	Mafinga Mountains	●		●		13000			●		
40	South Luangwa NP	●		●	●	905000	●				
41	Lukususi NP	●		●		272000	●				
42	Nyanje Hills	●		●		5000			●		●

GT - Globally threatened species
RR - Restricted-range species
BR - Biome-restricted species
GIC - Globally important congregations

NP - National Park
GMA - Game Management Area
N/LF - National/Local Forest

PO - Privately owned
U - unprotected

2. Acknowledgements

A great many people have helped during the slow gestation of this book. The late Dylan Aspinwall initiated work on the IBA programme in Zambia and data from his extensive fieldwork for the forthcoming Zambian avifauna have been invaluable in compiling the Zambian inventory. Dylan has remained an inspiration to all ornithologists in Zambia and to him we shall always remain grateful. I would like to thank Bob Dowsett and Francoise Dowsett-Lemaire who have been an endless source of advice and information throughout the project. I owe a great debt to Leon Bennun and Peter Njoroge as their excellent book *Important Birds Areas in Kenya* set the standard for African inventories and this work is based heavily on theirs. Thanks to Paddy Fleming, Chair of the Zambian Ornithological Society, who has been tremendously patient and supportive and also Kenna Kelly, for producing the maps and putting up with my pedantic editing.

I would personally like to thank the two sponsors of this book. Firstly Eli Weiss and the WildiZe Foundation® and secondly everyone at NOF and NORAD. Without their very generous support, this book would not have been published.

The photographs included in this book were all kindly donated, at very short notice, by the photographers listed at the front of the book. To them all I am extremely grateful.

For the many ways in which they have helped, I would also like to extend my sincere thanks to (in alphabetical order): Neil & Liz Baker, Ivan Bampton, Carl Beel, Rich Beilfuss, Phil Berry, Mike & Trish Bingham, Paul Bourdin, Gus & Eileen Bowden, Don Broadley, Ian Bruce-Miller, Clide Carter, Wilbroad Chansa, Dispencer Chizuwa, John Colebrook-Robjent, Pete Conant, Colin Congdon, Woody Cotterill, Tim Dodman, Bob Douthwaite, Leanne Edwards, Edmund & Kim Farmer, Pete & Lynn Fisher, Lincoln Fishpool, Mike Fleming, the Flynn family, Fil & Tony Green, Lazaro Hamusikili, Ron Hartley, Charlie & Jo Harvey, John Jearey, Kate Knox, Ron & Meg Landless, Rolf Lindholm, Rory Macdougall, Janice May, Jörg Mellenthin, Mike & Lari Merrett, Rory & Shefali Nefdt, Leo O'Keefe, Ivan Olding, Wouter Peters, Caroline Pollock, Adam & Clare Pope, Robin & Jo Pope, Viv Raubenheimer, David & Sheila Siddle, Derek Solomon, Ian Stevenson, Bob Stjernstedt, Chris & Tilde Stuart, Rod Tether, Esther Townsend, Tony Tree, Stephanie Tyler, Paul Van Daele, Elsabe Van der Westhuizen, Simon Wallington, Louise Warburton, John Woodhouse, Gerard Zytkow and anyone who has ever sent me their records.

Finally, I would like to thank all my friends in Zambia, my family, and my wife Andrea in particular, for all their support.

PL

Wattled Crane, Kafue Lechwe, Egyptian Geese and fishermen on the Kafue Flats (IBA 15). (Richard Beilfuss)

3. Introduction

3.1 About Zambia

◼ Geography

The Republic of Zambia is a landlocked tropical country with an area of 752,614km². It lies between about 8° and 18° south and 22° and 34° east. It is bordered by Angola to the west, the Democratic Republic of Congo (former Zaire) and Tanzania in the north, Malawi and Mozambique to the east and Zimbabwe, Botswana and Namibia in the south.

Most of Zambia is elevated plateau between 900m and 1250m a.s.l. and with a general decline in the south-west towards the Kalahari basin. The Middle Zambezi and Luano Valleys and the country around Lakes Mweru and Tanganyika constitute the most significant lowland areas along with the ancient rifted trough of the Luangwa Valley, which forms a southern extension of the East African Rift system. Most of these areas lie below 900m and Zambia's lowest point is where the Zambezi enters Mozambique at 325m. Only a small area in the north-east exceeds 2000m and can be classified as montane. These eastern highlands comprise the Nyika Plateau, the Mafinga and Makutu Mountains and they represent some of the southernmost formations in the chain of isolated peaks that runs from southern Kenya, through Tanzania to Malawi (the 'eastern arc'). Although a few other parts of Zambia (mainly in the east) approach such montane altitudes, none is as biogeographically significant as this small area.

About 70% of the country is drained by the Zambezi system which flows into the Indian Ocean. In addition to the Zambezi, major rivers include the Kafue, Lunsemfwa and Luangwa. The remaining area lies within the Congo catchment and thus eventually feeds the Atlantic. Here the main rivers are the Kalungwishi, the Chambeshi and the Luapula. Several major hydro-electric dams have been built, notably Itezhi-tezhi and Kafue Gorge on the Kafue River and Kariba on the Zambezi.

Due to its altitude, Zambia's climate is relatively mild, with 3 distinct seasons. The warm rainy season usually lasts 5-6 months between November and April. This is followed by a cool dry season between May and August and a hot dry season between September and November. Annual rainfall averages between about 600 and 1300mm, decreasing southwards and in the major low-lying river valleys. In some years the driest areas may receive as little as 500mm and the season may be confined to January, February and March. In contrast, the wettest areas may receive as much as 1500mm in a season lasting from September to May. Average annual rainfall has decreased through the 1980s and 1990s. In the hot season, daytime maximum temperatures average 27-38°C with the highest temperatures in the south-west and the low-lying areas. In the cool season the minimum temperatures average 2-15°C with the lowest temperatures in the south-west and on the highest ground.

◼ Biomes, habitats and bird communities

A biome is defined as a major regional ecological community, characterised by a distinctive flora and fauna. Any one biome is likely to comprise several, and often many, different habitats. The biomes described here are based on those defined by White (1983), Fishpool & Evans (2001) and Dowsett-Lemaire & Dowsett (1998).

Considering its large size, Zambia's landscapes and vegetation are remarkably uniform. Almost the entire country falls within the *Zambezian* biome which extends from the Atlantic almost to the Indian Ocean, and from about 3° to 26° south. The most characteristic vegetation is a mosaic of miombo woodland and grassy dambos. There are at least 8,500 species of vascular plant within this biome, of which over half are endemic (White 1983).

The eastern highlands belong to the *Afromontane* biome and support a combination of grassland and rain forest. In Mwinilunga District, North-western Province the flora and fauna include a number of species characteristic of the *Guineo-Congolian* biome, particularly in the forests. Zambia also holds near-endemic representatives of two further biomes, though these are of much less significance on a national scale. Several *Eastern* biome species

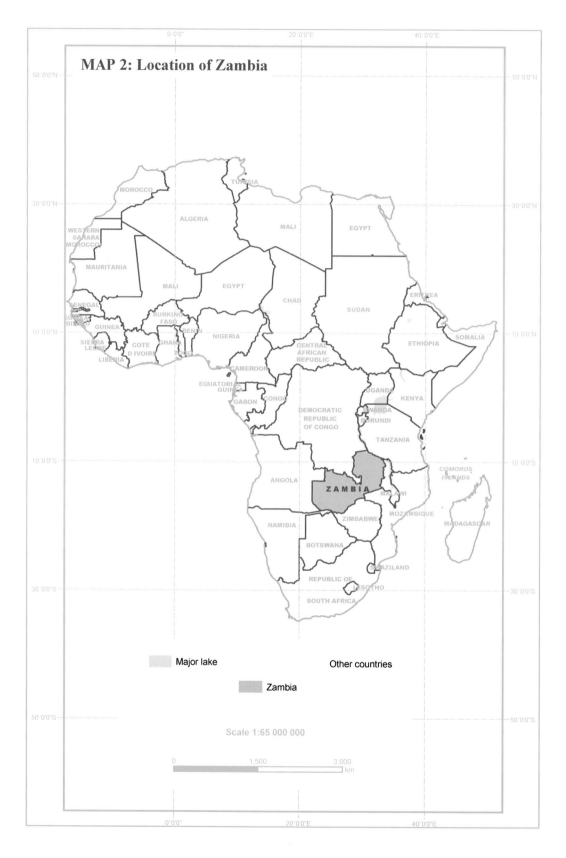

MAP 2: Location of Zambia

Major lake   Other countries

Zambia

Scale 1:65 000 000

0   1.500   3.000
                            km

occur, mainly in the south-east and the papyrus swamps of the lower Luapula River hold satellite populations of two warblers belonging to the **Lake Victoria Basin** biome. Each biome has endemic and near-endemic bird species and those that occur in Zambia are listed in Appendix 2.

The major habitat types in Zambia and their associated avifaunas are as follows:

Woodland

Miombo woodland covers about 50% of Zambia's surface (other woodland types constitute a further 10%) and it is dominated by *Brachystegia*, *Julbernardia* and *Isoberlinia* species. The canopy is usually light and 15-20m high, though it may be stunted on poor soils or very tall, dense and forest-like in other areas. The length of its deciduous period varies greatly according to rainfall. The ground layer typically comprises grasses and herbs. This structure maintains itself in areas of poor soil or low rainfall but elsewhere it is enforced by fire and if burning is avoided, miombo may revert to dry evergreen forest or transition woodland. In many areas, miombo forms a mosaic with grassy dambos along the drainage lines. *Uapaca* and *Protea* species are characteristic of the ecotone at dambo edges and where miombo is disturbed or on shallow soils *Uapaca* species may dominate. Termite mounds and rocky outcrops often support thickets and in wetter areas epiphytic vegetation may be well developed. Miombo is the dominant

A typical Zambian landscape: a grassy dambo along a drainage line in the miombo woodland. IBA 27 Mutinondo Wilderness. (Andrea Leonard)

vegetation of mid-elevation plateau (900-1700m). It is also characteristic of escarpments but rarely does it extend either below 600m or above 2000m.

Although there are numerous miombo formations, it is not yet clear how these affect bird distributions, which are often noticeably patchy on a local scale. Mixed-species bird parties are typical of this habitat. Characteristic species endemic to miombo include: Pale-billed Hornbill, Miombo Pied Barbet, Miombo Rock Thrush, Black-collared Eremomela, Red-capped Crombec, Yellow-bellied Hyliota, Trilling Cisticola, Böhm's Flycatcher, Rufous-

bellied Tit, Red-and-blue Sunbird, Miombo Double-collared Sunbird, Sousa's Shrike, Chestnut-mantled Sparrow-weaver, Bar-winged Weaver and Black-eared Seed-eater.

Most **mopane** woodland occurs in one of two blocks. The first lies at low altitudes in the Luangwa, Luano and Middle Zambezi Valleys and the second in a narrow belt between the Zambezi and the Kafue, north-west of Livingstone. Mopane (*Colophospermum mopane*) often grows in mono-specific stands and its structure of mature ('cathedral') mopane is not unlike miombo, however, it tolerates a wider range of soil types and is often associated with poorly-drained, alkaline soils with a high clay content. No birds are endemic to mopane, but the species spectrum is somewhat distinctive and can include: Three-banded Courser, Double-banded Sandgrouse, Lilian's or Black-cheeked Lovebird, Red-billed Hornbill, Southern Long-tailed Starling, Southern Grey-headed Sparrow and White-browed Sparrow-weaver.

Other types of **savanna woodland** (or undifferentiated woodland) occur in patches throughout the country. 'Munga' is dominated by *Acacia, Combretum* and *Terminalia* spp. and is often found on flat terrain with rich clay soils. In the west are areas of 'Kalahari woodland', which usually forms when mutemwa (see below) has been degraded by fire. The equivalent woodland in the north is 'chipya' which forms when dry evergreen forest has been burned. These habitats do not have endemic birds, yet their avifaunas are similar. Characteristic savanna woodland species include: Cape Turtle Dove, Striped Kingfisher, Little Bee-eater, Black-collared Barbet, Cardinal Woodpecker, Long-billed Crombec, Arrow-marked Babbler, Brubru, Southern Puffback and Yellow-fronted Canary. A few species have close associations with certain trees. For example, Red-necked Falcon, African Palm Swift and Collared Palm Thrush are usually found near *Borassus* and *Hyphaene* palms and Mottled Spinetail and Red-billed Buffalo Weaver are often near baobabs *Adansonia digitata*. Certain species, such as African Mourning Dove and Burnt-necked Eremomela are invariably associated with *Acacia* trees. Very little monodominant *Acacia* woodland occurs in Zambia, but there are a few small patches in the far south-west, home to species such as Acacia Pied Barbet, Crimson-breasted Shrike, Scaly-feathered Finch and Black-cheeked Waxbill.

A certain amount of **scrub** occurs naturally although most constitutes a transitional stage in woodland regeneration or degeneration. It is common in areas of much human activity and characteristic species include: White-browed Scrub Robin, Rattling Cisticola, Tawny-flanked Prinia, Black-crowned Tchagra and Yellow Bishop.

Evergreen forest

Moist evergreen forest or 'mushitu' is typically found on drainage lines north of about 14°S. Whereas riparian forest tends to occur in thin, dual strips along a watercourse, mushitu tends to form single isolated blocks, which may be rather broad and are often in the centre of dambos. Surface water may or may not be present, though there is usually a deep bed of damp leaf litter. The avifauna of a mushitu is always very different to that of the surrounding habitat and characteristic species include: Golden-rumped Tinkerbird, Purple-throated Cuckoo-shrike, Little Greenbul, Cabanis's Greenbul, West African Thrush, Bocage's Robin, Evergreen Forest Warbler, Laura's Warbler, Grey Apalis, Blue-mantled Flycatcher, Olive Sunbird, Many-coloured Bush Shrike, Square-tailed Drongo, Splendid Glossy Starling and Dark-backed Weaver. In northern Mwinilunga District, such forests are particularly well developed and in addition to the above species, a number of birds characteristic of the Guineo-Congolian biome occur, including: Afep Pigeon, Olive Long-tailed Cuckoo, Honeyguide Greenbul, Bristlebill, Rufous Ant Thrush, Buff-throated Apalis, Red-bellied Paradise Flycatcher, Bates's and Green-throated Sunbirds.

Small pockets of **dry evergreen forest** (including types dominated by *Marquesia, Parinari* and *Syzygium guineense* ssp. *afromontanum*) occur across much of northern Zambia, but they are extremely vulnerable to fire damage and many have been reduced to Chipya (see 'savanna woodland'). Perhaps the most significant dry evergreen forest type is 'mavunda' (dominated by *Cryptosepalum pseudotaxus*) which is found in several large blocks in the north-west. Mavunda is almost endemic to Zambia and ornithologically it is more interesting, supporting a combination of miombo species in the canopy and mushitu and thicket species in the lower strata. In Zambia, Gorgeous Bush Shrike is restricted to this habitat and other characteristic species include: Crested Guineafowl, Purple-throated Cuckoo-shrike, Margaret's Batis and Square-tailed Drongo. Still known only from the type specimen, White-chested Tinkerbird, if it is a valid species, may be endemic to this habitat.

Riparian forest is widespread and very variable, ranging from narrow fringes of *Syzygium cordatum* to broad strips of diverse forest vegetation. In more northerly areas, the distinctions between this and mushitu may become blurred. Species dependent on the combination of forest and waterway include White-backed Night Heron, African Finfoot, Pel's Fishing Owl and Half-collared Kingfisher. Palm-nut Vulture occurs where there are sufficient

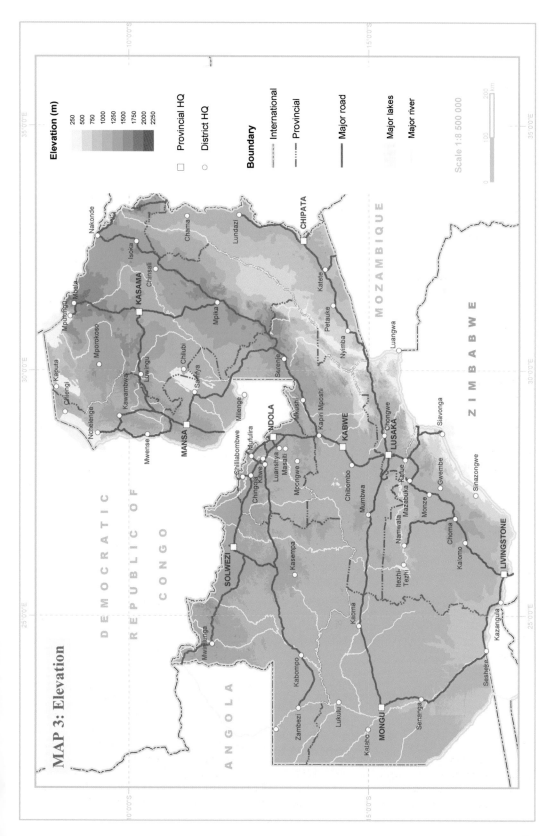

MAP 3: Elevation

Elevation (m)
250
500
750
1000
1250
1500
1750
2000
2250

□ Provincial HQ
○ District HQ

Boundary
International
Provincial

Major road

Major lakes
Major river

Scale 1:8 500 000

0   100   200
km

9

numbers of the palm *Raphia farinifera*.

Zambia has a small amount of **Afromontane rain forest** and this is virtually confined to the eastern highlands. The avifauna shares very few species with the other types of Zambian forest. Characteristic birds include: Bar-tailed Trogon, Moustached Green Tinkerbird, Eastern Mountain Greenbul, Yellow-streaked Bulbul, Orange Thrush, White-chested Alethe, Starred Robin, Sharpe's Akalat, Olive-flanked Robin, Chestnut-headed Apalis, African Hill Babbler, Eastern Double-collared Sunbird, Fülleborn's Black Boubou, Waller's Red-winged Starling and Red-faced Crimsonwing.

Where moist forest is regenerating or degenerating (usually following fire damage) the vegetation becomes evergreen shrubland or bracken-briar. A number of birds inhabit this tangled growth along forest margins but rarely enter the forest such as Black-tailed Grey Waxbill. Bracken-briar is particularly well developed on the Nyika Plateau where typical birds include Cape Robin, Cinnamon Bracken Warbler, Mountain Yellow Warbler, Black-lored Cisticola and Streaky Seed-eater.

Deciduous forest and thicket

On Kalahari Sands in the south-west are stretches of forest dominated by Zambezi Teak *Baikiaea plurijuga* with a dense thicket understorey known as **mutemwa**. It is very vulnerable to fire damage and is quickly reduced to Kalahari woodland (see 'savanna woodland') when burned.

Extensive **thicket** occurs in the low-lying area between Lakes Mweru and Tanganyika where it is known as 'Itigi'. Typical birds include Green Coucal, White-throated Nicator and the migratory African Pitta. The latter two species are found in similar habitat in the Luano, Lower Luangwa and Middle Zambezi Valleys alongside Barred Long-tailed Cuckoo, Sombre Bulbul, Eastern Bearded Scrub Robin and Livingstone's Flycatcher.

Generally smaller areas of thicket occur over much, but not all, of the plateau and most notably in parts of Southern Province. The birds inhabiting them are the most widespread of thicket species and include: Yellow-bellied Greenbul, Terrestrial Bulbul, Bleating Bush Warbler, Melba Finch and Red-throated Twinspot. Such patches may be very small and found within other habitats such as on termite mounds within miombo.

Grassland and dambos

A large proportion of Zambia's wetter grasslands take the form of **dambos**. These occur on shallow drainage lines over most of the plateau and range from the narrow and relatively dry to the broad, spongy and wet. Some may even contain perennial rivers or areas of permanent swamp and thus the differences between the wettest dambos and the more permanent wetlands are negligible. Birds inhabiting the grassy areas include: Long-toed Flufftail, Fülleborn's Longclaw, Broad-tailed Warbler, Pale-crowned and Stout Cisticolas, Marsh Whydah, Fawn-breasted Waxbill, Locust Finch and Black-chinned Quailfinch. Seasonal visitors include Blue Quail, Streaky-breasted Flufftail and Great Snipe.

Dry grassland occurs patchily over much of Zambia, but is most extensive in the west where characteristic species include: White-throated Francolin, White-bellied Bustard, Clapper Lark, Pink-billed Lark and Cloud Cisticola. Species that occur more widely include: Crowned Plover, Rufous-naped Lark, Buffy Pipit and Desert Cisticola.

Afromontane grassland in the eastern highlands is home to species such as Red-winged Francolin, Common Quail (subspecies *erlangeri*), Red-tailed Flufftail, Blue Swallow and Wing-snapping Cisticola.

Major wetlands

Zambia is rich in large wetlands and therefore supports large numbers of resident and migratory waterbirds. Many rivers, such as the Kafue and Zambezi have wide **floodplains** which, when dry, hold birds such as: Denham's Bustard, Common Pratincole, Richard's Pipit, Quailfinch and many of the species characteristic of dry grassland. When inundated, the spectrum changes dramatically and species can include a wide variety of herons, egrets, ibises, spoonbills, ducks and geese. As floodwaters recede, areas of mud are exposed and these are especially favoured by waders.

An important habitat not only for resident species, but for large numbers of breeding waterbirds is **swamp**. Resident swamp-dwellers include: Common Bittern, Little Bittern, Purple Heron,

Shoebill, Purple Gallinule, Red-chested Flufftail, Coppery-tailed Coucal, Little Rush Warbler, Lesser Swamp Warbler, Greater Black-backed and Chirping Cisticolas, Swamp Flycatcher, Slender-billed and Yellow-backed Weavers. The formations are variable, but only areas dominated by papyrus *Cyperus papyrus* show significant differences in avifauna and are the preferred habitat of species such as: Greater Swamp Warbler, Papyrus Yellow Warbler and White-winged Warbler.

Zambia has several large **lakes** and **dams** such as Bangweulu, Mweru, Tanganyika and Kariba. The margins of these may support a limited number of species, but areas of open water are often less rich in birds. In shallower parts species of cormorant and pelican may be found and gulls and marsh terns (*Chlidonias spp.*) may be the only birds to occur over deeper water.

In some areas, notably on Kalahari Sands in the west, there are **pans**. The more permanent wetlands that are rich in floating vegetation hold White-backed Duck and African Pygmy Goose and Lesser Jacana. The more seasonal attract a wide variety of waterbirds such as Slaty Egret, White-faced Whistling Duck and Red-billed Teal. Throughout the country, many small areas are flooded during the rains, often in dambos. These can attract Dwarf Bittern, Striped Crake and Lesser Moorhen.

Rivers such as the Zambezi and Luangwa have well defined channels along much of their length and support fair numbers of waterbirds, especially when floodwaters fill adjacent ox-bow lakes. They also provide two further ornithologically important habitats: sand bars and sand cliffs. Species associated with the former include: Egyptian Goose, Water Dikkop, White-fronted Sand Plover, White-crowned Plover and African Skimmer. Those making extensive use of sand cliffs for breeding include: Horus Swift, White-fronted Bee-eater, Southern Carmine Bee-eater and African Sand Martin.

Other habitats and factors affecting bird distribution

Small rocky outcrops and woodland on rocky ground occur widely but areas of extensive rock exposures (such as cliffs or large kopjes) are more prevalent in the south-eastern half of the country. Species that are typically associated with rocky habitats (some more widely distributed than others) include: Augur Buzzard, Black Eagle, Taita

Falcon, Peregrine Falcon, Freckled Rock Nightjar, African Black Swift, African Rock Martin, Striped Pipit, Boulder Chat, Familiar Chat, Mocking Chat, Rock-loving Cisticola, White-necked Raven and Red-winged Starling.

A few aerial feeders such as European Swift, European Bee-eater and House Martin occur in the sky irrespective of the habitat below. Many dry season visitors require bare open ground and usually this only becomes available after a bush fire. Species characteristic of burnt ground include: Bronze-winged Courser and Dusky Lark. Areas dominated by termite mounds and supporting only scattered shrubs are known as 'termitaria' and characteristic species include Capped Wheatear and Sooty Chat.

Large mammals (domestic and wild) play an important role in the lives of some birds, the most obvious being the two species of oxpecker. Cattle Egret, Yellow Wagtail and Wattled Starling also frequently feed around them. Vultures and to a lesser extent Marabou Storks depend on their carcasses. Two further food sources attract a wide variety of birds; insects fleeing bush fires fall prey to such species as Yellow-billed Kite, Fork-tailed Drongo and Lilac-breasted Roller and at flying termite emergences almost any species can be found enjoying a free feast.

Lastly, man's influence on bird distribution has been significant. Artificial waterbodies have affected the movements and distribution of many waterbirds and cleared arable land has had the same effect on species typical of bare ground. Many man-made constructions are utilised by birds. For example, pylons and overhead cables are used as perches by many species and large buildings, bridges and culverts often provide nest sites for swifts and swallows.

References: Dowsett-Lemaire in Dowsett *et al.* (in prep.), White 1983

■ Population and economics

More than 95% of Zambia's population are black Africans of Bantu origin. These can be divided into 16 major cultural groupings and over 70 different dialects are spoken. There are now also significant communities of European and Indian descent. In 2000 the population was estimated to be 9.89 million with an annual growth rate of 2.4%. The average population density is 13.1 people per km^2. The pop-

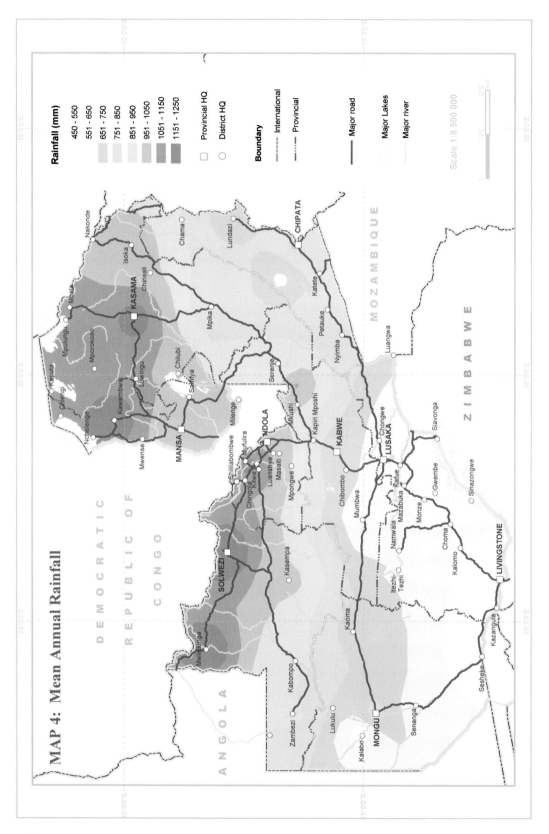

MAP 4: Mean Annual Rainfall

Rainfall (mm)

450 - 550
551 - 650
651 - 750
751 - 850
851 - 950
951 - 1050
1051 - 1150
1151 - 1250

□ Provincial HQ
○ District HQ

Boundary

International
Provincial

Major road

Major Lakes

Major river

Scale 1:8 500 000

MAP 5: Administrative

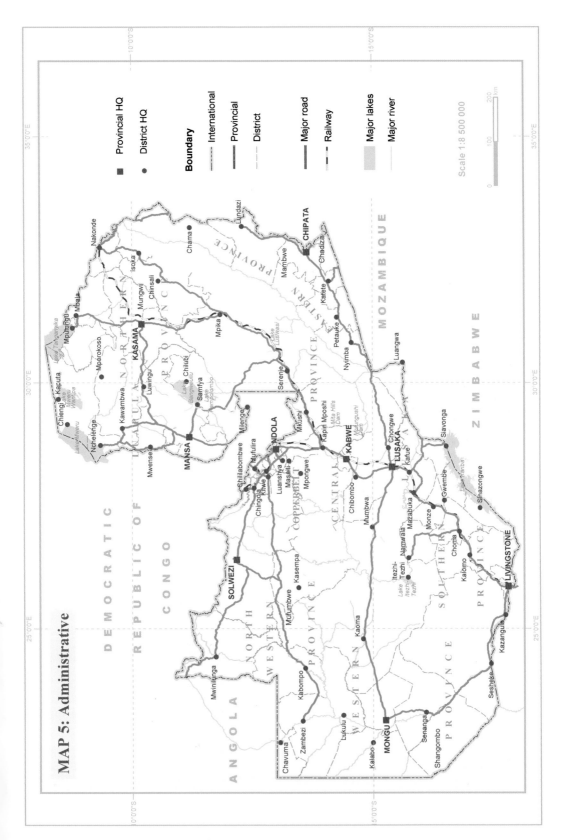

Scale 1:8 500 000

Provincial HQ ■
District HQ ●

Boundary
- International
- Provincial
- District
- Major road
- Railway
- Major lakes
- Major river

ulation is slowly becoming more urbanised and the capital city, Lusaka, has an estimated population of 1.6 million. The major industrial and mining towns further north (known collectively as the Copperbelt) have a total population of about 1 million. Zambia has 9 provinces divided into 72 districts. See map 5.

Average life expectancy is 48 for men and 52 for women and the mortality rate for children under the age of 5 is about 20%. Women have an average of 6.5 children and there is 1 physician for every 1,111 inhabitants. Only 50% of the population has access to safe water and calorie consumption is 89% of required intake. There is 1 primary school teacher for every 44 students and the literacy rate for those over 15 is about 81% for men and 60% for women. Between 1990 and 2000 the average literacy rate has declined from 74.8% to 70.1%. If children over 5 are included, the literacy rate is 55.3%. Zambia has a low income economy and income distribution is very inequitable. Recent estimates suggest that 58% of all Zambians live in extreme poverty, 15% are moderately poor and only 27% live above the poverty line.

The majority of rural Zambians are agriculturalists practising shifting axe and hoe cultivation on the plateau and semi-permanent hoe and ox-plough cultivation in the rift-valley areas and western parts of the country. This is complemented by fisheries and livestock practices, though the latter is confined to areas outside the tsetse fly belt.

GNP per capita in 1994 was $350. Annual inflation peaked at 187% in 1993 but was down to 24% in 1997. However problems associated with the privatisation of Zambia Consolidated Copper Mines (ZCCM) and an attempted coup slowed investment and foreign aid in 1998. A huge national debt (estimated to be over US$6 billion) and a weak currency are both major constraints on economic development.

Zambia is world's largest producer of cobalt and the fourth largest producer of copper. Copper accounts for about 68% of export earnings and 7% of GDP. Manufacturing accounts for about 30% of GDP. Agriculture accounts for around 20% of GDP but employs 85% of the workforce. The main crops are maize, cassava, sorghum (the primary staples), millet, ground nuts, soya beans, sunflowers, tobacco, cotton and sugarcane. The export of vegetables and flowers to Europe has increased markedly in recent years. Tourism remains one of the least developed sectors, yet it is widely agreed to hold the greatest potential. The most popular tourist destinations are currently Livingstone (and the Victoria Falls) and South Luangwa National Park.

Black Lechwe grazing in the Bangweulu basin (IBA 28) at sunrise. (Richard Beilfuss)

3.2 Conservation infrastructure

▪ Institutional structures

1. *The Ministry of Tourism, Environment and Natural Resources*: at present, this is the ministry most concerned with biodiversity conservation in Zambia. Within the ministry there are five semi-autonomous commissions, agencies and authorities with greater or lesser importance for conservation in Zambia. The Zambia Wildlife Authority (ZAWA) is by far the most important.

- The Zambia Wildlife Authority (ZAWA) was recently established by The Zambia Wildlife Act No. 12 of 1998 as a semi-autonomous entity which replaced the National Parks and Wildlife Department. The functions of ZAWA include the control, management, conservation, protection and administration of National Parks, Game Management Areas (GMAs), Bird Sanctuaries and Wildlife Sanctuaries. ZAWA is also responsible for the issuing of all licences and permits relating to the capture, hunting, sale, import and export of animals and birds, as well as those for tour operators and guides. The Directorate of ZAWA is presided over by a Director General who reports to a Board. ZAWA has five major departments: Finance and Administration; Commercial; Operations; Research and Planning; and Game Management Areas (GMAs). The Operations Department is responsible for the management of National Parks. There are four Commands within the Operations Department: North, South, East and West; and under each of the regional Commands there are Area Management Units (AMUs). The National Parks are patrolled by Game Scouts (Wildlife Police Officers) who are stationed at Scout Camps and Park gates. The GMA Department is responsible for the management and conservation of GMAs working through Community Resource Boards.

- The relatively new Environmental Council of Zambia (ECZ) is well funded and is notably influential where conservation legislation is concerned. It was established by the Environmental Protection and Pollution Control Act and its function is "to protect the environment and control pollution, so as to provide for the health and welfare of persons, animals, plants and the environment". It has particular responsibility for water, air, waste disposal, pesticides and toxic substances, noise and ionising radiation. It is also responsible for the implementation of the broader based National Environmental Action Plan (NEAP) but this has been slow to get under way.

- The Forestry Department is responsible for the conservation of National and Local Forests. In theory, the utilisation of all products from these conserved areas requires the authority of the Forestry Department and the payment of appropriate royalties.

- The National Museums Board (NMB) is responsible for operating and maintaining, inter alia, the National Museum in Lusaka, the Livingstone Museum and Moto Moto Museum in Mbala.

- The National Heritage Conservation Commission (NHCC) is responsible for the preservation and protection of national monuments, buildings and sites.

2. *Other government ministries and departments:* several other government ministries and departments deal with issues relevant to biodiversity conservation.

- The importance of Ministry of Agriculture Food and Fisheries (MAFF) lies in its legal authority to police water and soil conservation measures and to regulate and police the use of hazardous agricultural chemicals. Regrettably, although much of the legislation has been on the statute book for over forty years, it is rarely enforced. For example, it is an offence in Zambia, punishable by a fine or prison sentence, to cultivate a garden or field within one hundred meters of a stream or river bank. MAFF is required by law to police this statute.

- The Ministry of Lands is the agency through which any changes in land classification is brought about. For example, if it was deemed necessary to increase the coverage of a Game Management Area (GMA) to accommodate an IBA, then it would be ZAWA which would make the application for status change to the Ministry of Lands.

- The Customs Department of the Zambia Revenue Authority (ZRA) is responsible for ensuring that birds for export have proper permits from ZAWA and are not protected species. Officers do not have any training in this area.

3. *Non-governmental organisations (NGOs):* there are many NGOs involved in biodiversity conservation in Zambia including:

- The Zambian Ornithological Society (ZOS) was formed in 1969 and its object is to stimulate interest in and to further the study and conservation of birds in Zambia. The affairs of the Society are managed by a democratically elected executive committee and a series of Working Groups. ZOS has always had a committed core membership with a high degree of technical skills and a small overall membership. However, ZOS has always produced a monthly newsletter and arranged frequent walks and field outings. In addition, ZOS has published several books, some annual bird reports and a field checklist (in doing so, maintaining the national bird list). ZOS is currently involved in the IBA programme, a bird atlas project and the African Waterfowl Census. ZOS operates a ringing scheme, a nest record card scheme and it maintains species lists for all National Parks and IBAs. Recently ZOS has begun to develop what had been a limited conservation and advocacy agenda and it is hoped that the IBA programme will help to focus efforts in this area. ZOS is the affiliate of BirdLife International in Zambia.

- The Wildlife and Environment Conservation Society of Zambia (WECSZ) is a democratically managed, independent, membership based NGO. Although the Society has been in existence since the 1950s, and has been a significant force in the conservation arena at times, it has recently passed through a very difficult period and is currently undergoing major restructuring. During this process WESCZ has identified three specific objectives. It will: i) support the monitoring of biodiversity, protected area and resource management targets, agreed from time to time so as to be in balance with Zambia's needs and resources; ii) involve itself in contributing to long-term environmental education targets for the young people of

Zambia, that is provided both through and alongside the formal education system (the 'Chongololo Clubs' Programme for schools remains a core activity); iii) disseminate high quality environmental information, facilitate debate and lobby actively on environmental issues, to selected target groups, and especially to decision makers.

- The Wildlife Producers Association of Zambia (WPAZ) represents and lobbies on behalf of the rapidly growing game farming industry in Zambia. See 'Protected Area Systems' below.

- The Tourism Council of Zambia (TCZ) is the apex organisation to which a number of other tourism, safari operators, hotels and lodge operators associations (at regional and national level) are affiliated. The agency acts as a lobby group for all private sector tourism related activities in Zambia.

- The Zambia National Farmers Union (ZNFU) is a well organised NGO which represents the four hundred or so commercial farmers in Zambia and the large small-scale farmer lobby. The ZNFU has a permanent headquarters staff but is structured around a series of commodity associations such as coffee, wheat, and maize. Included in the permanent headquarters structure is an environmental protection unit (The Environmental Conservation Association of Zambia - ECAZ) which would be the focal point of any IBA conservation plan involving Commercial farmers.

- The Tour Guides Association (TGA) is a relatively new but very important agency. Membership of TGA is reserved for those tour guides who have passed the very stringent and wide ranging exams that are convened by the Tourism Council of Zambia. These are people who are out in the field regularly and they represent a highly significant pool of monitoring expertise.

- The Entomological Society of Zambia (ESZ) is a membership orientated, democratically managed society.

- Conservation Lower Zambezi (CLZ) works on law enforcement and research support in the Lower Zambezi National Park area. There is an aim intend to expand into community conservation education.

- Frankfurt Zoological Society (FZS) continues to work in the North Luangwa National Park area.

4. *International agencies:* there are four organisations of importance to Zambian biodiversity conservation. In order of priority they are:

- The Zambezi River Authority (not to be confused with the Zambia Revenue Authority) has its headquarters in Lusaka and is the agency established for bi-lateral and multi-lateral consultation over matters concerning the input, output and use of water in the Zambezi River. There are eight States in the basin: Angola, Botswana, Malawi, Mozambique, Namibia, Tanzania, Zambia and Zimbabwe. In terms of total land area within the basin, Zambia is the greatest followed by Zimbabwe and Angola. The Authority has identified 13 sub-catchments in the Zambezi basin and established a GIS database for each sub-catchment, covering population, meteorology, hydrology, wetlands, forestry, agriculture, irrigation, fisheries, hydro-power, transport, land-use, tourism and industry. There are at least 8 sites on the Zambezi River which are (or could be) of major ecological concern to Zambia and which require constant monitoring by environmentalists. See 3.3 Conservation issues for details.

- The World Wide Fund for Nature (WWF) has been involved in conservation in Zambia since 1962. Over the past decade WWF has spent in excess of US$20 million on environmental projects in the country. WWF has a Southern Africa Regional Programme Office in Harare and a Zambian Coordination Office in Lusaka. WWF currently supports the following ongoing projects in Zambia: i) the preparation of a children's version of the National Environmental Action Plan (NEAP) in conjunction with WECSZ; ii) the development of a Wetlands Conservation Programme for Zambia in conjunction with ECZ; iii) community based conservation in the Bangweulu Swamps based in Samfya District; iv) training and capacity building through the Zambia Environmental Education Project; v) Partners for Wetlands Project for the Kafue Flats and associated project modules - Mazabuka Wetlands Rehabilitation, Tourism Commercialisation,

Buffer Zone Management and Infrastructure improvement modules.

- Membership of the International Union for the Conservation of Nature (IUCN) is open to Governments, Government Agencies and NGOs. IUCN has its Regional Office for Southern Africa (ROSA) in Harare and the Country Office of Zambia (COZ) in Lusaka. Major IUCN initiatives in Zambia include the following: i) Zambia National Conservation Strategy; ii) Zambia Global Environment Facility (GEF) Report; iii) Zambia Environmental Support Programme; iv) Zambia Environmental Assessment Programme; v) National Parks and protected area planning (e.g. management plans for South Luangwa and Kasanka National Parks); vi) environmental impact assessments (e.g. for the Victoria Falls and the impact of the 1991/92 drought); vii) National Environmental Action Plan (NEAP); viii) Integrated Management Natural Resources Programmes (e.g. Upper Zambezi Programme); ix) capacity building for Zambian NGOs.

- The donor community has always been strongly committed to the environmental protection cause.

5. *Zambia Electricity Supply Corporation (ZESCO):* ZESCO is the only parastatal of significant relevance to biodiversity conservation. ZESCO is responsible for the generation, transmission and distribution of electric power in Zambia (except generation at Kariba). It is unlikely that the Corporation will ever be wholly privatised, but gradual privatisation will occur as new generating capacity is brought on line and new transmission lines are privately funded. The Corporation has an Environmental Unit to assess the environmental impact of its operations. See also 3.3 Conservation issues.

■ Conservation legislation

All wild animals and birds are protected under the Zambia Wildlife Act and it is a criminal offence to hunt, kill, capture or be in possession of any wild animal or bird without a licence. All animals and birds are categorised as either game animals or protected animals. The game animal schedules are currently under revision but the only significant bird families hunted legally (in specified seasons and in specified numbers) are likely to be wildfowl *Anatidae* and francolins and guineafowl *Phasianidae*. (The Zambian Ornithological Society has made proposals for the revision of the bird schedules and until these are adopted there are potential weaknesses in the legislation.) Protected animals have specified levels of protection and they are species for which the penalty for an offence is enhanced. In addition, the legislation permits the Minister of Tourism, Environment and Natural Resources to issue a special licence for the hunting or capture of any animal or bird and the Director General of ZAWA may license the export of specified animals and birds.

■ Protected area systems

There are 19 National Parks in Zambia, covering 63,820km^2 or 8.5% of the country and most of its important ecosystems. In addition, 36 Game Management Areas (GMAs) account for about 22%, thus in total about 30% of Zambia's land surface is under the jurisdiction of the Zambia Wildlife Authority (ZAWA, formerly the National Parks and Wildlife Service). The two categories of protected area differ in three main respects: entrance into and residence in GMAs is unrestricted, and within their limits controlled hunting takes place. These areas together form the basis of a wildlife management concept which affords protection of breeding resources within the National Parks, and provision for sustainable utilisation of wildlife in the surrounding GMAs. Clearly ZAWA is the most important Department concerned with conservation and management of the natural environment in Zambia.

About 70,000km^2 of Zambia's forests and woodlands (9% of the country) are managed as Protection and Production Forest Reserves by the Forest Department. The Forest Act recognises two types of forest reserve: National and Local. National Forests are meant for the conservation and development of forests with a view to securing supplies of timber and other forest produce, providing protection against floods, erosion and desiccation and maintaining the flow of rivers. The Act provides that Local Forests shall be used exclusively for securing supplies of timber and affording protection for land and water supplies in local areas. In recent years a particularly worrying trend of degazetting many national and local forests has developed.

There are smaller areas of natural, historical and archaeological significance to Zambia. A few Bird and Wildlife Sanctuaries come under the control of ZAWA. The National Monuments Commission and the National Museums Board are responsible for sites and artefacts of scenic, natural, cultural, historical and archaeological significance. The National Heritage Conservation Commission is responsible for National Heritage Sites.

Although not statutory, protection of some natural resources is provided by privately controlled estates. Game ranching is a rapidly expanding industry in Zambia and several such ranches are managed as private nature reserves or conservancies (e.g. IBAs 1, 16, 22, 27, 30). Some game ranches are run for hunting or game-bird shooting safaris, others concentrate on breeding, others are open to the paying public, and yet others are a mere indulgence for their owners. No matter what their purpose, however, they represent the most intensively conserved blocks of land in the country with management dedicated to the conservation of flora and fauna and having a high density of well paid, trained and equipped patrol staff.

■ International conventions and agreements

1. *The Convention on Biological Diversity* (CBD) identifies the responsibility of states to conserve their biological diversity and use their biological resources sustainably. Covering almost every aspect of conservation and sustainable use, the CBD has become an important framework for conservation related activities on the regional and national level. It requires that the contracting parties anticipate, prevent and address the causes of reduction or loss of biological diversity. The convention notes that 'the fundamental requirement for the conservation of biological diversity is the *in situ* conservation of ecosystems and natural habitats and the maintenance and recovery of viable populations of species in their natural surroundings.' To achieve this, contracting parties are required as far as possible to:

- Establish a system of protected areas where special measures are taken to conserve biological diversity.

- Develop, where necessary, guidelines for the selection, establishment and management of protected areas or areas where special measures need to be taken to conserve biological diversity.

- Regulate or manage biological diversity whether within or outside protected areas, with a view to ensuring its conservation and sustainable use.
- Promote the protection of ecosystems, natural habitats and the maintenance of viable populations of species in natural surroundings.
- Promote environmentally sound and sustainable development in areas adjacent to protected areas with a view to furthering protection of these areas.
- Rehabilitate and restore degraded ecosystems and promote the recovery of threatened species, *inter alia*, through the development and implementation of action plans or other management strategies.
- Prevent the introduction of, control or eradicate those alien species which threaten ecosystems, habitats or species.

The convention does not provide guidelines to parties for setting priorities among sites that are important for biological diversity. Instead it gives a broad list that indicates the components of biological diversity that are important for its conservation and sustainable use. The IBA process contributes to setting priorities for conservation action, thus helping to fulfil national obligations under this convention such as the development of National Biodiversity Strategies and Action Plans (required from the parties by article 6a). Zambia ratified the CBD on 28-05-93.

2. *The Ramsar Convention* (also known as the Convention on Wetlands of International Importance especially as Waterfowl Habitat) aims to ensure the 'wise use' of wetlands for the benefit of people, in a way that is compatible with the maintaining of the natural properties of the ecosystem. The convention also establishes certain guidelines for the formulation and implementation of wetland policies. These include the drawing up of national inventories of wetlands, determining priorities for each site, undertaking impact studies for projects which may affect wetlands, regulating the use of wild fauna and flora so as to avoid overexploitation, and drafting legislation that encourages wetland conservation. Contracting parties must designate at least one site for inclusion in the list of wetlands of international importance, on the basis of the site's international significance in terms of ecology, botany, zoology, limnology or hydrology. Criteria for assessing importance have been formulated by the Conference of the Parties, and include specific thresholds for waterbird populations. Zambia became a contracting party on 28-12-91 when portions of the Kafue Flats and Bangweulu Swamps were designated as Wetland Sites of International Importance under the convention.

3. *The World Heritage Convention* (also known as the Convention concerning the Protection of the World Cultural and Natural Heritage) aims to protect areas of outstanding global cultural or natural value. The following are considered as natural heritage: (a) natural features consisting of physical and biological formations or groups of such formations, which are of outstanding universal value from the aesthetic or scientific point of view; (b) geological and physiographical formations and precisely delineated areas which constitute the habitat of threatened species of animals and plants of universal value from the point of view of science or conservation; (c) natural sites or precisely delineated areas of outstanding universal value from the point of view of science, conservation or natural beauty. In addition the convention requires that each party recognises its duty to ensure the identification, protection, conservation, presentation and transmission to future generations of the natural heritage situated within its territory. The primary concern of the convention is the protection of habitats and ecosystems rather than species. To achieve its objectives, contracting states must try to integrate heritage protection into comprehensive planning programmes, to set up services for heritage protection, to develop scientific research, and to take legal, scientific, technical, administrative and financial measures necessary for heritage identification, protection, conservation and presentation. Since the sites constitute a world heritage of value to the international community, states are enjoined to co-operate in their conservation and preservation. The only site to have been declared a World Heritage Site in Zambia to date is the Victoria Falls. Zambia ratified the convention on 04-06-84.

4. Zambia is a party to the *Algiers Convention* (also known as the African Convention on the Conservation of Nature and Natural Resources). Contracting parties are obliged to ensure the con-

servation, rational use and development of soil, water, floral and faunal resources.

5. The *Convention on International Trade in Endangered Species of Wild Flora and Fauna* (CITES) aims to protect threatened species from detrimental effects of international trade. The species of Annex I, due to their status as being threatened by extinction, are not allowed to be traded commercially, while those of Annex II are only allowed to enter the international trade under specific controlled circumstances. Many threatened African species, for which IBAs play a major role, are covered by the Annexes, including, *inter alia*, all raptors, owls and parrots. Notable, many African species that are heavily traded, internationally or domestically, are not included in the CITES annexes, this being particularly true for passerines. Zambia's date of entry into force is 17-08-81.

6. Zambia has ratified the *UNCCD* (the United Nations Convention to Combat Desertification in those Countries Experiencing Serious Drought and/or Desertification, Particularly in Africa) which aims to combat desertification and mitigate the effects of drought. Desertification is defined as land degradation in arid, semi-arid and dry sub-humid areas, resulting from factors such as climatic variations and human activities. The convention's main tools are regional and national action programmes. The convention pursues a bottom-up approach, which asks for effective participation at the local, national and regional levels of non-governmental organisations and local populations in policy planning and decision making. With its strong focus on Africa it is obvious that many measures to be undertaken for its implementation will benefit IBAs and the wider environment. Similarly, activities to safeguard IBAs will support the implementation of National Action Programmes under the UNCCD. Article 8 of the regional implementation annex for Africa demands the National Action Programmes to include measures to conserve natural resources by ensuring integrated and sustainable management of natural resources, and training with regard to public awareness and environmental education campaigns. This clearly demands a close co-operation with the implementation of National Biodiversity Strategies and Action Plans under the Convention on Biological Diversity.

7. *The Bonn Convention* (also known as the Convention on the Conservation of Migratory Species of Wild Animals) aims to protect migratory species that cross borders, where conservation deficiencies in one state will affect the measures undertaken by other states. The convention also facilitates international Agreements between states for the protection and management of migratory species that have an unfavourable conservation status and would benefit from international co-operation. Agreements are the main tools for implementing the Bonn convention and are more specific and focused than the convention itself. States need not be a party to the convention itself to sign a particular Agreement. The *Agreement on the Conservation of African-Eurasian Migratory*

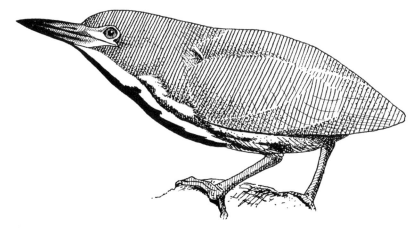

Dwarf Bittern

Waterbirds (AEWA) aims to create the legal basis for a concerted conservation policy among the range states of all migratory waterbird species and populations, which migrate in the African-Eurasian fly-way, irrespective of their current conservation status. The agreement has a comprehensive action plan and provides a framework for conservation action, monitoring, research and management of several globally important bird-migration systems. As such, it has close links to the IBA programme and to the Ramsar Convention. Zambia is in the process of signing the AEWA.

8. The *United Nations Framework Convention on Climate Change* (UNFCCC) is one of the most widely accepted global conventions. Its ultimate objective is to stabilise greenhouse-gas concentrations in the atmosphere at a level that would prevent dangerous anthropogenic interference with the climate system. Such a level should be achieved within a time frame sufficient to allow ecosystems to adapt naturally to climate change. The Kyoto Protocol to the UNFCCC contains individual emission limitations and reductions commitments for a range of developed-country parties. Climate change is one of the most serious long-term threats to ecosystems. A large number of IBAs is likely to face shifts in ecosystem composition with serious consequences - though hard to predict - for the majority of species. Thus, any advocacy strategy for IBAs cannot afford to neglect the implementation of the UNFCCC. Zambia ratified the convention on 28-05-93 and signed the Kyoto Protocol on 05-08-98.

9. Zambia is a party to *The Lusaka Agreement on Cooperative Enforcement Operations Directed at Illegal Trade in Wild Fauna and Flora* which aims to combat environmental crime.

3.3 Conservation issues

Of the environmental threats facing Zambia, degradation and loss of habitat is by far the most serious. Large areas of woodland and forest are being seriously affected by clearance for agriculture and the cutting of trees for fuel. Although currently a problem only in the most populated parts of the country, this is an issue which requires tackling immediately. Traditional 'slash and burn' farming practices (chitemene) were once kind to miombo and allowed swift regeneration, but in recent times the cutting has become increasingly harsh, fallow periods have been reduced and regeneration suppressed. In addition, increasing poverty often precludes the use of fertilizer and further promotes this method. In some areas, notably northern Mwinilunga, the pressure to find fertile land has led people to clear mushitus (patches of moist evergreen forest), when once they were left untouched and valued as rich hunting grounds. Inevitably, the soils beneath such forests are poor and their agricultural value quickly lost (Leonard & Van Daele 1999). This area holds many taxa with restricted ranges in Zambia (Cotterill 2002a) and urgent action is required to protect the remaining areas of undisturbed habitat.

Compounding the problem is the continued official degazetting of many forest reserves; a process generally driven by political, not environmental, considerations. A further aspect of timber exploitation is the illegal or ineffectively regulated export of certain hardwoods (notably Zambezi Teak *Baikiaea plurijuga* and Mukwa *Pterocarpus angolensis*) which, combined with fires (whether drought related or purpose lit) has resulted in the virtual eradication of undisturbed mutemwa.

Fire is used indiscriminately by a wide range of people throughout the country. Fires are lit for many reasons: to help clear land for agriculture, to burn cut vegetation, to promote fresh grazing, to flush animals for hunting, to kill pests such as ticks or snakes, or often simply to improve access (ranging from clearing an overgrown path to removing large areas of undergrowth to facilitate the locating and felling of hardwood trees). The use of fire for such purposes is not always detrimental to the health of the environment - it is uncontrolled manner in which they are used, resulting in quick-spreading fires and vast areas being burnt for no reason. Peaty dambos are particularly vulnerable to fire damage in years of severe drought.

Harsh burning towards the end of the dry season may also reduce the capacity of an area to hold water, resulting in excessive run off and erosion during the rains. In some areas, soil erosion has also become a serious problem through factors such as agricultural malpractice, over-grazing and poor road construction.

Zambian wetlands face a number of serious problems. Throughout the country many wetlands suffer from severe over-fishing and closed fishing seasons are not always respected. Sometimes, indiscriminate poisoning is used to harvest fish. Furthermore, the growing fishing communities cause increasing disturbance to sensitive wetlands and to sensitive species such as Shoebills *Balaeniceps rex*. Pollution, both small-scale and industrial, has become a problem in certain areas.

The Zambezi River Authority has identified several potential areas for concern along the Zambezi, including three potential hydro-electric dam sites identified by the Angolan authorities, an irrigated sugar scheme in the Caprivi Strip, water abstraction schemes in Botswana and Zimbabwe, proposed hydro-electric dams in the Batoka and Mupata Gorges and the ongoing regulation of storage levels in the Kariba Dam affecting flow levels downstream as far as Cabora Bassa. Some of these projects have been suspended for environmental reasons, but it is nevertheless prudent to be aware of threats that may return.

Elsewhere, ZESCO plans to build two new hydro-electric schemes in Luapula Province and three in the Northern Province, although these are likely to be run-of-river (no storage) projects and it is not yet clear how they could affect the environment. Without question, the ZESCO operations of greatest concern are those within the Kafue basin. The disregard for the initial agreement to simulate the flood regime on the Kafue Flats has already resulted in significant environmental change and the need for conservation action in the area is urgent. Much of the problem stems from increasing competition for water between power generation, agriculture (most notably sugar cane) and domestic/industrial use (Lusaka). Often there is insufficient water left over to implement the agreed flood regime. This competition is only likely to get worse. See also IBA 15: Kafue Flats.

Invasive alien plants are an increasing problem in several areas. *Mimosa pigra* has spread extremely rapidly around the Kafue Flats, perhaps as a result of the altered flood regime. *Eichhornia crassipes* (water hyacinth) is also very widespread in both the Kafue and Zambezi systems and *Pistia stratiotes* (Nile cabbage) is abundant along the Luangwa. Away from wetlands, species such as *Lantana camara* (lantana) and *Tithonia rotundifolia* (Mexican daisy) now dominate large areas locally.

The effects of climate change have been felt, particularly by the large numbers of farmers that rely on rain-fed crops. It is now well established that in

White-spotted Flufftail

typical '*El Nino*' years, the southern areas of the country get considerably drier and the northern areas get wetter. Recently, such years have occurred with increasing frequency and when they do, widespread crop failure is not uncommon in the south of the country.

Several ornithological issues are worthy of mention. Chaplin's Barbet deserves close attention in the near future, not only because it is the country's only true endemic, but because of its apparent close association with a single tree species. Its level of dependence on *Ficus sycomorus* requires investigation, as does the current status of the tree. A threat which continues to face certain species is that of illegal live export. Recently, both Shoebills and Wattled Cranes have been seen leaving the country and it seems likely that this was not an isolated incident. The possibility of resumption in the illegal trade of Black-

cheeked Lovebird should never be forgotten. There is widespread trapping, snaring, liming and catapulting of birds. This is mainly for food, but in some instances it is for illegal cagebird trading (see also IBA 19: Chisamba). There is also widespread poaching of mammals, particularly in and around the strongholds in certain National Parks. Although sometimes considered an issue of the past, there are still regular reports of farmers using poison to eradicate predators from their land.

Perhaps the most serious problem facing Zambian conservation is the lack of action in tackling these issues. This usually reflects a lack of capacity rather than a lack of awareness amongst Zambian institutions. Similarly, the legislative framework is more than adequate in catering for Zambia's conservation needs, but the enforcement and implementation of that legislation is often ineffective.

3.4 The IBA programme

■ What is the IBA programme?

The aim of the Important Bird Areas (IBA) programme is to identify and protect a global network of sites, at a biogeographic scale, critical for the long-term viability of naturally occurring bird populations, across the range of those species for which a sites-based approach is appropriate. Furthermore, although the network is defined by its bird fauna, it also aims to provide an initial basis for the conservation of all species of flora and fauna.

IBAs are identified using standardised, internationally agreed criteria and they provide a practical tool for conservation. Wherever possible, sites should be easy to define and must be amenable to being conserved. In selecting IBAs, the existing protected area network (see Protected area systems above) is, for practical purposes, considered first but additional sites are often brought onto the conservation agenda for the first time.

IBAs are one of an armoury of approaches to conservation. They are not the whole or the only answer. Some bird species are not well protected by the IBA system and thus the programme should form part of a wider, integrated approach to conservation that includes sites, species and habitat protection (Tucker & Heath 1994). Nonetheless,

IBAs do have many strengths. They are objectively defined using established criteria, which helps to give the results of the process weight and credibility. This also means that IBAs effectively form a global conservation currency. The criteria are simple and robust enough that they can be applied uniformly and cost-effectively. Information about IBAs is generated by local organisations, working on the ground. This means that the site identification process can be a powerful way to build institutional capacity and set an effective conservation agenda; it is far more than a technical research exercise. For these reasons, IBAs can be a practical and effective lever for conservation.

■ Biological rationale

Some sites are exceptionally important for the survival of animals and plants that depend upon the ecosystems in which they occur. Vigorous protection of the most critical sites is one important approach to conservation. Many bird species may be effectively conserved by this means. Patterns of bird distribution are such that it is often possible to select sites that support many species. These sites, carefully identified on the basis of the bird numbers and species that they hold, are termed Important Bird Areas. IBAs are selected in this way so that when taken together they form a network throughout the species' biogeographic distributions. This network may be considered as a minimum essential to ensure the survival of these species across their ranges, should remaining habitat elsewhere be lost. These sites may include the best examples of the species' natural habitat (particularly in habitats already much degraded), or 'typical examples' (mainly for habitats as yet little modified). Because all are, or may increasingly become, refuges, if any one site is lost the consequences may be disproportionately large.

Moreover, birds have been shown to be effective indicators of biodiversity in other plant and animal groups - especially when used to define a set of sites for conservation (Howard *et al.* 1998). Thus, although the IBA network is defined by its bird fauna, its conservation would ensure the survival of a correspondingly large number of other taxa.

While sites are selected using scientifically defensible, quantitative criteria, the IBA concept is pragmatic. Thus, the existing protected area network is taken fully into consideration. In many cases it will form the backbone of the network with additional sites proposed to fill in the gaps. Ideally, each site should be large enough to support self-sustaining populations of as many of the species as possible for which it was identified or, in the case of migrants, provide their requirements for the duration of their presence.

Some bird species are, however, not amenable to conservation through a sites-based approach and require different treatment. These include species that are widely dispersed at low densities, or nomadic birds that range over large distances. For others, the sites-based approach needs to be combined with conservation measures in the wider environment.

■ Categories and criteria

The category and criteria definitions given in these notes are the standard guidelines for the identification of IBAs. Since definitions of this sort cannot cover all possibilities, they are not inflexible rules. These guidelines have been followed closely in selecting Zambian IBAs, with the recognition that the need for scientific objectivity and standardisation has to be balanced by common sense and practical objectives.

For some of the categories quantitative thresholds are used in site selection. Others are more qualitative and require only that particular groups of species be present. Each category is supported by an appropriate species list and, where necessary,

population thresholds (Fishpool & Evans 2001, Wetlands International 2002). The species that are relevant for Zambia are listed in Tables 2, 3 and 4 and Appendices 2 and 3.

Globally threatened species
(Category A1 in Fishpool & Evans 2001)
The site regularly holds significant numbers of a globally threatened species, or other species of global conservation concern.

Sites are identified under this category for those species most threatened with global extinction. This includes species classified as 'Critical', 'Endangered' and 'Vulnerable', according to the recent universally recognised criteria for global threat status (IUCN 1994), as well as those designated 'Conservation Dependent', 'Data Deficient' or 'Near-threatened'. Species in the latter three categories, although strictly not globally threatened, are considered to be of sufficient global conservation concern to merit inclusion under this category. All such species are listed by BirdLife International (2000).

In general, the regular presence of a Critical or Endangered species, irrespective of its abundance at the site, is considered sufficient to propose the site as an IBA. For other categories, a site may need to hold more than a defined threshold to qualify. Population size thresholds for site selection and the methods of applying this category are necessarily flexible according to region, species and current knowledge. Some guidelines are given by Fishpool & Evans (2001).

The words 'regular' and 'significant' in the category definition are intended to exclude instances of vagrancy, marginal occurrence, ancient or historical records. 'Regularly' includes seasonal presence (and presence at longer intervals, if suitable conditions themselves only occur at extended intervals, e.g. temporary wetlands). In addition, the category allows for the inclusion of sites that have the potential to hold species of global conservation concern, following habitat restoration work or reintroductions.

Restricted-range species
(Category A2 in Fishpool & Evans 2001)
The site is known or thought to hold a significant component of a group of species whose breeding distributions define an Endemic Bird Area (EBA) or Secondary Area (SA).

Sites are identified under this category for species belonging to Endemic Bird Areas (EBAs). EBAs are defined as places where two or more species of restricted range, i.e. with world distributions of less than 50,000 km^2, occur together (Stattersfield *et al.* 1998). Also included here are species of Secondary Areas. A Secondary Area (SA) typically supports one restricted-range species with a distribution that does not overlap with any other such species. Only one EBA extends into Zambia (EBA 105: Tanzania-Malawi mountains) and there are a further two Secondary Areas.

> **Biome-restricted assemblages**
> (Category A3 in Fishpool & Evans 2001)
> *The site is known or thought to hold a significant component of a group of species whose distributions are largely or wholly confined to one biome.*

This category applies to groups of species with largely shared distributions of greater than 50,000 km^2, which occur mostly or wholly within all or part of a particular biome. Many of these assemblages are found in large areas of relatively intact and continuous habitat where delimiting IBAs may be particularly difficult. Biome endemics are species whose entire (global) breeding distribution lies within the defined boundaries of the biome. Biome near-endemics are species with more than 90% of their breeding distribution within the biome.

A biome may be defined as a major regional ecological community characterised by distinctive life forms and principal plant species. The system of biome classification used here is based on the work of White (1983), Fishpool & Evans (2001) and Dowsett-Lemaire & Dowsett (1998). More than one habitat type, and therefore bird community, often occurs within a biome and this will need to be reflected by the set of sites identified. In many cases the application of the category will be habitat driven; thus, the quality and representational value of the habitat types within sites may determine their selection. This is often because it has been impractical or impossible to produce comprehensive species inventories for each site so far.

The number of sites selected per country under this category should take into account both the size of the country and the relative amount of a given biome within it. The size of the site is also relevant

here; it is preferable to select a few, large sites that reflect the distribution of biomes across the country rather than many small ones confined to only a part of it. This will ensure that a greater number of species are represented per site and take account of their geographical distribution. Sites should not, however, be so large that they are not amenable to conservation and, in some cases, small sites with high population densities may be preferable to large ones with lower densities. Common sense has to be used to ensure that a large number of sites each holding only a few of the biome-restricted species are not chosen. Some sites may, however, be chosen for one or a few species which would otherwise be under-represented, such as those species confined to a relatively small part of the biome.

Some EBAs and many biomes cross political boundaries; where so, the networks of sites should try to ensure that, as far as possible, all relevant species occur in IBAs in those countries where the EBA or biome is well represented. Thus, biomes require that the networks of sites, chosen by complementarity analysis, take account of both the geographical spread of the biome and the political boundaries that cross it.

> **Globally important congregations**
> (Category A4 in Fishpool & Evans 2001)
> *A site may qualify on any one or more of the four criteria listed below:*
> *(i)* *The site is known or thought to hold, on a regular basis, 1% or more of a biogeographic population of a congregatory waterbird species.*
> *(ii)* *The site is known or thought to hold, on a regular basis, 1% or more of the global population of a congregatory seabird or terrestrial species.*
> *(iii)* *The site is known or thought to hold, on a regular basis, at least 20,000 waterbirds, or at least 10,000 pairs of seabirds, of one or more species.*
> *(iv)* *The site is known or thought to exceed thresholds set for migratory species at bottleneck sites.*

This category is applied to those species that are (perceived to be) vulnerable, at the population level, to the destruction or degradation of sites, by virtue of their congregatory behaviour at any stage in their life-cycles.

Table 2: Globally threatened species that occur in Zambia and their status.

species	status in Zambia
Vulnerable	
Madagascar Squacco Heron	a rare dry season migrant from Madagascar with most records from May-October
Slaty Egret	a widespread species of flooded grassland, rarely common and with no breeding proof to date; a significant proportion of the world population occurs in Zambia
Cape Vulture	a rare vagrant known from about 6 records
Lappet-faced Vulture	a relatively common and widespread breeding resident
Greater Spotted Eagle	a very rare, but possibly regular, Palearctic migrant to the Luangwa Valley, known only from records of birds tracked by satellite telemetry
Lesser Kestrel	a fairly common Palearctic migrant, recorded mainly on passage
Corn Crake	a Palearctic migrant, widespread, almost certainly under-recorded and probably not uncommon
Wattled Crane	a widespread breeding resident, but common in only a few localities (Kafue Flats, Bangweulu, Liuwa Plain); a significant proportion of the world population occurs in Zambia
Black-cheeked Lovebird	a localised breeding resident, effectively endemic and with a distribution centred on the small areas of mopane woodland north-west of Livingstone
Blue Swallow	a very localised Afrotropical migrant, breeding in small numbers on the Nyika Plateau (more numerous in the adjacent Malawi portion) and also recorded on passage
Papyrus Yellow Warbler	a fairly common, but highly localised breeding resident of papyrus swamp in the mouth of the Luapula River
Near-threatened	
Shoebill	an uncommon breeding resident in swamp in the north of the country with largest numbers in the Bangweulu Swamps
Lesser Flamingo	a rare vagrant that has attempted to breed in the far north on a very few occasions
Pallid Harrier	a widespread Palearctic migrant, not uncommon in suitable habitat
Taita Falcon	a rare and very localised breeding resident
Denham's Bustard	a widespread breeding resident and local migrant that is generally uncommon
Great Snipe	a widespread Palearctic migrant that can be locally common and is probably under-recorded
African Skimmer	a fairly widespread, breeding Afrotropical migrant that can be locally common
Chaplin's Barbet	a localised breeding resident and endemic, known from a relatively small area centred on the Kafue flats, from about 14° south through much of Southern Province; generally associated with Sycamore Fig trees (*Ficus sycomorus*) in open country
Olive-headed Weaver	a very localised breeding resident, confined to mature miombo with *Usnea* lichen near the Malawi border
Data-deficient	
Black-winged Pratincole	a scarce Palearctic migrant, recorded mainly on passage in the west of the country, sometimes in large numbers; occasionally winters in small numbers
Grimwood's Longclaw	a localised breeding resident of wet dambos in North-western Province

The term 'waterbird' is used here in the same sense as the Ramsar Convention uses 'waterfowl' and covers the list of families as more precisely defined by Wetlands International (2002). The same source also lists the waterbird population estimates used in the application of this category. Population estimates of non-waterbirds are listed by Fishpool & Evans (2001).

■ Zambia's ornithological importance

For a landlocked country dominated by a single biome, Zambia has a comparatively rich avifauna. To date, 750 species have been recorded (Leonard 2001a, Leonard 2003). Of this total, well over 600 species are residents or Afrotropical migrants which breed or are assumed to do so and there is breeding proof for at least 470. About 100 are non-breeding migrants or vagrants from the Palearctic region and the remainder comprise non-breeding Afrotropical migrants and vagrants.

Zambia's only true endemic species is Chaplin's Barbet, although Black-cheeked Lovebird is virtually so and quite a number of other species have the greater proportion of their range within Zambia. If recognised as a valid species, White-chested Tinkerbird *Pogoniulus makawai* is endemic. However, it is still known only from the holotype and many authorities now consider it to be an aberrant Golden-rumped Tinkerbird. The possibility of it being rediscovered cannot be excluded, but it is not treated as a valid species in this book. (See IBA 5 for further details.) Endemic and near-endemic subspecies are not treated comprehensively in this book, but the most significant taxa are listed by Aspinwall & Leonard (1998).

BirdLife International (2000) lists 22 globally threatened species that occur in Zambia. No species classified as 'Critical' or 'Endangered' occurs, but Zambia holds 11 species classified as 'Vulnerable', 9 species classified as 'Near-threatened' and 2 species classified as 'Data-deficient'. These are listed in Table 2 which outlines the current status of each. Appendix 1 lists the IBAs in which each species has been recorded. It is possible that White-winged Flufftail *Sarothrura ayresii* (classified as 'Endangered') occurs in Zambia, if only sporadically, but at present there are no confirmed records. 8 restricted-range species occur in Zambia. 6 of these belong to EBA 105 Tanzania-Malawi mountains and they occur in the Eastern Highlands. The two remaining species occur in Secondary Areas; Black-cheeked Lovebird in s051 Southern Zambia and Lake Tanganyika Weaver in s055 South-west Tanzanian swamps. Species in this category are listed in Table 3.

In Zambia, 138 species belong to biome-restricted assemblages. The most significant assemblage is the Zambezian with 57 endemics and near-endemics. The Afromontane assemblage is also notable, despite being mainly relevant to just a small corner of the country. It holds 56 endemics and near-endemics, including 2 species belonging to a sub-category within this biome known as 'Sub-Afromontane' (a small group of species which occur in mid-altitude forest but rarely reach true montane levels). 17 Guineo-Congolian near-endemics give Mwinilunga District a very distinct flavour but the remaining two biomes (Eastern, Lake Victoria Basin) have only a small impact on the Zambian avifauna. Table 4 lists the number of endemics and near-endemics occurring in each biome in Zambia and the total number per biome.

Table 3: Restricted Range species that occur in Zambia and the IBAs in which they occur.

Area code	Species	IBAs in which species occur
EBA 105	Sharpe's Akalat	38 Nyika NP, 39 Mafinga Mountains
	Churring Cisticola	38 Nyika NP
	Black-lored Cisticola	38 Nyika NP, 39 Mafinga Mountains
	Chestnut-headed Apalis	38 Nyika NP, 39 Mafinga Mountains
	Fülleborn's Black Boubou	38 Nyika NP
	Mountain Marsh Whydah	38 Nyika NP
s051	Black-cheeked Lovebird	12 Machile, 14 Kafue NP
s055	Lake Tanganyika Weaver	36 Saise River

Table 4: The number of biome-restricted species occurring in Zambia.

biome	number of endemics in Zambia	number of near-endemics in Zambia	total number of endemics + near-endemics in Zambia / total in biome as a whole
Afromontane	34	20	56 / c.230
- Sub-Afromontane	2	–	–
Eastern	-	6	6 / 45
Guineo-Congolian	–	17	17 / c.250
Lake Victoria Basin	–	2	2 / 9
Zambezian	39	18	57 / 64

Appendix 2 gives species lists for each biome and Appendix 1 lists the IBAs in which each species has been recorded.

It should be noted that since the publication of Fishpool & Evans (2001), a number of revisions have been made to the arrangement of biomes (based on White 1983, Dowsett-Lemaire & Dowsett 1998 and Dowsett, Aspinwall & Dowsett-Lemaire in prep.) and thus the lists of biome-restricted species. The Kalahari-Highveld biome is no longer represented in Zambia as the inclusion of Burchell's Sandgrouse (Zambia's only potential representative) is debatable. Furthermore, although Brown-chested Wattled Plover may qualify for the Sudan-Guinea Savanna biome, its status as a vagrant in Zambia does not seem to warrant the inclusion of the biome within this work.

Zambia has several sites that are important for congregatory birds, the most important being Liuwa Plain National Park (IBA 8), the Kafue Flats (IBA 15) and the Bangweulu Swamps (IBA 28). Unfortunately, data are lacking for many species and many sites, so this category has not been applied extensively. Further fieldwork will surely reveal that this category is in fact far more widely applicable in Zambia. It should be noted that not all waterbirds have been listed under this criterion. For example, although the estimated number of Shoebills in the Bangweulu Swamps exceeds the 1% population threshold, this species is not congregatory by nature. In such instances, the data are mentioned under the relevant site accounts. Sites and species qualifying under this category are listed in Appendix 3.

At present Zambia does not have its own 'red data book' nor is it incorporated into a regional work such as that prepared for East Africa (Bennun & Njoroge 1996). However, Zambia has a number of species that are clearly of regional or national conservation concern and it was felt prudent to include some indication of this in the present work. Following informal discussion with a number of workers, both within and beyond Zambia's borders, a preliminary species list has been drawn up. It is hoped that this will form the starting point for a more comprehensive survey and, in time, Zambian red data lists.

It should be noted that this category (hereafter referred to as 'Species of regional conservation concern') has not been used as a criterion for the identification of IBAs. However, it does support the choice of a site. Very broadly, the criteria used to identify species for inclusion in this category are based on those for global threat status (IUCN 1994). At present, species already listed as globally threatened are not listed in this category. Table 5 lists the species currently included in this category with an outline of the reasons for their inclusion.

It is likely that further work will greatly expand this list, particularly once criteria are better defined. Furthermore, some species may merit inclusion due to the fact that large proportions of their ranges lie within Zambia. Such species are not necessarily threatened, but Zambia has a special responsibility to protect them. Species which may qualify on this basis include: Long-toed Flufftail, Lilian's Lovebird, Miombo Pied Barbet, Black-collared Eremomela, Laura's Warbler, Böhm's Flycatcher, Red-and-blue Sunbird, Oustalet's White-bellied Sunbird, Shelley's Sunbird, White-winged Starling and Chestnut-mantled Sparrow-weaver.

Table 5: Species of regional conservation concern.

species	reasons for inclusion
Great Crested Grebe	Very localised, not recorded in Zambia since 1994 and has undergone a parallel dramatic decline in East Africa.
Common Bittern	The Afrotropical race *B. s. capensis* is very localised and has disappeared from large areas of its former range in Southern Africa, Zambia may represent the last stronghold.
Goliath Heron	A low density species that has declined in some areas and about which there is concern elsewhere.
Saddle-billed Stork	A low density species that has declined in some areas and about which there is concern elsewhere.
Bateleur	Although currently still common over much of the country, this species has become very rare in several commercial farming areas and is very sensitive to disturbance, its range has also contracted considerably in Southern Africa.
African Marsh Harrier	Although currently still common over much of the country, this species has become very uncommon in some commercial farming areas and there is concern about its status in Southern Africa.
White-spotted Flufftail	Although probably not as threatened in other parts of its range, in Zambia it only occurs at a very few unprotected forest sites in northern Mwinilunga District which are under severe threat of destruction.
Southern Crowned Crane	A localised species about which there is concern elsewhere and which is sometimes the target of poachers.
White-bellied Bustard	Once much more widespread in Zambia, now mainly restricted to areas west of the Zambezi.
Yellow-throated Sandgrouse	Has apparently declined on the Kafue Flats which is a stronghold, perhaps due to changes in the flood regime, there is also concern about its status in Southern Africa.
Shining-blue Kingfisher	Although probably not as threatened in other parts of its range, in Zambia it only occurs at a very few unprotected forest sites in North-western Province which are very vulnerable to clearance.
White-bellied Kingfisher	Although probably not as threatened in other parts of its range, in Zambia it only occurs at a very few unprotected forest sites in northern Mwinilunga District which are under severe threat of destruction.
Southern Ground Hornbill	Although currently still common over much of the country, this species has become very rare in several commercial farming areas, its range has also contracted considerably in Southern Africa.
Brown-eared Woodpecker	Although probably not as threatened in other parts of its range, in Zambia it only occurs at a very few unprotected forest sites in northern Mwinilunga District which are under severe threat of destruction.
Joyful Greenbul	Although probably not as threatened in other parts of its range, in Zambia it is known only from one unprotected site in northern Kaputa District (Lambwe Chikwama 8°27'S 29°22'E) which was largely cleared of forest in the late 1990s. The last confirmed record was on 12-12-83 and the species probably no longer occurs in Zambia.
Shrike-Flycatcher	Although probably not as threatened in other parts of its range, in Zambia it only occurs at a very few unprotected forest sites in northern Mwinilunga District which are under severe threat of destruction.

Margaret's Batis	Although not currently threatened, this species is localised, poorly known and often occurs at low densities, its range does not extend far beyond Zambia and it would be very vulnerable to forest clearance.
Chestnut Wattle-eye	Although probably not as threatened in other parts of its range, in Zambia it only occurs at a very few unprotected forest sites in northern Mwinilunga District which are under severe threat of destruction.
Spotted Thrush-Babbler	Although possibly not as threatened in other parts of its range, in Zambia it only occurs at a very few unprotected sites in northern Mwinilunga and Chiengi Districts which are under severe threat of destruction.
Yellow-billed Oxpecker	A localised species that is dependent on large mammals and which has declined in, or disappeared from large parts of its former range due to the decline of mammal populations and the use of poisonous cattle dips.
Red-billed Oxpecker	This species remains more widespread than the previous species, but it is vulnerable for the same reasons.
Bar-winged Weaver	A localised and specialised bird which is sensitive to disturbance and which has already disappeared from some areas due to habitat destruction.

Refs: Barnes 1998, Bennun & Njoroge 1996

In conclusion, Zambia's importance lies in her extensive woodlands and wetlands which support large populations of many species. Zambia boasts large tracts of pristine wilderness which are probably less exposed to environmental, population, industrial and political pressures than many neighbouring countries. Zambia is also fortunate not to have large numbers of threatened species. However, this could quickly change if appropriate conservation measures are not implemented and if the current conservation infrastructure is not properly maintained.

Refs: Barnes 1998, Bennun & Njoroge 1996

■ Selection of sites

The initial identification of potential IBAs took place at a workshop at which species lists for the four categories were compared with published sources (Benson *et al.* 1971, Dowsett & Forbes-Watson 1993), unpublished atlas data (Dowsett *et al.* in prep.), unpublished National Park data and personal knowledge. The initial section of sites was made using the list of globally threatened species and this site list was then checked against the other categories to identify gaps in the coverage. Sites added to the list thereafter were mainly chosen to ensure adequate representation of biome-restricted assemblages as the other categories were well covered.

Certain other points were taken into consideration when choosing sites. As far as possible, IBAs were chosen that were already protected areas and, ideally, National Parks. Sites without pre-defined or obvious natural boundaries were, as far as possible, different in character or habitat or ornithological importance from the surrounding area. A further aim was that sites, either alone or with other sites, should be self-sufficient areas which provide all the requirements of the birds (that they are important for) which use it during the time they are present.

The first inventory was published as a chapter in Fishpool & Evans (2001). Following this, a similar process was used to revise, update and expand the Zambian IBA network to produce the current directory. A number of new sites were added not only on the basis of the accepted criteria, but also because they helped to incorporate aspects of Zambia's flora and fauna that had not been covered previously.

■ The Zambian IBA network – coverage and gaps

Forty-two sites have been identified in this inventory (see Table 1 and Map 1) and together they cover a combined area of 10,538,250ha; approximately 14% of Zambia's total land surface. At present, about 82% of the area covered by IBAs receives some form of protection (National Park: 60%, Game Management Area: 19%, National Forest: 2%, privately owned: 1%). IBAs range in size from 250 to 2,240,000ha. The median size is 50,000ha, while the mean size is 250,000ha - showing the disproportionate effect of a few very large sites.

Only four sites do not qualify under the globally threatened species category and most globally threatened species are very well covered by the network. However, several species have poorer coverage for a number of different reasons. Although present in many large IBAs, Lappet-faced Vultures tend to occur only at low densities. Denham's Bustard is also widespread and also occurs at low densities. Chaplin's Barbet is a common resident in only 3 IBAs and is scarce or rare in 2 others. Considering that this is Zambia's only endemic species, this coverage seems insufficient. A problem in identifying suitable IBAs for this species is the localised and very fragmented nature of its preferred habitat. Although Olive-headed Weaver is covered by a single National Park site, it is not common in this area. Unfortunately the areas in which it is more common (closer to the Malawi border) are under immediate threat of destruction and it may already be too late to locate areas which would make suitable IBAs with a realistic chance of protection.

The network covers Zambia's few restricted-range species and all biome-restricted assemblages very comprehensively, with every site qualifying under the latter category. Only one biome-restricted species is not covered by the current network: Joyful Greenbul (an Afromontane near-endemic) which is no more than marginal in Zambia and known from only one site where suitable habitat probably no longer exists (see Table 5).

Many sites require more fieldwork but a few in particular are worthy of mention. Sites with poorly defined boundaries include: 3 Chitunta Plain, 6 Minyanya Plain, 7 Mbulo Forest, 9 Barotse Floodplains, 17 Mutulanganga, 20 Lukanga Swamp, 21 Imanda, 24 Wonder Gorge, 36 Saise River and 42 Nyanje Hills. Sites with relatively poorly documented avifaunas include: 2 Source of the Zambezi (particularly the miombo), 7 Mbulo Forest, 9 Barotse Floodplains, 11 Simungoma (particularly the northern half), 17 Mutulanganga (particularly away from the road), 20 Lukanga Swamp,

22 Chimfunshi Wildlife Orphanage, 23 North Swaka, 24 Wonder Gorge, 26 Lavushi Manda NP (particularly non-miombo habitats), 28 Bangweulu Swamps (particularly Isangano NP), 31 Luapula Mouth, 32 Lusenga Plain NP, 33 Kalungwishi, 34 Mweru Wantipa NP (particularly the western areas), 35 Sumbu NP & Tondwa GMA (particularly Tondwa away from the pan), 36 Saise River, 39 Mafinga Mountains, 41 Lukususi NP (particularly non-miombo habitats) and 42 Nyanje Hills. Particularly lacking for many sites are data for the category: Globally important congregations.

The wide geographical spread has ensured that substantial areas of all major habitat types have been included. However, a number of general areas remain poorly represented in the inventory. Miombo and mushitu in the north of the country require better coverage, but more work is needed to identify suitable sites with a realistic future of protection. Worthy of consideration are the National Forests in Solwezi, Kasempa, Kaoma, Kasama and Mbala Districts. The Muchinga Escarpment supports large stretches of miombo and may also be important for Taita Falcon, but at present, data are lacking. Fortunately, the area is very inaccessible and the habitat is unlikely to be disturbed in the near future. The pans in and around Mongu District once held a population of Great Crested Grebes and although not recorded for several years (Van Daele & Leonard 2001) their rediscovery, coupled with the occurrence of several globally threatened species, could earn part of the area IBA status. The Matabele Plain (c.16°20'S 23°08'E) is poorly known but may be important for waterbirds. At least 5 Slaty Egrets were present in April 1999 (Leonard *et al.* 2001c). Luambe National Park is the only Zambian National Park not included in the current IBA network. However, further exploration may show that it merits inclusion and two globally threatened species are already known to occur (Lappet-faced Vulture, African Skimmer). Very few areas in Zambia remain completely unexplored by ornithologists, but examples include several areas along the Angola border, a block of mavunda between Kaoma and Kabompo, northern Sesheke and Senanga Districts, the Jivundu Swamps in Solwezi District, much of the Luano and Lukusashi Valleys and many escarpment areas. In addition, many areas have not been visited during the rains when access becomes very difficult.

Only 18 species on the Zambian list have not been

recorded in an IBA and when rare vagrants are excluded, the present network affords protection for all but 5 species on the national list. These 5 species are all of marginal occurrence in Zambia, better represented in other countries and none is globally threatened:

Shining-blue Kingfisher - a species of regional conservation concern (see Table 5) but one which does not occur at any sites presently suitable for IBA status.

Fischer's Sparrow-Lark - a species which is locally common in fields and open ground on the Malawi border. It is unlikely to become threatened in Zambia.

Joyful Greenbul - see above and in Table 5. Probably no longer occurs in Zambia.

Orange-cheeked Waxbill - locally common in scrub in the area north of Lake Mweru. It is unlikely to become threatened in Zambia.

Streaky-headed Seed-eater - a scarce woodland bird in the south-west, this species is likely to be found in IBA 10 Sioma Ngwezi NP in the future.

Bangweulu fisherman at dawn. (Edmund Farmer)

3.5 The next steps

◼ What needs to be done

The initial process of identifying and documenting IBAs is perhaps the easiest stage in the programme as a whole. Furthermore, the completion of this stage is futile unless it is followed by direct and ongoing conservation action. Individual action plans for the conservation of every site are beyond the scope of this book. However, listed below are the main strategies and methods which need to be employed in order to achieve sustainable IBA conservation. These are based on the recommendations set out by Fishpool & Evans (2001).

1. Research
- assessing the threats to sites
- establishing suitable boundaries where undefined
- further ornithological fieldwork for poorly known sites
- surveys of flora and fauna other than birds
- establishing a scientifically researched list of regionally threatened bird species

2. Monitoring
- establish monitoring programmes involving, wherever possible, relevant local stake-holders
- evaluation and, if necessary, revision of the programme at local and national levels

3. Planning
- ensure that IBAs are adequately incorporated into all local, national and regional planning

4. Taking site action
- identify local stakeholders
- develop and maintain site support groups
- conduct socio-economic surveys where necessary
- develop and implement management or action plans
- conservation and development projects
- habitat restoration and rehabilitation
- provide alternative resources for local people
- share benefits

5. Education
- education and awareness raising at a local level near sites
- integration of IBA information into teaching materials and into the curricula of teacher training institutions

6. Communications
- maximise the use of information on IBAs in a wide range of public fora
- specific campaigns to promote the conservation of species, sites and habitats

7. Advocacy
- ensure IBA information is available to all decision-makers and planners
- continual awareness raising for decision makers
- lobby for appropriate legislation on site conservation
- lobby for gazettement and designation of unprotected IBAs

8. Building partnerships
- identifying of stakeholders and collaborators for IBA conservation
- establish and develop partnerships with as many of the above as necessary to pursue IBA conservation

9. Working locally
- build democratic structures through which people can pursue action for IBA conservation

10. Working nationally
- continue to evaluate and develop National IBA strategy
- fundraise to buy unprotected sites
- enforce conservation policies
- promote ecotourism
- ensure National strategy is incorporated in regional and global planning

◼ Prioritising action

As resources are scarce, it is unlikely that immediate conservation action can be taken for all of Zambia's 42 IBAs. This means that priorities need to be set and the following section aims to provide an initial stage in identifying areas where efforts and resources should be targeted. It is important to remember, however, that **all** IBAs are priority sites for biodiversity conservation.

In this exercise, priorities have been set by combining a measure of estimated threat with a measure of ornithological importance. Both immediate and likely future threats have been taken into account as well as each site's current protected status. Each site has been given a score of between 1 (minimal) and 20 (critical) to indicate its estimated threat status. Each site has also been given a score of between 1 (lowest) and 5 (highest) to indicate its ornithological importance in each of the four categories (see Categories and criteria above) using the methodology employed in Bennun & Njoroge (1999). The scores have then been added to produce a final score out of 40 by which the sites have been ranked.

To date, no survey work has been undertaken to establish a quantifiable threat status for each site, so what follows is based on what is known and documented in the site accounts and ideally this exercise should be repeated once better data are available. Furthermore, it would be desirable to use a measure of overall biodiversity as opposed to ornithological importance, but at present, data are lacking. The methods are necessarily crude, but it is hoped that this section will stimulate further investigations along similar lines in the future.

■ Limitations of this book

Some IBAs remain very poorly known and this seriously impedes conservation planning. Furthermore, although birds are excellent indicators, there are undoubtedly a few areas in Zambia that are vital for biodiversity conservation but which have not been identified by this programme. This highlights, once again, the importance of continual research, evaluation and revision in a programme as far-reaching as this. This book should be treated as a starting point and not the final word in the development of an IBA-based conservation strategy.

African Buffalo (Mike Harrison)

Table 6: A preliminary ranking of sites' needs for conservation action.

IBA number	IBA name	ornithological importance	estimated threat status	overall score
15	Kafue Flats	12	15	27
4	Jimbe Drainage	8	15	23
38	Nyika NP	13	10	23
28	Bangweulu Swamps & Isangano NP	9	12	21
33	Kalungwishi	6	11	17
9	Barotse Floodplains	6	10	16
14	Kafue NP	9	7	16
2	Source of the Zambezi	4	11	15
8	Liuwa Plain NP	7	8	15
12	Machile	6	9	15
5	West Lunga NP & Lukwakwa GMA	6	9	15
11	Simungoma	4	10	14
17	Mutulanganga	3	11	14
20	Lukanga Swamp	5	9	14
39	Mafinga Mountains	7	7	14
19	Chisamba	5	8	13
21	Imanda	2	11	13
23	North Swaka	5	8	13
31	Luapula Mouth	4	9	13
34	Mweru Wantipa NP	4	9	13
37	Uningi Pans	4	9	13
40	South Luangwa NP	6	7	13
3	Chitunta Plain	5	7	12
18	Lower Zambezi NP	5	7	12
35	Sumbu NP & Tondwa GMA	5	7	12
36	Saise River	3	9	12
1	Hillwood	7	4	11
7	Mbulo Forest	2	9	11
13	Mosi-Oa-Tunya NP & Batoka Gorge	5	6	11
30	Shiwa Ng'andu	6	5	11
41	Lukususi NP	4	7	11
42	Nyanje Hills	2	9	11
27	Mutinondo Wilderness	5	6	11
16	Nkanga River Conservation Area	5	5	10
22	Chimfunshi Wildlife Orphanage	5	5	10
32	Lusenga Plain NP	4	6	10
10	Sioma Ngwezi NP	3	6	9
26	Lavushi Manda NP	3	6	9
29	North Luangwa NP	5	4	9
6	Minyanya Plain	3	5	8
24	Wonder Gorge	2	6	8
25	Kasanka NP	5	3	8

4. Site Accounts

4.1 Presentation of data

The main part of this directory consists of detailed descriptions of the 42 sites listed as Important Bird Areas in Zambia. The sites are ordered roughly according to Province and in such a way that those close to each other are listed together, starting in the north-west, moving to the south, then through central and northern areas and finally to the east.

■ Heading box

This includes important information about each site as follows:

Reference number - The site number or IBA number precedes the site name. Sites are numbered in the sequence in which they are presented. Note that the reference number is often different from the International site code (see below).

Site name - In most cases sites had established names. For other sites names (and other localities mentioned in the text), those on the standard 1:250,000 maps are used. It should be noted that some names have many different spellings. E.g. 'Wantipa' is sometimes spelt 'wa Ntipa', 'Sumbu' is often spelt 'Nsumbu' and 'Saise' is sometimes spelt 'Saisi'.

Location - Both the administrative district(s) and province(s) in which the site is located are given. The co-ordinates of a site are given. If the area of a site is 10,000ha or less then the co-ordinates given are an approximate central point. For larger sites, the approximate ranges are given to indicate the most northerly, southerly, westerly and easterly limits of a site.

Area - The approximate area of the IBA is given in hectares (100ha = 1km^2). Some of these have been taken from published sources (Clarke & Loe 1974, Jachmann 2000) whilst others have been calculated during the production of the maps. Sources do not always agree and sites with poorly defined boundaries have only a very approximate figure given.

Altitude - The approximate altitudinal range of the site is given in metres above sea level. These are derived mainly from the standard 1:250,000 maps of Zambia.

Status - The protection status of the site is indicated. Different parts of a site may have different status and some particular areas may have more than one status. The main status types are: National Park, Game Management Area, National and Local Forest, National Monument, Ramsar site and private land. 'Unprotected' generally refers to government or trust land.

Categories - The category or categories under which the IBA is listed are indicated (globally threatened species, restricted-range species, biome-restricted assemblages, globally important congregations).

International site code - This is the code given to sites in the international directory (Fishpool & Evans 2001) and is given for reference. Eleven sites have been added to the network since then and these do not have such codes.

Map page number - indicates the page on which a site's map may be found. In some cases, site maps have been combined where sites are geographically close.

■ Site Description

The site description contains summary information on habitats, location and boundaries, history (where relevant), climate, vegetation and ecology. Not all this information is available for all sites. Where sites form part of trans-boundary protected areas this is indicated.

■ Birds

This section is designed to give an overview of the site's avifauna, often in relation to its habitats. It is not designed to be comprehensive. Birds that are often considered to be special or interesting are mentioned, particularly if they are not listed for one of the categories. There is some information on the ornithological importance of the site, but in general the species for which the site is listed are presented separately in a summary box within the text (see below). A rough indication of whether a site is ornithologically well known or not is given and the total number of species recorded at a site is indicated. Note that full site checklists are given in Appendix 1.

■ Other flora and fauna

This section briefly outlines the importance of the

site for other flora and fauna with the focus on threatened and endemic species. Where species have been classified, their current conservation threat category is given (see also Glossary and abbreviation below) as listed on www.redlist.org. In many cases data are either sparse or totally lacking and much of what is written is based on the knowledge and observations of numerous field-workers. Primary references include Ansell (1978) for mammals, Broadley (1971) for reptiles and amphibians, Broadley *et al.* (2003) for snakes, Heath *et al.* (2002) for butterflies and Flora Zambesiaca online for plants at:
http://www.kew.org/floras/fz/intro.html

▪ Conservation issues

This section outlines the main threats currently facing the site and the problems that seem likely to arise in the future.

▪ Information for visitors

This section is included for the benefit of future fieldworkers and tourists who are interested in visiting the site. It includes directions and advice on getting to the site, details of available accommodation, contacts and relevant websites as well as various other points dealing with practicalities and logistics. Other sites of interest nearby are mentioned. The aim of this section is to encourage data collection and tourism, which in turn will raise the profile of a site and increase its chance of protection. At the back of the book are some general tips for travellers that are relevant to many sites.

▪ Summary Box

These boxes contain a summary of all the reasons a site qualifies as an IBA. There are lists of all the globally threatened and restricted-range species that occur or have occurred at the site, along with their threat status and an outline of their status within the site. The biomes represented are listed along with the number of endemic and near-endemic species from each that occur. If a site qualifies under Globally important congregations, the species it qualifies under are listed, along with the relevant count figures.

All species of regional conservation concern that occur are listed along with an outline of their status within the site. It should be noted again that this category is not used as a criterion for identifying

IBAs, but it is included here as it supports the choice of most sites. In many cases, very little information has been published about the status of species within sites so the descriptions are often vague and generally based on the knowledge of field workers who are familiar with particular sites.

▪ Maps

The maps are intended to give an overall idea of the site's location, size and shape. The maps are not intended to be definitive for demarcating the boundaries of any IBA. Maps for some IBAs are combined. The following features are included in each map:

- lines of latitude and longitude to indicate position
- a scale in kilometres
- the IBA boundary
- established protected areas
- international, provincial and district boundaries
- the main rivers, drainage lines and wetland areas
- the main roads, railways and other roads and tracks relevant to the IBA
- the main towns, villages and missions
- the main tourist facilities
- a thumbnail sketch of the site's position within Zambia

▪ Taxonomy and nomenclature

For birds, the English and scientific names and the taxonomic treatment used in this book largely follow Dowsett & Forbes-Watson (1993). Details of how these differ from the names and treatment used by Fishpool & Evans (2001) are given in Appendix 4 along with the implications for each category's species list. Scientific names have not been used in the main text, but they are listed for all Zambian species in Appendix 1. For mammals, names and taxonomy largely follow Kingdon (1997).

▪ Glossary and abbreviations

a.s.l. above sea level

chipya woodland with tall grass that forms when dry evergreen forest is burned, characteristic of some areas in the north of Zambia (N.B. 'lake basin chipya' is a well developed form found on alluvial soils)

chitemene traditional shifting 'slash and burn' cultivation which, if practised sensitively, allows relatively swift woodland regeneration

CR critically endangered (IUCN conservation status category)

dambo a grassy drainage line through woodland (sometimes known as a 'vlei')

DD data-deficient (IUCN conservation status category)

DRC The Democratic Republic of Congo (former Zaïre)

EBA Endemic Bird Area

EN endangered (IUCN conservation status category)

GMA Game Management Area

IBA Important Bird Area

Itigi a distinctive thicket type found in the low-lying areas between Lakes Mweru and Tanganyika

kopje a rather bare, granite hill or collection of boulders

LF Local Forest

LR/cd Lower risk/conservation dependent (IUCN conservation status category)

LR/nt Lower risk/near-threatened (IUCN conservation status category)

mavunda dry evergreen forest dominated by *Cryptosepalum pseudotaxus* and with a dense

understorey, on Kalahari sand in north-western Zambia

miombo woodland dominated by *Brachystegia, Julbernardia* and *Isoberlinia* spp.

mopane woodland dominated by *Colophospermum mopane*

munga a type of savanna or undifferentiated woodland usually on heavy soils and dominated by *Acacia, Combretum and Terminalia* spp.

mushitu moist evergreen forest, sometimes known as 'swamp forest', typically found in isolated blocks on drainage lines in the north of the country

mutemwa dry deciduous forest on Kalahari sand, dominated by Zambezi Teak *Baikiaea plurijuga* and with a dense understorey

NF National Forest

NP National Park

termitaria grassy or scrubby terrain with a high density of termite mounds

VU Vulnerable (IUCN conservation status category)

ZAWA the Zambia Wildlife Authority

ZESCO Zambia Electricity Supply Corporation

ZOS the Zambian Ornithological Society

Zambia's National emblem - the African Fish Eagle. (Andrea Leonard)

4.2 Site accounts

Greater Black-backed Cisticola

1 Hillwood

Admin region: Mwinilunga District, North-western Province
Co-ordinates: 11°15'S 24°19'E
Area: 3,200ha   **Altitude:** 1350-1430m
Status: private farm
Categories: Globally threatened species, Biome-restricted species
International site code: ZM001   **Map:** p 44

■ Site description

Hillwood is one of the few large scale commercial farms in northern Mwinilunga District and a thriving community has grown around it. It was founded and is still run by members of the Fisher family who first arrived in the area as missionaries at the end of the nineteenth century (Fisher 1991). In addition to the livestock and arable farming, a game ranch has been established called Nchila Wildlife Reserve. The farm is bisected by the Sakeji River and over much of the area the vegetation remains relatively undisturbed. The three dominant habitats are grassy plains, woodland and forest. The grasslands range from very wet, peaty dambos to drier, sandy areas typical of the region's watersheds. In many areas the miombo woodland forms a mosaic with patches of dry evergreen forest and along the drainage lines are strips of wet, evergreen gallery forest. In a few places these broaden to form large mushitus, the local name for which is 'lito'.

■ Birds

Forest birds comprise an important element of Hillwood's avifauna. Many of these belong to the Guineo-Congolian biome and, within Zambia, many are restricted to northern Mwinilunga District such as Afep Pigeon, Honeyguide Greenbul, Bristlebill, Rufous Ant Thrush, Buff-throated Apalis, Red-bellied Paradise Flycatcher and Bates's Sunbird. Other interesting forest species include Buff-spotted Flufftail, Bronze-naped Pigeon, Olive Long-tailed Cuckoo, Blue-breasted Kingfisher, both Western and Eastern Least Honeyguides, Grey-winged Robin and Bannerman's Sunbird. Both Evergreen Forest and Bamboo Warblers occur in dense forest undergrowth and White-chinned Prinia and Black-bellied Seed-cracker are occasional along the forest margins, the latter where it is swampy. Splendid

Starlings are common visitors between about July and November. Crested Guineafowl of the distinctive subspecies *kathleenae* were once regular but have apparently declined and there have been no records for several years. Orange-tufted and Green-throated Sunbirds appear to be irregular visitors and the status of African Pitta is uncertain but it appears to be a very rare passage migrant.

Common birds in the grassland include Angola Lark, Black-tailed Cisticola, Natal Nightjar, Locust Finch and Black-chinned Quailfinch. Both Rosy-

Black-collared Bulbul (Peter Leonard)

breasted and Fülleborn's Longclaws are present in good numbers though strangely Grimwood's Longclaw has yet to be found (though it is known from a nearby locality on the Zambezi at 11°11'S 24°22'E (Oatley, 1969)). Black-and-rufous Swallow is regular in the dry season whereas Black-rumped Buttonquail, Denham's Bustard and Short-tailed Pipit are probably more common during the rains. The miombo holds a wide array of Zambezian endemics and both Black-collared Bulbul and Whistling Cisticola are common in areas of scrub and bracken-briar.

See summary box for key species. The site is well known and the total number of species recorded to date is 388.

■ Other flora and fauna

Relatively well known. Mammals of interest include Ansell's Musk Shrew *Crocidura ansellorum* (CR) which, on present evidence, is endemic to Zambia, Angola Fruit Bat *Lissonycteris angolensis,* Anchieta's Pipistrelle *Pipistrellus anchietai* (VU) (Cotterill 2002a), Red-tailed Monkey *Cercopithecus ascanius,* Tree Pangolin *Manis (Phataginus) tricuspis* and African Palm Civet *Nandinia binotata.* Angola Pied Colobus *Colobus angolensis* has been recorded, but is probably only a wanderer here. The Sakeji Horseshoe Bat *Rhinolophus sakejiensis* is a recently described species known from just beyond the eastern boundary of Hillwood (Cotterill 2002a,b) and it is likely to occur. The butterfly *Eicochrysops pinheyi*, a Zambian endemic, is quite common. Reptiles of note include the hinged terrapin *Pelusios nanus*, the dwarf gecko *Lygodactylus heeneni*, the snakes *Philothamnus carinatus, Causus lichtensteinii, Thelotornis kirtlandii* and an undescribed species of whip snake *Psammophis* sp. Nov. A number of endemic dragonflies occur including *Prodasineura flavifacies, Ceriagrion sakeji, Ischuragrion nodosum, Aciagrion nodosum, Onychogomphus quirkii, Onychogomphus kitchingmani, Anax mouri, Crocothemis brevistigma* and *Trithemis bifida.* A new species of beetle, *Prothymidia sibyllae*, was recently discovered at Hillwood (Schüle 2002). As has been noted on many occasions (e.g. Cotterill 2002a), much flora and fauna

Globally threatened species		
Pallid Harrier	Near-threatened	scarce passage migrant
Lesser Kestrel	Vulnerable	scarce passage migrant
Corn Crake	Vulnerable	occasional non-breeding visitor
Wattled Crane	Vulnerable	rare visitor
Denham's Bustard	Near-threatened	regular, possibly breeds, most records Oct-Apr
Black-winged Pratincole	Data deficient	occasional passage migrant
Great Snipe	Near-threatened	regular non-breeding visitor
Biome-restricted species		
Afromontane	-	5 near-endemics
Sub-Afromontane	1 endemic	-
Eastern	-	1 near-endemic
Guineo-Congolian	-	12 near-endemics
Zambezian	16 endemics	17 near-endemics
Species of regional conservation concern		
Goliath Heron	rare visitor	
Saddle-billed Stork	rare visitor	
Bateleur	occasional, may breed	
African Marsh Harrier	regular	
White-spotted Flufftail	rare, only one record in Sept 1998	
White-bellied Bustard	occasional	
Southern Ground Hornbill	regular	
Brown-eared Woodpecker	rare, only one record in Apr 1998	

with restricted ranges occurs and the biodiversity of the area is very rich. Several species of large mammal have been reintroduced within the game ranch.

■ Conservation issues

Hillwood itself is well protected but much forest in the surrounding areas is being cleared. See 3.3 Conservation Issues and IBA 4 for details.

■ Information for visitors

Hillwood is about 70km north of Mwinilunga town and although the quality of the road surface is variable it is easily reached in a vehicle with reasonable clearance. It is advisable to carry some extra fuel as the supply in Mwinilunga is erratic. Hillwood also has an airstrip. There is a self-catering camp within Nchila Wildlife Reserve with chalet accommodation and a certain amount of farm produce can be bought on site. There is also a campsite outside the

Tree Pangolin (Peter Leonard)

reserve beside the Sakeji River. The farm sees a steady trickle of the more adventurous tourists and other places of interest nearby include Kalene Hill and the Zambezi Rapids (where both Forbes's Plover and Cassin's Grey Flycatcher can be found). For more information or to make bookings contact: Nchila@uuplus.com or visit www.nchila-wildlife-reserve.com   .

---

2 Source of the Zambezi

Admin region: Mwinilunga District, North-western Province
Co-ordinates: 11°22'S 24°19'E
Area: 250ha   **Altitude:** 1445-1490m
Status: National Forest, National Monument
Categories: Biome-restricted species
International site code: ZM002   **Map:** p 44

■ Site description

Zambezi Source National Forest (No. 80) constitutes the site. It lies along the Congo border about 50km north of Mwinilunga town. The focus of the site is the strip of gallery mushitu along the small valley that constitutes the source of the Zambezi. The forest is surrounded by rich miombo and such woodland covers most of the reserve's area. Beyond the boundary are a few scattered villages.

■ Birds

Of most interest are the forest species, many of which belong to the Guineo-Congolian biome. These include Afep Pigeon, Olive Long-tailed Cuckoo, Blue-breasted Kingfisher, Western Least

Honeyguide, Purple-throated Cuckoo-shrike, Honeyguide Greenbul, Bristlebill, Rufous Ant Thrush, Grey-winged Robin, Buff-throated Apalis, Red-bellied Paradise Flycatcher, Bates's and Bannerman's Sunbirds. Bamboo Warbler is uncommon in the undergrowth at the forest edge and Sooty Flycatcher was found for the first time in April 1998.

A large number of miombo species are present, many of which are Zambezian endemics such as Pale-billed Hornbill, Anchieta's Barbet, Black-collared Eremomela, Böhm's Flycatcher and Sousa's Shrike. Benson et al. (1971) reported Grimwood's Longclaw from this site but the locality in question lies further downstream (see under IBA 1 Hillwood and also Dowsett 1973).

Mushitu at the Source of the Zambezi. (Peter Ryan)

Böhm's Flycatcher (Mike Harrison)

See summary box for key species. The forest avifauna is well known but the miombo has been less well explored. The total number of species recorded to date is 194.

■ Other flora and fauna

Mammals include Tree Pangolin *Manis (Phataginus) tricuspis* and the long-footed rat *Malacomys longipes*. In addition, Red-tailed Monkey *Cercopithecus ascanius* and African Palm Civet *Nandinia binotata* have been recorded in the same quarter-degree square (Ansell 1978). Reptiles include the forest lizard *Adolfus africanus* and the dagger-tooth tree snake *Rhamnophis aethiopissa*. The endemic dragonfly *Nesciothemis fitzgeraldi* has been recorded. It is likely that the site holds much flora and fauna with limited distributions in Zambia and the biodiversity of the area is very rich (Cotterill 2002a).

■ Conservation issues

Being a National Monument, this is a relatively high profile site and therefore perhaps under less threat of habitat destruction than many. However, the surrounding woodland is slowly being cleared for small-scale farming and the site may be in danger of becoming an 'island'. Trees within the area are sometimes felled for honey and subsistence hunting and trapping would appear to be increasing.

■ Information for visitors

This IBA is easily reached from the Mwinilunga-Ikelenge road. At the turn-off is a gate manned by an attendant. All visitors sign a register and pay a small entrance fee. From the gate it is about 4km to the parking spot from where you can walk down into the mushitu that constitutes the source. Camping is permitted here, but there are no facilities so visitors must be self-sufficient. Motorists are advised to carry some extra fuel as the supply in Mwinilunga is erratic.

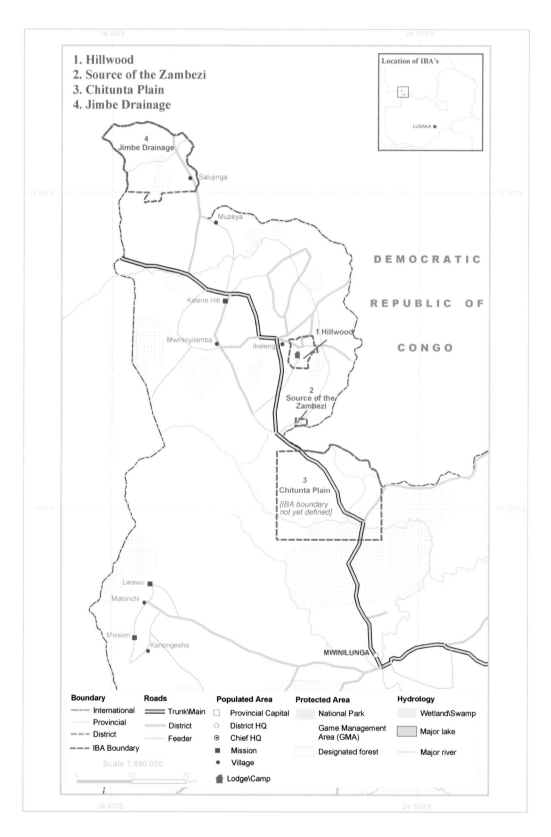

1. Hillwood
2. Source of the Zambezi
3. Chitunta Plain
4. Jimbe Drainage

Location of IBA's

LUSAKA ■

4
Jimbe Drainage

● Salujinga

● Muzeya

D E M O C R A T I C

● Kalene Hill ■

R E P U B L I C   O F

1 Hillwood

● Mwininyilamba   ● Ikeleng

C O N G O

2
Source of the
Zambezi

3
Chitunta Plain

[IBA boundary
not yet defined]

Lwawu ■
Matonchi ●

Mission ■
● Kanongesha

MWINILUNGA

Boundary
--·--·-- International
———— Provincial
═ ═ ═ District
— — — IBA Boundary

Roads
═══ Trunk\Main
———— District
———— Feeder

Populated Area
□ Provincial Capital
○ District HQ
◉ Chief HQ
■ Mission
● Village
⌂ Lodge\Camp

Protected Area
National Park
Game Management
Area (GMA)
Designated forest

Hydrology
Wetland\Swamp
Major lake
Major river

Scale 1:650 000
0   10   20
km

44

Biome-restricted species		
Afromontane	-	3 near-endemics
Sub-Afromontane	1 endemic	-
Eastern	-	1 near-endemic
Guineo-Congolian	-	10 near-endemics
Zambezian	10 endemics	9 near-endemics
Species of regional conservation concern		
Bateleur	occasional, may breed	
Southern Ground Hornbill	occasional	

3 Chitunta Plain

Admin region: Mwinilunga District, North-western Province
Co-ordinates: 11°30'S 24°23'E
Area: at least 10,000ha   **Altitude:** 1360-1400m
Status: unprotected
Categories: Globally threatened species, Biome-restricted species
International site code: ZM003   **Map:** p 44

■ Site description

This IBA lies about 30km north of Mwinilunga town and it comprises the lower half of the Chitunta River and a section of the Luakera above the confluence of the two. Both flow through wide grasslands that are a mixture of dambo, floodplain and dry plain. Some areas are characterised by high densities of small, black *Cubitermes* termite mounds and the stunted woodland is typical of the ecotone between grassland and miombo. There are many similar sites in the district but this remains a prime example, the best known and most studied due to its accessibility.

The site is poorly defined at present and further work is required to establish a suitable boundary. Furthermore, the possibility of extending the site needs to be investigated. On the southern side lies what was once the Luakera River National Forest (No. 35) although this has been degazetted. To the east is Kakula National Forest (No. 94) and another private farm belonging to the Fisher family (see IBA 1 Hillwood) called Nkwazhi.

■ Birds

The Chitunta Plain has a very rich grassland avifauna and it is the best known locality for

Grimwood's Longclaw

Grimwood's Longclaw. This species is common in the wet grassland near the rivers where it occurs

45

alongside both Rosy-breasted and Fülleborn's Longclaws. Other interesting grassland species include Angola Lark, Blue Quail, Black-rumped Buttonquail, Great Snipe, Natal Nightjar, Short-tailed Pipit, Locust Finch, Black-chinned Quailfinch and at least eleven species of cisticola including Black-tailed, Wing-snapping, Stout and Lesser Black-backed. Black-and-rufous Swallow is common in the dry season, Angola and Pearl-breasted are occasional and both South African and Red-throated Cliff Swallows have been recorded on passage. Denham's Bustard and Sooty Chat are not uncommon and tend to favour the edges of the plains. Red-throated Wryneck may also be regular in the stunted miombo and the Chitunta Plain is the only Zambian locality from which it has been reported with any regularity. Bocage's Weaver has a very small Zambian range and breeds colonially in shrubs along the main channel of the Luakera River.

See summary box for key species. The grassland habitats have been well explored, other habitats less so and the total number of species recorded to date is 256.

■ Other flora and fauna

The butterfly *Eicochrysops pinheyi*, a Zambian endemic, is quite common and the endemic drag-onfly *Onychogomphus kitchingmani* has been recorded. Otherwise data are lacking.

The Chitunta Plain. (Peter Ryan)

■ Conservation issues

The site is not protected, but it is relatively undis-turbed. There is some subsistence hunting, fishing and cultivation and cattle sometimes graze.

■ Information for visitors

This site is bisected by the Mwinilunga-Ikelenge road and is thus easy to reach. However, there are few other tracks and exploration must be carried out on foot. There are no facilities, but the local res-idents welcome campers. Visitors should be self-sufficient and motorists are advised to carry some extra fuel as the supply in Mwinilunga is erratic.

Globally threatened species		
Pallid Harrier	Near-threatened	occasional passage migrant and non-breeding visitor
Lesser Kestrel	Vulnerable	occasional passage migrant
Wattled Crane	Vulnerable	occasional visitor
Denham's Bustard	Near-threatened	regular, possibly breeds, most records Oct-Apr
Black-winged Pratincole	Data deficient	occasional passage migrant
Great Snipe	Near-threatened	regular non-breeding visitor
Grimwood's Longclaw	Data deficient	common breeding resident
Biome-restricted species		
Afromontane	-	1 near-endemic
Eastern	-	1 near-endemic
Zambezian	13 endemics	12 near-endemics
Species of regional conservation concern		
Bateleur	occasional, may breed	
African Marsh Harrier	regular, may breed	
Southern Crowned Crane	very rare visitor	
Southern Ground Hornbill	fairly common resident	

4 Jimbe Drainage

Admin region: Mwinilunga District, North-western Province
Co-ordinates: 10°57'S 24°03'E
Area: 15,600ha (LF: c.1000ha; unprotected: c.14,600ha)
Altitude: 1250m
Status: unprotected, Local Forest
Categories: Globally threatened species, Biome-restricted species
International site code: ZM031   **Map:** p 44

■ Site description

Although miombo is dominant, the site is most important for its strips of mushitu. These gallery forests line a network of streams that drain into the Jimbe river and the fauna and flora contain a very strong Guineo-Congolian element. Within Zambia, many taxa are wholly restricted to this site. The area lies at the northernmost tip of North-western Province and is bordered by the Democratic Republic of Congo to the north and east. Here the Zambezi-Congo watershed marks the international boundary and the broad Chana Chamuhina plain straddles the area. Nearby, the Salujinga road supports a string of villages. By contrast, western parts of the site lie adjacent to Angola and are very sparsely populated owing to the many years of civil conflict in that country. The site incorporates Muhonge Local Forest (No. 73) in the south but most of the area is unprotected.

■ Birds

The site holds 16 of Zambia's 17 Guineo-Congolian species. Of these, Chestnut Wattle-eye and Shrike-Flycatcher are known only from this

Chestnut Wattle-eyes

site. White-spotted Flufftail, White-bellied Kingfisher and Brown-eared Woodpecker are probably all regular and can be no more than rare further south. Other interesting forest species include Margaret's Batis and elusive birds like Spotted Thrush-Babbler and Bamboo Warbler. Compact Weaver is not known from elsewhere in Zambia and probably breeds in areas where forest and grassland meet. Grey Kestrel is not yet formally on the Zambian list, but there is a recent sight record from here (Van Daele, 1999a). Many grassland species inhabit the plain such as Denham's and White-bellied Bustards, Angola Lark and Black-and-rufous Swallow. A wide range of Zambezian endemics occur (Leonard & Van Daele 1999a, 1999b).

See summary box for key species. The area is fairly well known. Total number of species recorded to date: 310.

Shrike-Flycatcher

■ Other flora and fauna

The biodiversity is very rich and many taxa with very limited Zambian distributions occur (e.g. Ansell 1978, Broadley 1991, FitzPatrick 1999). Mammals include Red-tailed Monkey *Cercopithecus ascanius*, Thomas's Galago *Galagoides thomasi*, Hammer Bat *Hypsignathus monstrosus* (P. Van Daele *in litt.*), the dwarf epauletted fruit bat *Micropteropus pusillus*, Giant Otter Shrew *Potamogale velox*, Beecroft's Anomalure *Anomalurus beecrofti*, the long-footed rat *Malacomys longipes*, the hump-nosed mouse *Hybomys univittatus*, the creek rat *Pelomys minor*, African Palm Civet *Nandinia binotata* and Tree Pangolin *Manis (Phataginus) tricuspis*. Angola Pied Colobus *Colobus angolensis* has been recorded, but its status is not clear. Reptiles and amphibians of note include the night adder *Causus lichtensteini*, the vine snake *Thelotornis kirtlandii*, the water snakes *Grayia ornata, G. tholloni*, the bold-eyed tree snake *Thrasops jacksonii*, the green snake *Philothamnus carinatus*, the ridged frog *Ptychadena bunoderma* and the reed frog *Hyperolius major*. Endemic dragonflies include *Prodasineura flavifacies*,

Forest clearance for small-scale farming along the Jimbe River. (Peter Leonard)

Ischuragrion nodosum, Aciagrion nodosum and *Anax mouri*.

■ Conservation issues

The greatest threat is posed by forest clearance for small scale farming. Particularly favoured are the broad mushitus found at headwaters and along the level stretches of streams where the ground is more waterlogged. Such areas probably supported the greatest diversity of flora and fauna yet very few

Globally threatened species		
Lesser Kestrel	Vulnerable	passage migrant
Wattled Crane	Vulnerable	status uncertain
Denham's Bustard	Near-threatened	regular, possibly breeds
Black-winged Pratincole	Data deficient	passage migrant
Biome-restricted species		
Afromontane	-	4 near-endemics
Sub-Afromontane	1 endemic	-
Guineo-Congolian	-	16 near-endemics
Zambezian	17 endemics	15 near-endemics
Species of regional conservation concern		
Bateleur	occasional, may breed	
White-spotted Flufftail	locally common breeding resident	
White-bellied Bustard	breeding resident	
White-bellied Kingfisher	few records, probably scarce breeding resident	
Southern Ground Hornbill	regular resident	
Brown-eared Woodpecker	uncommon, presumed breeding resident	
Shrike-Flycatcher	two records, possibly rare breeding resident	
Margaret's Batis	scarce and localised resident	
Chestnut Wattle-eye	locally fairly common breeding resident	
Spotted Thrush-Babbler	localised breeding resident	

now remain untouched and many have been clear felled (Aspinwall 1976, Beel 1995, Leonard & Van Daele 1999a). Where the drainage lines are steeper, the forest strips narrower and the land less suitable for cultivation, the disturbance is still minimal, but with an ever-growing human population the chances of disturbance increase and therefore action is urgently required to protect such areas. A rather destructive hunting practice involves making cut lines through the forest and fishermen often use extremely potent poisons which can leave long stretches of a waterway devoid of life.

■ Information for visitors

The area is remote, but the roads from Mwinilunga town are mostly in good condition. Beyond Salujinga it is possible to drive about another 5km to the village of Kayuka but from here exploration is easiest on foot. The local residents welcome campers, but there are no facilities so visitors must be self-sufficient. Motorists are advised to carry some extra fuel as the supply in Mwinilunga is erratic. Local residents are often keen to act as guides or porters for a basic wage. For a more detailed map of the area, see Leonard & Van Daele (1999a). Being close to two international boundaries, there are occasionally security problems in the area and it is wise to check with other travellers or local authorities before venturing into this exciting part of Zambia.

5 West Lunga National Park and Lukwakwa GMA

Admin region: Mwinilunga and Kabompo Districts, North-western Province
Co-ordinates: 12°30'-13°11'S 24°15'-25°01'E
Area: c.445,000ha (NP: 168,400ha; GMA: 276,600ha)
Altitude: 1100-1400m
Status: National Park, Game Management Area
Categories: Globally threatened species, Biome-restricted species
International site code: ZM004   **Map:** p 52

■ Site description

The site is divided into two parts, bisected from north to south by the West Lunga River. Lukwakwa GMA (No. 5) constitutes the western half and its western boundary is the Mwinilunga-Kabompo road. West Lunga National Park, the eastern half, stretches to the Kabompo River. The most important habitat is mavunda found on Kalahari Sands. This tall, dry evergreen forest is dominated by the tree *Cryptosepalum pseudotaxus*. It is three storeyed with an impenetrable shrub-scrambler layer and a total lack of surface water (Fanshawe 1961, Cottrell & Loveridge 1966). It is found over much of the area with some of the most extensive blocks in Lukwakwa. West Lunga also supports considerable areas of miombo and chipya and through the whole IBA runs a network of rivers and streams that are flanked by dambos, strips of riparian forest and swamp. In the north-western corner of Lukwakwa is the broad Mayau Plain and there are a few rocky outcrops in the central areas.

■ Birds

Mavunda holds a very interesting selection of species. In the canopy are many birds typical of miombo such as Red-capped Crombec, Southern Hyliota, Rufous-bellied Tit, Spotted Creeper and Bar-winged Weaver. However, in the mid and lower strata, forest and thicket birds predominate and again there is an unusual mixture of species with some typical of mushitu such as Blue-mantled Flycatcher and others characteristic of drier thickets such as Yellow-bellied Greenbul. Restricted to this habitat in Zambia is the Gorgeous Bush Shrike and other species that are typical include Crested Guineafowl (of the distinctive subspecies *kathleenae*), Purple-throated Cuckoo-shrike, Margaret's Batis and Square-tailed Drongo. Both Eastern and Western Least Honeyguides have been recorded as well as the Guineo-Congolian near-endemic Olive Long-tailed Cuckoo. Bronze-naped Pigeon occurs in the moist riparian forests along the Kabompo River near Jivundu where Rameron

Schalow's Turaco (Bob Medland)

Pigeon has also been found, though only as a wanderer. Other species recorded here include Crowned Eagle, African Finfoot, Pel's Fishing Owl, Böhm's Bee-eater, Thick-billed Weaver and Green Twinspot. Several breeding colonies of Southern Carmine Bee-eaters are amongst the most northerly for the species.

In 1965 a new species of tinkerbird *Pogoniulus sp.* was described from Lukwakwa (Benson & Irwin 1965), named White-chested Tinkerbird *Pogoniulus makawai*. The type locality, Mayau, is easily accessible and lies on the western boundary of the IBA at about 12°45'S 24°16'E. However, several attempts to relocate the species have failed and it is still known from but a single specimen. Some authors now consider it to be no more than an aberrant Golden-rumped Tinkerbird (Dowsett & Dowsett-Lemaire 1980, 1993, see also Goodwin 1965). If the species is valid then it may prove to be endemic to mavunda and the protection of this IBA would be critical for its survival. Fishpool & Evans (2001) treat the species as valid and list it as Globally threatened and of Restricted Range (in doing so creating the Secondary Area s052). Both Yellow-fronted and Golden-rumped Tinkerbirds are common in mavunda.

In other habitats a wide range of Zambezian endemics occur including the long-tailed race of Neddicky *Cisticola fulvicapilla angusticauda* and Sharp-tailed Starling. In time the site might prove to be an important area for Great Snipe judging by a report of 15+ from a short visit in December 1988 (Berkvens 1988) which also yielded a sighting of

the elusive Striped Crake. Wattled Cranes have been recorded regularly in several areas, including Mayau Plain but Slaty Egret is probably no more than a vagrant. It seems likely that oxpeckers have declined as the large mammals populations have been much reduced by poaching.

See summary box for key species. The areas around Mayau and Jivundu have been well explored but there remain many very poorly known areas in this IBA. The total number of species recorded to date is 407 (West Lunga NP: 368, Lukwakwa GMA: 249 (not including White-chested Tinkerbird)).

■ Other flora and fauna

The NP had one of the largest protected populations of Sitatunga *Tragelaphus spekei* (LR/cd) in Zambia (R. J. Dowsett *in litt.*), though current data are lacking and poaching has reduced the numbers of most large mammals in recent years. Small numbers of African Buffalo *Syncerus caffer* (LR/cd) apparently still exist (McIntyre 1999), Hippopotamus *Hippopotamus amphibius* are found along the main rivers and African Elephants

Mavunda on the Mwinilunga-Kabompo road.
(Peter Ryan)

Loxodonta africana (EN) still occur in the north-west of the NP and adjacent areas of the GMA (J. Mellenthin *in litt.*). A wide variety of antelope occur in small numbers including Puku *Kobus vardoni* (LR/cd), Impala *Aepyceros melampus* (LR/cd), Bushbuck *Tragelaphus scriptus*, Hartebeest *Alcelaphus buselaphus lichtensteinii* (LR/cd), Southern Reedbuck *Redunca arundinum* (LR/cd), Yellow-backed *Cephalophus silvicultor* (LR/cd) and Blue Duikers *C. monticola* and Sable *Hippotragus niger* (LR/cd). Buk (1995) reported two Wild Dog *Lycaon pictus* (EN) sightings, though this species may now be extinct in the area. Other mammals include Spot-necked Otter *Lutra maculicollis* (VU), Gentle (Blue) Monkey *Cercopithecus mitis* and the climbing shrew *Sylvisorex megalura*. Butterflies include *Mylothris mavunda* which is, on present evidence, endemic to the area, while it is the stronghold of *Charaxes variata*.

■ **Conservation issues**

Fire is a constant threat to the mavunda in many places (see introduction) and particularly in areas close to Mwinilunga-Kabompo road. Many such fires are accidental, but others are used to clear land for cultivation. The mavunda in the NP was once much more extensive but large areas have been reduced to chipya by indiscriminate burning by both poachers and park staff. Much of the IBA was once rich in large mammals but poaching has decimated populations and now even the tsetse fly population is alarmingly low. The general area has long been one of the most sparsely populated in the country, but parts of Mufumbwe District are rapidly being settled and cleared, thus gradually closing a major game corridor to Kafue NP (IBA 14). On the eastern side towards Solwezi, the Maheba Refugee Settlement continues to grow and generate further poaching problems. Fish populations are declining as the number of fishermen increases and Nile Crocodiles *Crocodylus niloticus* are now frequently killed, presumably out of fear. Bird hunting is common and recent reports have included the 'harvesting' of an entire colony of Carmine Bee-eaters by draping a fishing net over it and the liming and subsequent felling of a tree in which about 200 Green Pigeons were regularly roosting (J. Mellenthin *in litt.*).

Globally threatened species		
Slaty Egret	Vulnerable	rare visitor
Lappet-faced Vulture	Vulnerable	status uncertain
Wattled Crane	Vulnerable	regular and almost certainly breeds
Denham's Bustard	Near-threatened	regular and almost certainly breeds
Great Snipe	Near-threatened	non-breeding visitor
Biome-restricted species		
Afromontane	-	3 near-endemics
Sub-Afromontane	1 endemic	-
Eastern	-	2 near-endemics
Guineo-Congolian	-	1 near-endemic
Zambezian	17 endemics	15 near-endemics
Species of regional conservation concern		
Goliath Heron	uncommon	
Saddle-billed Stork	regular breeding resident	
Bateleur	common and almost certainly breeds	
African Marsh Harrier	regular	
White-bellied Bustard	status unknown	
Southern Ground Hornbill	fairly common breeding resident	
Margaret's Batis	uncommon	
Yellow-billed Oxpecker	status unknown	
Red-billed Oxpecker	status unknown	
Bar-winged Weaver	fairly common breeding resident	

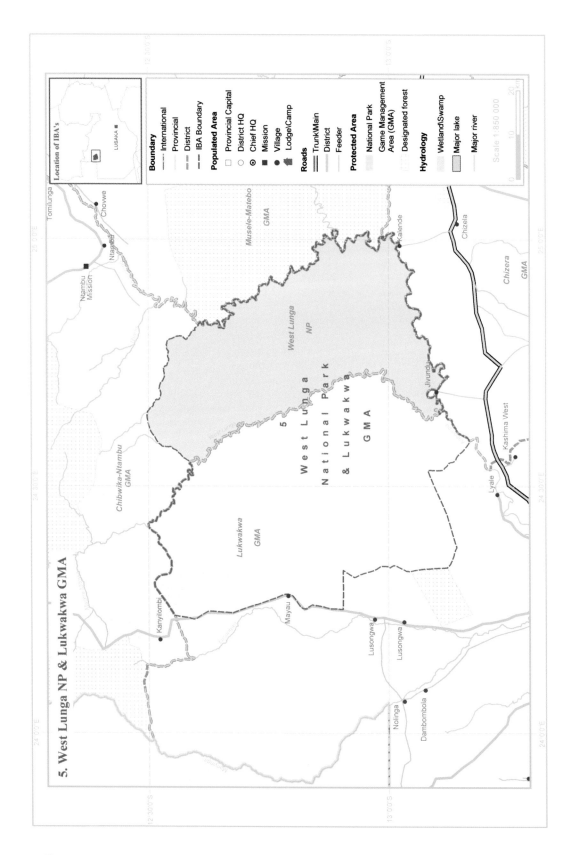

5. West Lunga NP & Lukwakwa GMA

■ Information for visitors

The Mwinilunga-Kabompo road follows the western boundary of the IBA and provides access to some of the richest blocks of mavunda and Mayau, the type locality of White-chested Tinkerbird. However, it can be difficult to travel far from the main road and only a few poor tracks lead deeper into Lukwakwa. Most people wishing to visit West Lunga travel to the park headquarters at Jivundu on the banks of the Kabompo. The signed turn is about 80km east of Kabompo town and

Jivundu is a further 12km off the main road. At Jivundu there was a pontoon enabling access to the park, but this is seemingly out of use and the internal road network is now almost non-existent. The only practical ways of exploring the area now are either on foot or by boat and it is worth consulting the resident ZAWA scouts at Jivundu before doing so. It was once possible to approach the park from Ntambu to the north-east but this road is no longer passable owing to damaged bridges. There are no tourist facilities so visitors need to be self-sufficient.

---

6 Minyanya Plain

Admin region: Chavuma District, North-western Province
Co-ordinates: c.13°0'-13°15'S 22°0'-22°30'E
Area: at least 50,000ha   **Altitude:** c.1070m
Status: unprotected
Categories: Globally threatened species, Biome-restricted species
International site code: ---   **Map:** p 55

■ Site description

A vast area of rather flat grassy plains that can be broadly divided into wetter and drier types, depending on slight differences in elevation (Aspinwall 1979). There are scattered pockets of scrub and in the depressions small clumps of *Syzygium* forest. Bordering the plains are stretches of rather open Kalahari woodland and *Burkea* savanna. There is very little surface water in the dry season and much of the area is very sparsely populated. The site is poorly defined at present and further work is required to establish a suitable boundary.

■ Birds

A very rich grassland avifauna, comprising species typical of both Western Province and Mwinilunga District. Typical of the former are Greater Kestrel, Black Crow and Long-tailed Whydah. Characteristic of the latter are Angola Lark and Black-tailed Cisticola. One of the most interesting birds to occur is White-throated Francolin, an essentially West African species that has a relict population in this small corner of Zambia and neighbouring Angola. It is a fairly common inhab-

Bronze-winged Coursers are regular in the dry woodlands bordering the plain.

53

Track across Minyanya Plain. (Peter Ryan)

itant of the drier plains, whereas Red-winged Francolins tend to be found in the wetter areas. Another species with a seemingly disjunct population in this area is Cloud Cisticola. However, recent observations in Sesheke District suggest that the species may be more widespread in Zambia than previously thought (Stjernstedt 2003). According to local residents, some areas become heavily inundated during the rains and large concentrations of waterbirds occur, but very few ornithologists have visited at this time.

See summary box for key species. The grassland has been well explored, other habitats less so. Total number of species recorded to date: 242.

■ Other flora and fauna

Not known.

■ Conservation issues

The area is very sparsely populated and not particularly suitable for agriculture so human disturbance is currently minimal. Perhaps the only potential threat is fire, although the extent to which this is a problem at present is not known.

■ Information for visitors

The area is remote and the roads rough in places. They are also very sandy so four wheel drive is important. In a vehicle with good clearance it is reasonably easy to explore much of the area off-road and the fact that the main track can become obscure means that a map, compass and GPS are vital tools. There are very few villages, let alone facilities, but self-sufficient travellers will find the area very pleasant for camping. Motorists are advised to carry some extra fuel as the supply in Zambezi is erratic. There are three pontoons which cross the Zambezi, at Chavuma, Chinyingi and Zambezi town. The one at Chinyingi is self-service and not motorised but the opportunity to see the famous suspension footbridge makes the effort worthwhile. Once on the east bank, visitors with time should consider following the beautiful circuit via Chinyama Litapi. See also IBA 7.

Globally threatened species		
Wattled Crane	Vulnerable	uncommon, may breed
Biome-restricted species		
Zambezian	10 endemics	10 near-endemics
Species of regional conservation concern		
Saddle-billed Stork	uncommon resident, may breed	
Bateleur	fairly common breeding resident	
African Marsh Harrier	regular	
White-bellied Bustard	fairly common breeding resident	
Southern Ground Hornbill	regular, probably breeds	

6. Minyanya Plain
7. Mbulo Forest

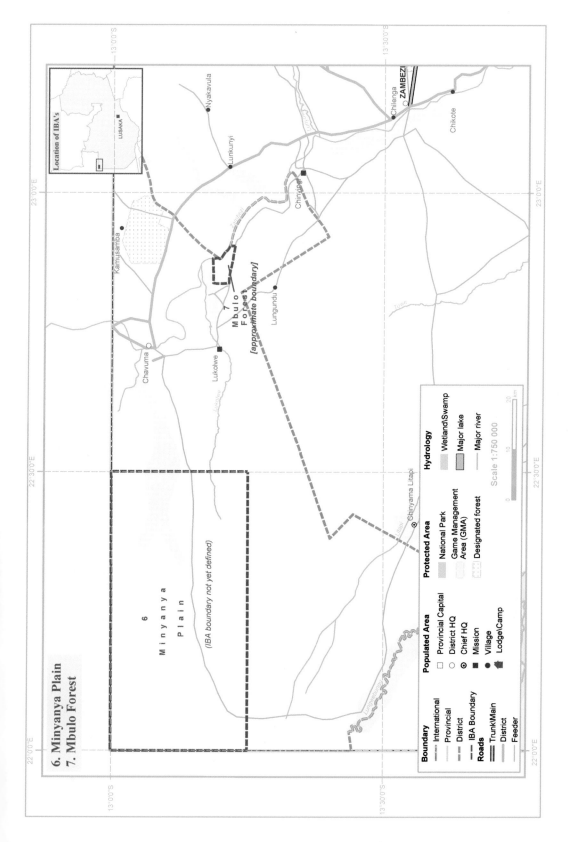

Location of IBA's

LUSAKA

Nyakavula

Lunkunyi

Chilenga
ZAMBEZI

Chikote

Kamusamba

Chinjung
Chinjungi

Chavuma

Lukolwe

7
M b u l o
F o r e s t
[approximate boundary]

Lungundu

6
M i n y a n y a
P l a i n

(IBA boundary not yet defined)

Chinyama Litapi

Boundary
International
Provincial
District
IBA Boundary
Roads
Trunk\Main
District
Feeder

Populated Area
□ Provincial Capital
○ District HQ
◉ Chief HQ
■ Mission
● Village
⛺ Lodge\Camp

Protected Area
National Park
Game Management Area (GMA)
Designated forest

Hydrology
Wetland\Swamp
Major lake
Major river

Scale 1:750 000

0   10   20
km

7 Mbulo Forest

Admin region: Chavuma District, North-western Province
Co-ordinates: 13°13'S 22°50'E
Area: at least 500ha   **Altitude:** 1050m
Status: unprotected
Categories: Globally threatened species, Biome-restricted species
International site code: --- **Map:** p 55

■ Site description

A large and extremely rich mushitu just west of the Zambezi river, between Lukolwe and Luzu. Such forests are uncommon in this district and Mbulo is a particularly fine example. It is between 1 and 2km long and as much as 0.5km wide in places. Much of the surrounding habitat is thin miombo, but to the north the mushitu is bordered by a small swampy stream. The Kamunoka Plain lies to the west and this grassland is included in the site. The general area is very sparsely populated and the forest very undisturbed. Furthermore, some local residents would appear to have superstitious fears of the forest. The site has seen very little fieldwork so far, but the small amount that has been carried out has revealed a very interesting range of species (Leonard 1998b).

■ Birds

A wide range of mushitu species occur, many on the very edge of their range such as Cinnamon Dove, Blue-breasted Kingfisher, Bannerman's Sunbird, Blue-mantled Flycatcher, Grey Apalis and Many-coloured Bush Shrike. Splendid Glossy Starlings occur in very large numbers during the breeding season from about August to November. Woolly-necked Storks appear to be regular and probably nest here as they have been found breeding nearby (Van Daele 1999b). Species more typical of forest edge and the surrounding woodland include Anchieta's Barbet, Scaly-fronted Honeyguide and Little Spotted Woodpecker. The plain supports many grassland species such as Natal Nightjar, Grimwood's Longclaw, Lesser Black-backed Cisticola and Parasitic Weaver.

See summary box for key species. The site remains poorly known. Total number of species recorded to date: 151.

Black-backed Barbets (Mike Harrison)

Edge of Mbulo Forest. (Peter Leonard)

■ Other flora and fauna

Poorly known, although the flora is likely to have Guineo-Congolian elements (M. Bingham *in litt.*). The hairy bat *Myotis welwitschii* has been recorded (P. Van Daele *in litt.*).

■ Conservation issues

Although the area receives no official protection, the combination of low population density and a superstitious fear of the forest has served to protect it well. A single, large forest tree was found cut for canoe-making and some small scale trapping and hunting is likely. In the late 1990s a few sections of the forest seemed to have died after several consecutive years of drought. As the soil had dried, the trees appeared to have lost vital support and simply toppled over.

■ Information for visitors

The forest lies to the north of the Lukolwe-Chinyingi road, just west of Luzu and although it almost reaches the road, it is not immediately obvious as in most places it is obscured by miombo. The roads are sandy so four wheel drive is important and motorists are advised to carry some extra fuel as the supply in Zambezi is erratic. Self-sufficient travellers will find the area very pleasant for camping. The area is beautiful and worth exploring and more information can be found in Leonard (1998). Note that the mushitu where the road crosses the Towe (South Kashiji) river is a good site for Shining-blue Kingfisher. See also IBA 6.

Globally threatened species		
Grimwood's Longclaw	Data deficient	regular, probably breeds
Lappet-faced Vulture	Vulnerable	occasional
Biome-restricted species		
Afromontane	-	3 near-endemics
Eastern	-	1 near-endemic
Zambezian	3 endemics	4 near-endemics
Species of regional conservation concern		
Bateleur	fairly common resident	
Southern Ground Hornbill	fairly common resident	

8 Liuwa Plain National Park

Admin region: Kalabo District, Western Province
Co-ordinates: 14°13'-14°51'S 22°18'-22°55'E
Area: 366,000 ha   **Altitude:** c.1050m
Status: National Park
Categories: Globally threatened species, Biome-restricted species, Globally important congregations
International site code: ZM005   **Map:** p 61

■ Site description

The park is basically a vast, flat, short-grass sand plain surrounded by two areas that are seasonally inundated. Two fairly large rivers, the Luambimba and the Luanginga, flank the park to the east and west respectively. During and after the rains much of this area floods or becomes partially inundated

Martial Eagle being mobbed by Pied Crows.

and as the dry season progresses this water recedes leaving numerous small pans. The plain covers an area measuring about 30 by 70km and the grasslands can be divided into two broad categories. Wetter types are found along the drainage lines and drier types on the slightly elevated areas, which may also be occupied by *Cubitermes* mounds and ground-creeping shrubs. The dominant grasses are *Loudetia simplex* and *Monocymbium ceresiiforme.* There are small stretches of *Diplorhynchus* scrub and the woodland that fringes the plain is dominated by Wild Syringa *Burkea africana* intermingled with small pockets of mutemwa (Zambezi Teak *Baikiaea plurijuga*). The more perennial streams and rivers support strips of riparian forest dominated by waterberries *Syzygium* spp.. The park was gazetted in 1972 and before that the area was protected by the Lozi Paramount Chief, the Litunga, but despite being a national park, the area supports a high human population.

■ Birds

Huge numbers of waterbirds can congregate, particularly as water levels are dropping. Slaty Egret is regular; groups of over 30 have been recorded on several occasions and in August 2001 over 100 were recorded (J. Mellenthin *in litt.*). At times, the site supports significant numbers of Wattled Cranes and over 1000 have been counted on several occasions (e.g. Leonard & Peters 1998) although the latest population estimate for the area is 600-700 (Kamweneshe & Beilfuss 2002). Southern Crowned Cranes are also common (>500 in Nov 2001, Kamweneshe & Beilfuss 2002) and the area would appear to be important for Saddle-billed Storks (Osborne 1978) with a recent population estimate of at least 200 (Kamweneshe & Beilfuss 2002). Spur-winged Goose can be numerous (>2000 in Nov 2001, Kamweneshe & Beilfuss 2002) and to date, it is the only known Zambian breeding locality for Whiskered Terns (Conant 1980).

A characteristic sight on the plains and near pans is huge flocks of certain gregarious waders. Both Ruff and Caspian Plovers can occur in very large numbers but it is perhaps the pratincoles for which Liuwa is more famous. Both Black-winged and Common Pratincoles can be abundant, the former on passage from their Palearctic breeding grounds and the latter a wandering resident. The migration of Black-winged seems to take place through a rather narrow corridor which passes across eastern Angola and western Zambia. On 15 November

1977 D. R. Aspinwall and P. A. Conant witnessed many thousands of southbound birds in Liuwa and the total count for that day alone was estimated to be countable in hundreds of thousands, with at least 100,000 counted and with a true figure possibly closer to 1,000,000 (Anon 1977, Aspinwall 1977). Records of tens of thousands have been reported fairly regularly and as recently as 1997(Leonard & Peters 1998).

Two larks are represented by subspecies that are virtually endemic to Liuwa and its immediate environs; Clapper Larks *Mirafra apiata jappi* are common and Pink-billed Larks *Spizocorys conirostris makawai* abundant on the plain. Of the other six species of lark known, Grey-backed Sparrow-Lark is perhaps the most numerous. Other typical grassland birds include Greater Kestrel, White-bellied Bustard and Long-tailed Whydah. Both Black Crows and Common Kestrels occur but are less common. Among a broad selection of raptors are Tawny and Martial Eagles, Secretary

Bird and the occasional Palm-nut Vulture. Recently, large numbers of Black-rumped Buttonquails have been recorded, though these may be seasonal (Beel 1996).

See summary box for key species. The park has been fairly well explored, though the wooded habitats have generally received less attention than the plain and the total number of species recorded to date is 328.

■ Other flora and fauna

A wide variety of mammals occur. Liuwa is best known for its particularly large numbers of Wildebeest *Connochaetes taurinus* (LR/cd) that comprise the second largest migratory population in the world. A recent survey counted 35,000 and estimates the total population to be even higher (Kamweneshe & Beilfuss 2002). The same survey counted 2500 Common Zebra *Equus (quagga) burchelli*. Both Tsessebe *Damaliscus lunatus* (LR/cd) and Red Lechwe *Kobus leche leche*

Wildebeest on the Liuwa Plains (Richard Beilfuss)

Liuwa Plains when flooded. (Richard Beilfuss)

(LR/cd) occur but their status is unclear. Lechwe appear to move in during the rains from the Luanginga plains and c.400 were recorded in June 2002 (J. Mellenthin *in litt.*). Other mammals include Lion *Panthera leo* (VU), Wild Dog *Lycaon pictus* (EN), Cheetah *Acinonyx jubatus* (VU), Spotted Hyaena *Crocuta crocuta*, Spot-necked Otter *Lutra maculicollis* (VU), Oribi *Ourebia ourebi* (LR/cd) and Southern Reedbuck *Redunca arundinum* (LR/cd). Interesting reptiles include the burrowing skink *Sepsina angolensis* and the skink *Mabuya capensis*.

Globally threatened species		
Slaty Egret	Vulnerable	regular visitor, concentrations of more than 10 not uncommon, may breed
Lappet-faced Vulture	Vulnerable	fairly common breeding resident
Pallid Harrier	Near-threatened	scarce passage migrant and probably non-breeding visitor
Lesser Kestrel	Vulnerable	passage migrant and probably non-breeding visitor
Wattled Crane	Vulnerable	common visitor and breeding resident
Denham's Bustard	Near-threatened	occasional, probably breeds
Black-winged Pratincole	Data deficient	abundant passage migrant
Great Snipe	Near-threatened	occasional non-breeding visitor, though may be more common than records suggest
African Skimmer	Near-threatened	occasional

Biome-restricted species		
Zambezian	6 endemics	8 near-endemics

Globally important congregations	
(i) regularly holds >1% of biogeographic population of a congregatory waterbird	
Black Egret	probably >1000 (Apr 1980)
Slaty Egret	>100 (Aug 2001)
Wattled Crane	>1,000 (Nov 1997)
Common Pratincole	"thousands" (Nov 1997)
Black-winged Pratincole	>10,000 (Nov 1997), 20,000 (Nov 1978), >100,000 (Nov 1977)
(iii) regularly holds >20,000 waterbirds	

Species of regional conservation concern	
Goliath Heron	occasional
Saddle-billed Stork	common breeding resident
Bateleur	common resident
African Marsh Harrier	occasional resident
Southern Crowned Crane	common resident
White-bellied Bustard	common resident
Yellow-throated Sandgrouse	occasional breeding visitor
Southern Ground Hornbill	fairly common resident

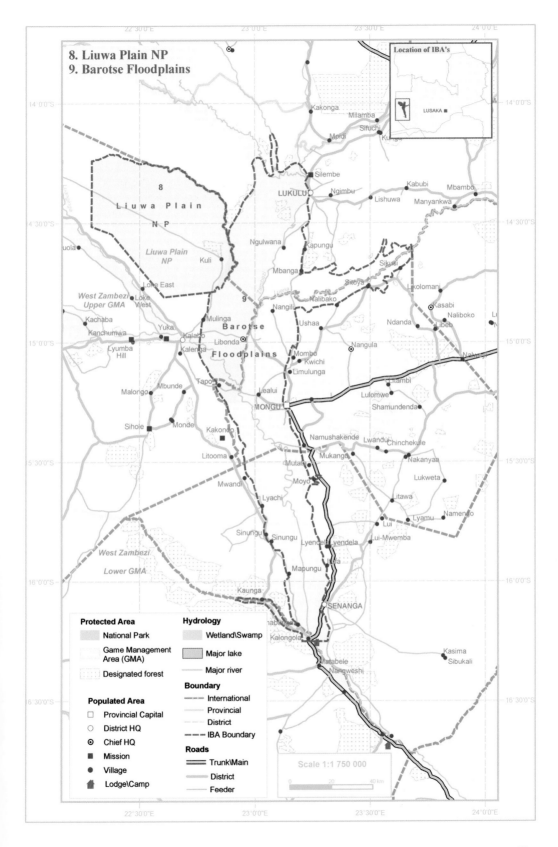

8. Liuwa Plain NP
9. Barotse Floodplains

Location of IBA's

LUSAKA ■

Kakonga
Milamba
Sifuchi
Kunga
Mpidi

Silembe
LUKULU
Ngimbu
Lishuwa
Kabubi
Mbambo
Manyankwa

8

Liuwa Plain
N P

Ngulwana
Kapungu
Mbanga
Sikusi
Sitoya
Likolomani

Liuwa Plain
NP
Kuli

uola

Lola East

West Zambezi
Upper GMA
Loke
West

9

Nangili
Nalibako
Ushaa
Ndanda
Kasabi
Naliboko
Libeb

Kachaba
Yuka
Mulinga
Barotse

Kanchumwa
Kalabo
Libonda
Mombo
Nangula
Nalwego
Kalenga
Floodplains
Kwichi
Lyumba
Hill
Limulunga

Malongo
Mbunde
Tapo
Lealui
Litambi
MONGU
Lulomwe
Shamundenda

Sihole
Monde
Kakondo

Litooma
Namushakende
Lwandu
Chinchekule
Nakanyaa
Mukango
Mutango
Lukweta
Mwandi
Moyo
Litawa
Lyachi
Namengo
Lui
Lyamu
Sinungu
Sinungu
Lyendela
Lui-Mwemba
Mapungu
Lula

West Zambezi
Lower GMA

Kaunga
SENANGA

Kalongola
Kasima
Sibukali

Matabele
Nangweshi

Protected Area
  National Park
  Game Management Area (GMA)
  Designated forest

Populated Area
□ Provincial Capital
○ District HQ
◉ Chief HQ
■ Mission
● Village
⌂ Lodge\Camp

Hydrology
  Wetland\Swamp
  Major lake
  Major river

Boundary
International
Provincial
District
IBA Boundary

Roads
Trunk\Main
District
Feeder

Scale 1:1 750 000
0   20   40 km

■ Conservation issues

Human encroachment needs very careful monitoring. According to NP staff there are over 160 villages within the boundary and consequently there are many cattle as well. Lions are killed as they prey on the cattle and the Lion population is likely to be declining. Over-grazing could become a problem and also the clearing of land for agriculture and wood for fuel. There is much illegal hunting, affecting both mammals and birds. For example, both species of crane are targeted with neck snares in shallow water. Illegal fishing is common and fire is also a threat.

■ Information for visitors

The park accessible only during the dry season and is reached from Kalabo where visitors are advised to visit the park office before continuing into the park itself. ZAWA scouts are often able to accompany visitors and their navigational skills can be invaluable once in the park where the road network is very limited and you may find yourself driving off-road for much of the time. Just outside Kalabo there is a pontoon to cross the Luanginga but when the water level is low motorists must ford the river. The area is very sandy and four wheel drive is almost essential. For the very adventurous it is also possible to approach the park from Lukulu where there is a pontoon across the Zambezi at the hospital. Continue by driving north-west at first and further on locals will be able to direct you to the points at which it is safe to cross the Lungwebungu and Luambimba rivers. There are no permanent tourist facilities in the park although safari operators attempt to set up camps from time to time and one or two companies have been operating mobile safaris in the park. Simple accommodation can be found in Kalabo but most visitors are self-sufficient campers. It is advisable to carry extra fuel as the supply in Kalabo is erratic and a GPS can be very useful.

9 Barotse Floodplains

Admin region: Lukulu, Kalabo, Mongu and Senanga Districts, Western Province
Co-ordinates: 14°20'-16°15'S 22°40'-23°30'E
Area: c.730,000ha (GMA: c.240,000ha, unprotected: c.490,000ha)
Altitude: 1000-1060m
Status: unprotected, Game Management Area
Categories: Globally threatened species, Biome-restricted species, Globally important congregations
International site code: ZM006   **Map:** p 61

■ Site description

The immense floodplain of the Zambezi (sometimes referred to as the Bulozi Plain) and the adjacent floodplains form a complex and highly seasonal wetland system. Following good rains, much of the area becomes inundated between about February and June but by the end of the dry season and at the beginning of the rains water is generally restricted to the main river channels and larger pools and there is very little permanent swamp. The terrain is not completely flat and the scattered small rises become islands when the water is high. These often support small stands of *Acacia albida*. There are small patches of thicket and *Syzygium guineense* along the main river channel and fringing some oxbows, but in general riparian vegetation is sparse. In some areas (particularly in the north) there are short grass plains on higher ground which are not flooded and there are also patches of *Diplorhynchus* scrub and mature *Borassus* forest in such parts.

When the flood waters rise, the area near Mongu hosts one of the most famous traditional ceremonies in Zambia known as the Ku-omboka. This involves the retreat of the Lozi King (the Litunga) from his dry season residence at Lealui to his palace on the higher ground at the edge of the plain in Limulunga. The King is transported in the royal barge, an enormous wooden canoe that was built around the beginning of the twentieth century. It is propelled by ninety-six polers and accompanied by a fleet of other, smaller boats (Reader 1998). During the dry season, the floodplains support dense populations of subsistence farmers and herdsmen, most of whom also leave their temporary villages with their cattle as the water rises.

Some of the land to the west of the main river channel falls within the West Zambezi Upper GMA (No. 1) but the majority is unprotected. Much of the area is poorly known and more work is required to define the exact limits of an IBA. Provisionally, the area incorporates all the terrain falling within the high water mark from the area of the Senanga Ferry north to and including the Luena Flats.

■ Birds

The area is poorly known but it is undoubtedly important for a wide variety of waterbirds and several observers have received local reports of substantial breeding colonies during flood periods (e.g. Van Daele & Stjernstedt 2001). Further fieldwork is likely to reveal that several species occur in numbers exceeding their 1% thresholds. Species that have been recorded in large numbers, but for which precise figures are lacking include Reed Cormorant, Openbill Stork, Spur-winged Goose, Common Pratincole, Caspian Plover, Whiskered Tern and African Skimmer.

The Luena area would appear to hold a rich variety of species and African Skimmers are known to breed. The eastern part of the Luena Flats has not been well explored, but some preliminary fieldwork suggests that it may hold a very interesting

African Skimmer

diversity of flora and fauna (Van Daele & Stjernstedt 2001).

A small number of Zambezian endemics occur, such as Coppery-tailed Coucal and Chirping Cisticola. The area is one of the few in Zambia where Avocets are regular and breeding is strongly suspected (Van Daele 2001). Southern Brown-throated Weavers are locally common, particularly near stands of *Phragmites*.

See summary box for key species. Despite being poorly known, the total number of species recorded to date is relatively high at 333.

■ Other flora and fauna

Very few large mammals remain (Timberlake 2000, Jeffery *et al.* 1996). Spot-necked Otter *Lutra maculicollis* (VU) and Spring Hare *Pedetes capensis* (VU) both occur, though their status is not known. There are several endemic reptiles and amphibians; the burrowing skink *Typhlacontias gracilis*, the blind legless skink *Typhlosaurus jappi*, the spade-snouted worm-lizard *Dalophia ellenbergeri*, the beaked snake *Rhamphiophis acutus jappi* and the shovel-snouted frog *Hemisus barotseensis*. The plated lizard *Gerrhosaurus auritus* occurs here at the northern limit of its range. Nile Crocodiles *Crocodylus niloticus* are still relatively common. The type specimens of the plants *Gloriosa sessiliflora* (*Colchicaceae*) and *Emiliella drummondii* (*Asteraceae*) were collected on the Barotse Plains and a *Crinum* species, common and widespread on the Bulozi Plain, has not yet been described (M. Bingham *in litt.*)

■ Conservation issues

Overgrazing, burning and subsistence farming have all affected the area (Van Daele & Stjernstedt 2001). Recently there have been attempts to re-establish the traditional land management practices, which would benefit the environment. The area is relatively densely populated and there is likely to be much subsistence hunting. There are a few traditional bird-hunting areas known as 'Sitaka' where nestlings are 'harvested' from breeding colonies and this must have an impact on the local populations. Dogs are numerous and pose a considerable threat to ground-nesting birds. Overfishing and use of fine-mesh mosquito nets for fishing are increasing problems.

■ Information for visitors

On the eastern side, tarmac roads run as far as Mongu and Senanga. There are dirt roads and tracks around and across much of the area, but many of these are seasonal. There are vehicle ferries at Lukulu, Mongu and Senanga and these also stop operating when the floodwaters are high. Accommodation can be found in the larger towns and there are several safari camps along the Zambezi between Senanga and Sesheke. The Kuomboka usually takes place in March or April and its date is announced in the national press a week or two in advance. For those wishing to explore the more obscure parts of the plains, both a local guide and a GPS are advisable in addition to the usual off-road requirements of good clearance and four

Nile Crocodile (Andrea Leonard)

wheel drive. Areas such as the Luena Flats are only easily accessible for a short period between about August and October.

Globally threatened species		
Slaty Egret	Vulnerable	occasional, possibly breeds
Lesser Flamingo	Near-threatened	rare visitor
Lappet-faced Vulture	Vulnerable	fairly common resident
Pallid Harrier	Near-threatened	non-breeding visitor
Lesser Kestrel	Vulnerable	non-breeding visitor and passage-migrant
Wattled Crane	Vulnerable	fairly common, probably breeds
Denham's Bustard	Near-threatened	occasional, status uncertain
Black-winged Pratincole	Data deficient	passage migrant
Great Snipe	Near-threatened	non-breeding visitor
African Skimmer	Near-threatened	breeding resident

Biome-restricted species		
Zambezian	4 endemics	4 near-endemics

Globally important congregations	
(i) regularly holds >1% of biogeographic population of a congregatory waterbird	
Wattled Crane	145 (date untraced)

Species of regional conservation concern	
Common Bittern	status uncertain, known from two localities, probably scarce breeding resident
Goliath Heron	uncommon breeding resident
Saddle-billed Stork	occasional, probably breeds
Bateleur	fairly common
African Marsh Harrier	common resident
Southern Crowned Crane	occasional
White-bellied Bustard	status uncertain
Yellow-throated Sandgrouse	regular visitor, probably breeds
Southern Ground Hornbill	fairly common
Yellow-billed Oxpecker	status uncertain
Red-billed Oxpecker	status uncertain

10 Sioma Ngwezi National Park

Admin region: Shangombo and Sesheke Districts, Western Province
Co-ordinates: 16°58'-17°37'S 23°03'-23°51'E
Area: 527,600ha   **Altitude:** 970-1000m
Status: National Park
Categories: Globally threatened species, Biome-restricted species
International site code: ZM007   **Map:** p 67

■ Site description

Situated in the dry south-west of the country, this is the third largest of Zambia's National Parks. Its southernmost boundary is the international border with Namibia and the Mashi River (also known as the Kwando) lies along the park's south-western boundary. (It should be noted though that the international border with Angola is delineated by the edge of the floodplain on the Zambian side and not the river.) Much of the area is flat, very sandy and dry with the only a few isolated pools providing permanent water. The vegetation is dominated by Kalahari woodland, a degraded form of mutemwa (Zambezi Teak *Baikiaea plurijuga*) that has usually been opened up as a result of burning. There are a few patches of undisturbed mutemwa, some stretches of mopane woodland and areas of grassland and thornveld where the vegetation is dominated by *Acacia* spp..

■ Birds

A number of species on the Zambian list are restricted to the dry south-west of the country in Sesheke and Shangombo districts. Most occur within the site and many favour the small areas of thornveld such as Acacia Pied Barbet, Tit-babbler, Marico Flycatcher, Crimson-breasted Shrike, Cape Glossy Starling and Black-cheeked Waxbill. Burchell's Starling prefers more open areas and is often in the vicinity of camel thorns *Acacia erioloba* and Burchell's Sandgrouse is found on or near the Mashi floodplain. In the latter area, Southern Brown-throated Weaver can be found in the reeds. Bradfield's Hornbill is more of a generalist and is frequent in Kalahari woodland, which tends to support a selection of species not dissimilar to, but poorer than miombo. Other Zambezian species occurring include Dickinson's Kestrel, Racket-tailed Roller, Sousa's Shrike and Sharp-tailed Starling. Rufous-cheeked Nightjar and

Fawn-coloured Lark are both characteristic birds of the area.

Both Slaty Egret and Wattled Crane have been recorded although further work is required to gauge their true status. Such exploration might also reveal the presence of Corn Crake and Great Snipe as both have been recorded from areas not far outside the park boundary. Similarly, Black-winged Pratincole is probably a common passage migrant.

See summary box for key species. The area is not particularly well known or explored and further work during the rains is desirable. The total number of species recorded to date is 324.

■ Other flora and fauna

Mammals known to occur include fairly large (though seasonally fluctuating) numbers of African Elephants *Loxodonta africana* (EN) and Zambia's only population of Southern Giraffes *Giraffa camelopardalis angolensis* (LR/cd). Antelope reported recently include Steinbuck *Raphicercus campestrus*, Sable *Hippotragus niger* (LR/cd) and Roan *H. equinus* (LR/cd). Spring Hare *Pedetes*

Burchell's Sandgrouse

Kudu (Andrea Leonard)

capensis (VU) is probably still common, but Cheetah *Acinonyx jubatus* (VU) was probably never more than scarce and may no longer occur. There were sightings of Wild Dog *Lycaon pictus* (EN) in the 1990s (Buk 1995) though the current status of this species is not known.

■ Conservation issues

The small number of settlements in the area present no significant threat and much of the area is un-

suitable for habitation. However, there is much illegal hunting and the pressure on larger mammals is ever-increasing. The restricted water availability merely compounds this problem. Reports of large-scale illegal timber extraction (notably Zambezi Teak *Baikiaea plurijuga*) require investigation.

■ Information for visitors

Most visitors reach the park from the Sesheke-Sioma road, turning west from this about 30km north of the Sesheke ferry. This sandy track leads to the park boundary at Ngwesi pools and then on through the park all the way to Imusho on the edge of the Mashi floodplain. It is also possible to travel from here to Shangombo on a road that runs parallel to the Mashi. A cut line along the Namibian border is fairly well maintained and provides access to the southernmost part of the park, though visitors are advised to check both the condition of the road and the security situation before embarking on such a trip. There are no facilities for visitors so self-sufficiency is vital. It is worth taking extra fuel and water as well as maps and navigational aids. High clearance and four wheel drive are both important. Recently, several tourist camps have been built along the banks of the Zambezi nearby and some of the operators have plans to take safaris into the park. Whether or not this happens, such camps can be a good source of local information, as is the ZAWA camp at Sioma Falls, a popular tourist spot on the Zambezi nearby.

Globally threatened species		
Slaty Egret	Vulnerable	status uncertain, probably regular
Wattled Crane	Vulnerable	status uncertain, probably regular
Biome-restricted species		
Eastern	-	1 near-endemic
Zambezian	9 endemics	8 near-endemics
Species of regional conservation concern		
Saddle-billed Stork	regular	
Bateleur	common	
African Marsh Harrier	probably regular	
Yellow-throated Sandgrouse	regular visitor, probably breeds	
Southern Ground Hornbill	common resident	
Yellow-billed Oxpecker	status uncertain	
Red-billed Oxpecker	status uncertain	

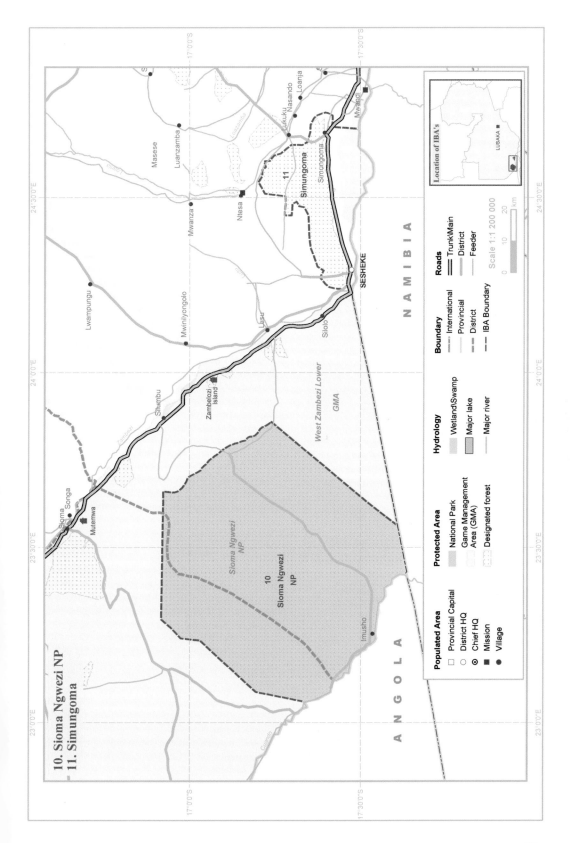

10. Sioma Ngwezi NP
11. Simungoma

Populated Area
☐ Provincial Capital
○ District HQ
◉ Chief HQ
■ Mission
● Village

Protected Area
National Park
Game Management Area (GMA)
Designated forest

Hydrology
Wetland\Swamp
Major lake
Major river

Boundary
International
Provincial
District
IBA Boundary

Roads
Trunk\Main
District
Feeder

Scale 1:1 200 000

Location of IBA's

LUSAKA ■

NAMIBIA

ANGOLA

SESHEKE

West Zambezi Lower GMA

10
Sioma Ngwezi NP

11
Simungoma

67

11 Simungoma

Admin region: Sesheke District, Western Province
Co-ordinates: 17°13'-17°32'S 24°15'-24°45'E
Area: c.100,000ha (NF: c.60,000ha; unprotected: c.40,000ha)
Altitude: 710-970m
Status: National Forest, unprotected
Categories: Globally threatened species, Biome-restricted species
International site code: ---   **Map:** p 67

■ Site description

An area of floodplain, woodland and mutemwa straddling the western end of the Livingstone-Sesheke road. The Zambezi marks the southern boundary (as well as the Namibian border) and a complex system of channels and ox-bows flank its main course. Both papyrus and *Phragmites* swamps are found in some of the more permanent wetlands and further away from the river are several ephemeral pans. A broad, sandy floodplain extends back for several kilometres and this is dotted with small elevations some of which become islands in years of heavy flood. Characteristic trees of these islands are *Phoenix reclinata* and very large *Acacia albida*. Beyond the plain is woodland of various types. Some areas are dominated by *Terminalia sericea,* but of more interest are the stands of *Acacia* woodland, a habitat that is uncommon in Zambia. To the north of the main road, the land rises and here the vege-tation is principally mutemwa (forest dominated by Zambezi Teak *Baikiaea plurijuga*). Most of this section falls within a National Forest (No. 194) and it includes some of the finest remaining examples of this endangered forest type. Where burnt and degraded the mutemwa becomes Kalahari woodland and there are also small scattered, grassy plains. The area has a relatively small human population, although the density is higher along the Zambezi where fishing is productive and cattle-herding feasible.

■ Birds

A very wide variety of waterbirds occur, particularly as the floodwaters recede at the end of the rains when pools regularly attract Slaty Egrets. Further fieldwork may show that both this species and African Skimmer occur in numbers that exceed their 1% thresholds. Both Southern Brown-throated Weaver and Swamp Boubou occur in riparian growth and many bank-nesting species are attracted to the sand cliffs along the Zambezi. It is the only locality in Zambia from which there are several records of both Burchell's Sandgrouse and Kori Bustard. The former appears to be a fairly common breeding resident whereas the latter is scarce. Three other species of bustard have been recorded; White-bellied inhabits the driest parts of the plain, Black-bellied Bustard is found throughout the grassland and scrub and Red-crested Korhaan is in the open woodland. Many other species with restricted Zambian ranges occur. Both Burchell's Starling and Cape Glossy Starling occur around the edges of the plain and scrubby woodland often supports Scaly-feathered Finch. Red-eyed Bulbul is an unpredictable wanderer found throughout the area but many species are more restricted to the *Acacia* woodland, including

Scaly-feathered Finches

Kori Bustard

Acacia Pied Barbet, Tit-babbler, Marico Flycatcher, Crimson-breasted Shrike, Black-cheeked Waxbill and Shaft-tailed Widow.

See summary box for key species. The floodplains and *Acacia* are relatively well known but the Mutemwa has not been well explored. Total number of species recorded to date: 321.

■ Other flora and fauna

Very poorly known. Spring Hare *Pedetes capensis* (VU) is common and African Elephants *Loxodonta africana* (EN) wander through occasionally. An Aardwolf *Proteles cristatus* was found dead on the main road close to the site in 1999 (P. Van Daele *in litt.*).

■ Conservation issues

Perhaps the greatest concern is the rapid demise of mutemwa. Very little undisturbed mutemwa remains anywhere as it is not fire-resistant and once burnt, it never fully recovers. Timber extraction, both legal and illegal, has also contributed to the problem as fire is used to open up the dense under-storey. Furthermore, very large, old trees are now a rare sight. Elsewhere within the IBA, over-fishing, hunting and snaring are encountered with some regularity and the human population along the Zambezi would appear to be growing.

■ Information for visitors

At the time of writing the main Livingstone-

Globally threatened species		
Slaty Egret	Vulnerable	common at times, may breed but exact status uncertain
Lappet-faced Vulture	Vulnerable	occasional, may breed
Lesser Kestrel	Vulnerable	occasional passage migrant and non-breeding visitor
Wattled Crane	Vulnerable	occasional visitor, exact status uncertain
African Skimmer	Near-threatened	regular breeding visitor
Biome-restricted species		
Eastern	-	2 near-endemics
Zambezian	5 endemics	2 near-endemics
Species of regional conservation concern		
Saddle-billed Stork	occasional	
Bateleur	fairly common breeding resident	
African Marsh Harrier	fairly common breeding resident	
White-bellied Bustard	rare resident	
Southern Ground Hornbill	uncommon resident	

69

Sesheke road is being resurfaced and this will provide easy access to the locality. However, there are not many other tracks within the site and visitors wanting to explore will require a sturdy four-wheel drive vehicle and navigational aids. The settlement from which the IBA takes its name is on the main road at the turn-off to Mulobezi. To reach the floodplain, turn south here, and follow one of the vague cattle or sand-sledge tracks which all lead to the river eventually. Within the woodland these tracks can be difficult to pass due to deep loose sand, but once on the floodplain, driving around is simple (as is getting lost - so be pre-

pared). Between Simungoma and Sesheke, several tracks lead north from the main road into the National Forest. These can also be very sandy. Once the main road is complete, day visits to this IBA will be easy from Livingstone. Alternatively, basic accommodation can be found in Sesheke and there are tourist lodges on the west bank of the Zambezi further upstream. Camping is easy and recommended for those who are self sufficient and numerous spots around the edge of the floodplain or on the 'islands' make ideal campsites. Some of the best pockets of *Acacia* woodland are along the main road, just east of Simungoma.

12 Machile

Admin region: Sesheke and Kalomo Districts, Western and Southern Provinces
Co-ordinates: 16°44'-17°27'S 24°58'-25°50'E
Area: c.477,000ha (GMA & LFs: c.155,000, unprotected: c.322,000)
Altitude: 950-1110m
Status: Game Management Area, Local Forests, unprotected
Categories: Globally threatened species, Restricted-range species, Biome-restricted species, Globally important congregations
International site code: ZM008   **Map:** p 73

■ Site description

An area dominated by mopane woodland, with some grassland, floodplain, thicket, savanna woodland and remnant mutemwa. It covers sections of the mid-Machile, Simatanga, Sichifulo and Sala rivers, though sources of permanent surface water are rather limited. Some of the floodplains are quite extensive, especially along the Sichifulo. The area is bisected by the Livingstone-Mulobezi railway line and there are small villages scattered throughout. The site's importance lies in its population of Black-cheeked Lovebirds and at present the most important areas within the site for this species are from Mulanga (16°55'S 25°17'E) east to Bombwe (17°07'S 25°20'E), west to Magumwi (17°07'S 25°06'E) and south to Adonsi (17°12'S 25°01'E) and also the Lunungu catchment (c.17°22'S 25°27'E) (Warburton 2003). Part of the area lies within Sichifulo GMA (No. 8) and the site also encompasses four Local Forests (Nos. 2, 24, 25,

37), three of which lie within the GMA. People are present generally at fairly low densities, partly due to the difficulty of farming on heavy mopane soils and also due to the scarcity of water in the dry season. However, the population is steadily increasing. Most villages are concentrated along the river and stream courses, where subsistence agriculture is the predominant occupation. Here, maize, sorghum and millet are important crops, whilst cattle are also raised. Seasonal hunters and fishermen also visit the area. There is very little economic development, though forestry was important earlier in the 20th Century. Water is in very short supply from June to December, as all rivers in the area are ephemeral. The only naturally occurring water sources are scattered shallow pools, few of which last the entire dry season. The block of mopane woodland within the region is associated with alluvial clay deposits left by an ancient wetland on what was probably an earlier course of the Kafue River (M. Bingham *in*

Black-cheeked Lovebirds (Louise Warburton)

litt.). Its isolation also explains the localised distribution of the Black-cheeked Lovebird (Warburton 2003).

■ Birds

This is the stronghold of the Black-cheeked Lovebird and supports about two thirds of the known population (total population estimated at c.8,000 individuals). This is Africa's most localised parrot, with a core range estimated at 2,500 km^2 (Dodman 1996a, Dodman *et al.* 2000). Only described in 1906, the Black-cheeked Lovebird suffered severe population decline through the 1920s due to capture for the bird trade. The population appears never to have recovered, despite a Zambian trade ban in 1930. The species is closely associated to mopane woodland and is never far from permanent sources of surface water as birds need to drink daily.

Other typical mopane birds include Red-billed Hornbill, Southern Grey-headed Sparrow, White-browed Sparrow-weaver and the Zambezian endemics Arnot's Chat and Southern Long-tailed Starling. Where there is savanna woodland dominated by *Acacia* spp. species may include Marico Flycatcher, Marico Sunbird, Scaly-feathered Finch and Black-cheeked Waxbill. Wattled Cranes occur in pairs or family groups at permanent wetlands towards the north of the area.

See summary box for key species. The area is fairly well known. Total number of species recorded to date: 302.

■ Other flora and fauna

Mammals known to occur include Spring Hare *Pedetes capensis* (VU), Spotted Hyaena *Crocuta crocuta* (LR/cd), small numbers of Lion *Panthera leo* (VU), Ground Pangolin *Smutsia temminckii* (LR/nt), African Elephant *Loxodonta africana* (EN), Hippopotamus *Hippopotamus amphibius*, African Buffalo *Syncerus caffer* (LR/cd), Sharpe's Grysbok *Raphicerus sharpei* (LR/cd), Oribi *Ourebia ourebi* (LR/cd), Impala *Aepyceros melampus* (LR/cd), Wildebeest *Connochaetes taurinus* (LR/cd)(Nov. 1999), Roan *Hippotragus equinus* (LR/cd) and Sable Antelopes *H. niger* (LR/cd) (L. Warburton *in litt.*).

■ Conservation issues

Desiccation due to climate change has perhaps resulted in the decrease of dry-season surface water upon which Black-cheeked Lovebirds depend. From 1950 to 1997 the average annual rainfall within the species' range declined by over 5mm (Warburton 2003). There is some small-scale hunting for local consumption, but overall the lovebird's continued existence is assisted by the creation and maintenance of dry season surface water supplies, particularly along the Sichifulo and Lunungu Rivers. However, the birds are very cautious drinkers and avoid water sources which are subject to disturbance at peak lovebird drinking times. Constant disturbance probably deters lovebirds and if no other suitable water is available the birds will desert the area. Of particular concern is the recent establishment of hand-pumped boreholes along the river catchments. It is logical to assume that the communities living close to the pumps will decrease their well and dam-digging activities and this will further deprive the lovebirds of drinking points (Warburton 2003). Other poten-

Mopane woodland towards the end of the dry season.
(Tim Dodman)

tial threats to the species include destruction of habitat for firewood, resumption of illegal trade and disease (principally the Psittacine Beak and Feather Disease Virus) (Warburton 2003). A detailed 4 year study of Black-cheeked Lovebirds to determine its ecological requirements and devise a conservation strategy for its survival has recently been completed (Warburton 2003).

Globally threatened species		
Lappet-faced Vulture	Vulnerable	resident, probably breeds
Lesser Kestrel	Vulnerable	passage migrant and non-breeding visitor
Wattled Crane	Vulnerable	visitor, some probably resident breeders
Black-cheeked Lovebird	Vulnerable	breeding resident (see text)

Restricted-range species		
Black-cheeked Lovebird	s051	breeding resident (see text)

Biome-restricted species		
Eastern	-	2 near-endemics
Zambezian	5 endemics	5 near-endemics

Globally important congregations	
(ii) regularly holds >1% global population of a terrestrial species	
Black-cheeked Lovebird	7,500 (Warburton 2003)

Species of regional conservation concern	
Goliath Heron	occasional
Saddle-billed Stork	occasional
Bateleur	common, probably breeds
Yellow-throated Sandgrouse	fairly common visitor, may breed
Southern Ground Hornbill	fairly common resident
Yellow-billed Oxpecker	common resident
Red-billed Oxpecker	common resident

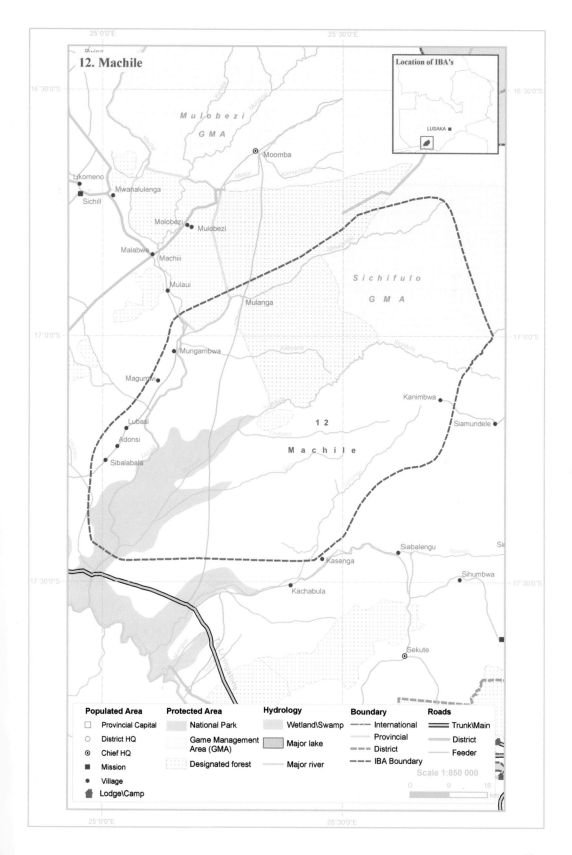

12. Machile

Location of IBA's

LUSAKA ■

Mulobezi GMA

Moomba

Likomeno
Mwanalulenga
Sichill
Molobezi
Mulobezi
Malabwe
Machiii
Mulaui
Mulanga

Sichifulo GMA

Mungambwa

Magumwi

Kanimbwa

Lubasi
Adonsi

Siamundele

1 2

Sibalabala

Machile

Siabalengu

Kasenga

Sihumbwa

Kachabula

Sekute

Populated Area
- ☐ Provincial Capital
- ○ District HQ
- ◉ Chief HQ
- ■ Mission
- • Village
- 🏠 Lodge\Camp

Protected Area
- National Park
- Game Management Area (GMA)
- Designated forest

Hydrology
- Wetland\Swamp
- Major lake
- Major river

Boundary
- International
- Provincial
- District
- IBA Boundary

Roads
- Trunk\Main
- District
- Feeder

Scale 1:850 000

0   9   18
km

73

■ Information for visitors

The area is relatively remote, undeveloped and largely roadless although the Livingstone-Sesheke road is currently being resurfaced. Visitors will require a sturdy four-wheel drive vehicle and those spending more time in the area must be self-sufficient, even for drinking water. The nearest fuel is in Livingstone. The area is only easily accessible during the drier months (May to November) and overnight visitors are advised to introduce themselves and their purpose to local village headmen (Warburton 2002).

13 Mosi-Oa-Tunya National Park and the Batoka Gorge

Admin region: Livingstone, Kazungula and Kalomo Districts, Southern Province
Co-ordinates: 17°49'-18°01'S 25°44'-26°34'E
Area: c. 8,600ha (NP: 6600ha, unprotected: c.2000ha)
Altitude: 600-900m
Status: National Park, World Heritage Site, National Monuments, unprotected
Categories: Globally threatened species, Biome-restricted species
International site code: ZM009   **Map:** p 77

■ Site description

Mosi-Oa-Tunya is loosely translated as 'the smoke that thunders'. This is the Kololo name for the great natural wonder more widely known as the Victoria Falls. Above this famous feature, the Zambezi reaches about 2km in width but below the falls, the river flows through the narrow Batoka Gorge for over 100km. The site comprises the Mosi-Oa-Tunya National Park and the adjacent Batoka Gorge, downstream as far as Sidinda Island (18°01'S 26°34'E). It lies adjacent to the Zimbabwean IBA ZW011: Batoka Gorge (Childes & Mundy 2001).

At 6600ha, the park is Zambia's smallest, but it is the most popular. It encompasses a 25km section of the north bank of the Zambezi both above and below the falls. There are 6 National Monuments within the park and an area of about 1000ha has been fenced and is managed as a zoological park. Above the falls are riparian habitats such as sand bars and cliffs, fringing forest and when the water is low, exposed rocks and rapids. Away from the main river mopane woodland dominates the shallow basaltic soils and baobabs *Adansonia digitata* are common. On the Kalahari sand there is Kalahari woodland and a few small patches of mutemwa.

The falls themselves reach a maximum height of 108m and the maximum mean flow of water is about 540 million litres per minute. The flow of the river is controlled, to an extent, by a hydroelectric power station though this only has a noticeable effect when water levels are low. Below the falls the river has carved an immense gorge through the basalt lava rocks. The first section runs in a series of close zigzags, each of which represents the line of a previous waterfall. Here the gorge is about 110m deep and characterised by precipitous cliffs. Further downstream the gorge reaches a depth of 350m, but it is considerably weathered and the sides are therefore more gently sloping.

■ Birds

The site is most important for the species occurring in and around the gorges and most notably the Taita Falcon. Unfortunately, many recent publications (e.g. Childes & Mundy 1998) have continued to herald this area as the species' stronghold when its status has undoubtedly changed. The most suitable habitat is found along the first 60km of gorge below the falls. Intensive surveys carried out along this stretch between 1989 and 1994 revealed 6 pairs of Taita Falcons and 13 pairs of Peregrine Falcons (Hartley 2000a), though the true figures were thought to be higher. Similar surveys between 1999 and 2001 yielded signs of occupation at two nesting cliffs, but only two sightings of Taita

The Victoria Falls (Andrea Leonard)

Falcon and the two most recent surveys did not record the species at all. Other birds of prey appear to be thriving and both Peregrine Falcons and Lanner Falcons are increasing (Hartley 2000b, Weaver *et al.* 2002) though whether or not this is directly linked to the decline of the Taita Falcon is not clear. The status of Taita Falcons is further clouded by regular reports from tour operators that almost certainly refer to Peregrine Falcons.

Raptors in general are particularly well represented and the 45 species known include Bat Hawk, Gymnogene, Augur Buzzard, Black Eagle and Crowned Eagle. Along the rocky sides of the gorges are species such as African Rock Martin, Striped Pipit, Mocking Chat and Rock-loving Cisticola. There are also breeding Black Storks and African Black Swifts of the subspecies *hollidayi* that is endemic to the area.

When water levels drop, rocky islands and sand bars are exposed along the river above the falls. Rock Pratincoles breed in large numbers on the rocks whereas sand bars attract species such as White-fronted Sand Plover and African Skimmer. The riparian forest is home to species such as White-backed Night Heron, Western Banded Snake Eagle, African Finfoot and Brown-necked Parrot.

A number of interesting species have been recorded on the boundary of the National Park at the Livingstone Sewage Ponds including several rare waders and a variety of crakes. Slaty Egret has occurred on a few occasions. The general area also holds large numbers of indigobirds, amongst which can be found odd individuals imitating Brown Firefinch (Stjernstedt 1998). Such birds are thought to be Village Indigobirds that have switched hosts (Payne *et al.* 2002) although they may deserve specific status.

See summary box for key species. The National Park and upper stretches of the Batoka Gorge are very well known. The lower stretches of the gorge have received very little attention. Total number of species recorded to date: 384 (Mosi-Oa-Tunya NP: 381, Batoka Gorge: 154).

■ Other flora and fauna

A wide variety of mammals occur, including African Elephant *Loxodonta africana* (EN). Several species of large mammal have been introduced into the zoological park, several of which are not indigenous to the area such as Southern Giraffe *Giraffa camelopardalis angolensis* and White Rhinoceros *Ceratotherium simum*. A number of rare and interesting wetland herbs have been col-

The Batoka Gorge (Wouter Peters)

lected from the falls' spray zone. *Canscora kirkii* (*Gentianaceae*) is endemic to the area. The basalts have many species which are rare elsewhere in Zambia such as *Acacia senegal* var. *leiorhachis* (*Mimosoideae*), *Bolusanthus speciosus* (*Papilionoideae*) and *Terminalia stuhlmannii* (*Combretaceae*). For a thorough survey of the area's flora and fauna, see Phillipson (1975).

■ Conservation issues

Perhaps the most significant potential threat to the site is a proposed hydroelectric dam near Moemba Falls (17°56'S 26°06'E). This would flood much of the gorge and reduce the available habitat for cliff-nesting species such as Taita Falcon. The general level of disturbance in the area continues to rise. Although this can be attributed, in part, to the ever-increasing human population, the effects of the expanding tourist industry are much more obvious. Both light aircraft and helicopters quarter the area constantly; they tend to remain at relatively low altitudes and will sometimes fly within the gorge itself. More and more 'adrenaline sports' are being established in the gorges, including abseiling and jet-boating and in addition to the immediate disturbance these create, new roads and other developments quickly follow in the surrounding areas.

Globally threatened species		
Slaty Egret	Vulnerable	rare visitor
Lesser Flamingo	Near-threatened	rare visitor
Lappet-faced Vulture	Vulnerable	uncommon, may breed
Pallid Harrier	Near-threatened	rare non-breeding visitor
Lesser Kestrel	Vulnerable	regular passage migrant
Taita Falcon	Near-threatened	rare breeding resident
Corn Crake	Vulnerable	uncommon non-breeding visitor
Great Snipe	Near-threatened	occasional non-breeding visitor
African Skimmer	Near-threatened	regular breeding visitor
Biome-restricted species		
Eastern	-	1 near-endemic
Zambezian	5 endemics	7 near-endemics
Species of regional conservation concern		
Goliath Heron	occasional	
Saddle-billed Stork	occasional	
Bateleur	regular	
African Marsh Harrier	uncommon	
Yellow-billed Oxpecker	scarce visitor	
Red-billed Oxpecker	regular	

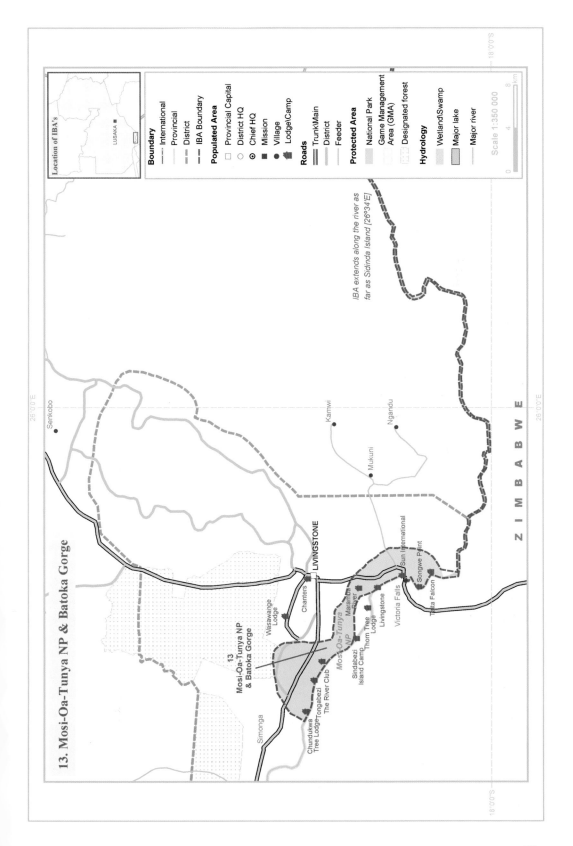

13. Mosi-Oa-Tunya NP & Batoka Gorge

13

Mosi-Oa-Tunya NP & Batoka Gorge

IBA extends along the river as far as Sidinda Island [26°34'E]

Boundary
- - - International
——— Provincial
- - - District
— — IBA Boundary

Populated Area
☐ Provincial Capital
○ District HQ
◉ Chief HQ
■ Mission
● Village
▲ Lodge/Camp

Roads
——— Trunk/Main
District
Feeder

Protected Area
National Park
Game Management Area (GMA)
Designated forest

Hydrology
Wetland/Swamp
Major lake
Major river

Scale 1:350 000

0   4   8 km

ZIMBABWE

Senkobo

Kamwi

Mukuni

Ngandu

LIVINGSTONE

Sun International

Songwe Point

Tata Falcon

Victoria Falls

Livingstone

Thorn Tree Lodge

Sindabezi Island Camp

Marambwa River

Chanters

Wasawange Lodge

Mosi-Oa-Tunya NP

The River Club

Tongabezi

Chundukwa Tree Lodge

Simonga

26°00'E

18°00'S

■ Information for visitors

Known as the 'tourist capital of Zambia', Livingstone offers facilities for every traveller, ranging from camp sites to five star hotels. The falls vary greatly through the year and are at their most dramatic between about February and May. However, one's view at this time is often restricted by the clouds of spray and between about May to August they are more easily seen. Towards the end of the dry season and at the beginning of the rains they can become very dry and it is also extremely hot at this time. To explore the gorge, turn left shortly before the border post and cross the railway, then follow any of a multitude of dirt tracks that lead off to various points along its length. To reach the sewage ponds, take the road to the zoological park and turn right after about 1km. As with all busy tourist towns, visitors should be alert to the possibility of pickpockets, confidence tricksters and other petty criminals typical of such areas.

14 Kafue National Park

Admin region: Mufumbwe, Kasempa, Mumbwa, Itezhi-tezhi, Kalomo Districts, North-western, Central, Southern Provinces
Co-ordinates: 14°03'-16°42'S 25°13'-26°46'E
Area: 2,240,000ha **Altitude:** 1000-1479m
Status: National Park
Categories: Globally threatened species, Restricted-range species, Biome-restricted species, Globally important congregations
International site code: ZM012 **Map:** p 82

■ Site description

About 200km west of Lusaka and spread over three provinces, Zambia's largest and oldest national park covers a broad section of the Kafue drainage above the Kafue Flats (IBA 15). The gently undulating terrain is dominated by the typically Zambezian miombo-dambo mosaic with smaller patches of munga and strips of riparian forest and thicket and along the major rivers. The Kafue river follows a relatively narrow and well-defined course through the park, becoming wider in only a few places where shallow, rocky rapids occur. Bisected by the Mongu road (M9), the park is conveniently divided into two sectors. The northern sector receives more rainfall and so the vegetation is richer and the miombo taller. In many areas such woodland is dominated by *Julbernardia paniculata*. In the north-western corner of the park are the Busanga swamps and adjacent floodplains. These are flanked by termitaria and there are scattered 'islands' of higher ground, some of which support vegetation such as enormous sycamore fig trees *Ficus sycomorus*. The southern sector of the park is drier and much of it falls on Kalahari sand. As a result there are stretches of Kalahari woodland and a few patches of mutemwa in addition to the miombo. The Ngoma forest is the best known block of mutemwa, though like so many similar blocks it has suffered fire damage. In the far south of the park grey alluvial clays support stands of mopane. Near the point where the Kafue River leaves the park is the Itezhi-Tezhi dam, behind which an area of 3-400km^2 has been flooded. Although the dam generates some electricity, its primary function is as a reservoir to regulate the flow to the Kafue Gorge hydroelectric dam further downstream.

■ Birds

A wide variety of Zambezian endemics and near-endemics occur including Racket-tailed Roller, Pale-billed Hornbill, Miombo Pied Barbet, Fülleborn's Longclaw, Central Bearded Scrub Robin, Red-capped Crombec, Böhm's Flycatcher and Sousa's Shrike. Along the main rivers are species such as White-backed Night Heron, Hadada, African Finfoot, Rock Pratincole, African Skimmer, Lady Ross's Turaco, Pel's Fishing Owl,

Black-cheeked Lovebirds coming to drink. (Louise Warburton)

Half-collared Kingfisher and Black-backed Barbet. In the riparian thickets Böhm's Bee-eater can be particularly numerous. Crested Guineafowl inhabit the mutemwa and other dense thickets in the south.

Large numbers of waterbirds may be found on the Busanga plains and during the rains there is much dispersal to smaller floodplains, dambos and pans throughout the park. Both Wattled Cranes and Saddle-billed Storks are typical of such small, quiet wetlands. Few waterfowl counts have been carried out, but species which may be found to occur in numbers exceeding their 1% threshold include Openbill Stork, Spur-winged Goose, Wattled Crane, Southern Crowned Crane, Common Pratincole, Caspian Plover and African Skimmer.

About a third of the total population of Black-cheeked Lovebirds are found in the southern sector, mainly in mopane and usually close to the scattered pools associated with the Nanzhila River around Kalenje, Nakabula, Mabiya and Chelenge. During the dry season the birds gather in large numbers at the remaining water sources. 800 were recorded at Mabiya Pools in September 1999 (Warburton 1999).

See summary box for key species. The area is well known, though there has been much less work during the rains. Total number of species recorded to date: 492.

■ Other flora and fauna

The site holds the largest number of antelope species of any national park in the world (Jachmann 2000) with 19 species occurring. Amongst the most common are Bushbuck *Tragelaphus scriptus*, Greater Kudu *T. strepsiceros* (LR/cd), Oribi *Ourebia ourebi* (LR/cd), Puku *Kobus vardoni* (LR/cd), Impala *Aepyceros melampus* (LR/cd) and Hartebeest *Alcelaphus buselaphus lichtensteinii* (LR/cd). Both Roan *Hippotragus equinus* (LR/cd) and Sable *H. niger* (LR/cd) antelopes also occur widely and the park probably holds the largest protected populations of both in Zambia. More localised species include a population of Red Lechwe *Kobus leche* (LR/cd) on the Busanga Plains estimated at around 3,400 in 1985 (Howard & Chabwela 1986) although there are no recent figures and their current status is uncertain. There are also about 1000 Sitatunga *Tragelaphus spekei* (LR/cd) in the adjacent swamps (May & Lindholm 2002). Yellow-backed Duiker *Cephalophus silvicultor* (LR/nt) can be found in

79

areas of dense vegetation and Steinbuck *Raphicercus campestris* is scarce on the Kalahari Sands in the south on the edge of its range. African Elephants *Loxodonta africana* (EN) occur widely but are rarely numerous and Black Rhinoceros *Diceros bicornis* (CR) is now almost certainly extinct. The park probably holds Zambia's largest population of Wild Dogs *Lycaon pictus* (EN) (Buk 1995) and Cheetah *Acinonyx jubatus* (VU) are still recorded with some regularity. Lions *Panthera leo*

(VU) are fairly common throughout the park and very common on the Busanga plains. Spring Hare *Pedetes capensis* (VU) is particularly common in the southern sector, and other red data mammals include Spot-necked Otter *Lutra maculicollis* (VU) and Anchieta's Pipistrelle *Pipistrellus anchietai* (VU).

■ Conservation issues

There is widespread illegal hunting and large sections of the park hold very few large mammals. The

Globally threatened species		
Slaty Egret	Vulnerable	irregular visitor, possibly breeds
Lesser Flamingo	Near-threatened	rare vagrant
Cape Vulture	Vulnerable	rare vagrant
Lappet-faced Vulture	Vulnerable	breeding resident
Pallid Harrier	Near-threatened	passage migrant and non-breeding visitor
Lesser Kestrel	Vulnerable	passage migrant and non-breeding visitor
Corn Crake	Vulnerable	non-breeding visitor
Wattled Crane	Vulnerable	breeding resident with >300 recorded in the early 1970s (Douthwaite 1974), but no recent counts of >100
Denham's Bustard	Near-threatened	breeding resident
Great Snipe	Near-threatened	non-breeding visitor
African Skimmer	Near-threatened	breeding visitor
Black-cheeked Lovebird	Vulnerable	localised breeding resident
Chaplin's Barbet	Near-threatened	uncommon and very localised resident

Restricted-range species		
Black-cheeked Lovebird	s051	localised breeding resident

Biome-restricted species		
Eastern	-	2 near-endemics
Zambezian	21 endemics	15 near-endemics

Globally important congregations	
(ii) regularly holds >1% global population of a terrestrial species	
Black-cheeked Lovebird	2,160 (Dodman 1996a)

Species of regional conservation concern	
Goliath Heron	uncommon breeding resident
Saddle-billed Stork	breeding resident
Bateleur	common breeding resident
African Marsh Harrier	breeding resident
Southern Crowned Crane	breeding resident
White-bellied Bustard	current status unclear, formerly an uncommon resident
Yellow-throated Sandgrouse	uncommon breeding visitor
Southern Ground Hornbill	common breeding resident
Yellow-billed Oxpecker	fairly common breeding resident
Red-billed Oxpecker	common breeding resident

Pel's Fishing Owl roosting in riparian forest. (Mike Harrison)

highest concentrations occur in the Lufupa-Busanga area in the north and the Nanzhila area in the south, although recent reports suggest that game populations in the latter are declining fast. Huge areas are burnt every year, sometimes repeatedly and such uncontrolled burning is a major conservation issue. Fire is a serious threat to mutemwa which never fully recovers once burnt. Much of the park is uninhabited and inaccessible to vehicles, but human encroachment needs to be assessed and carefully monitored. For limited periods, local fishermen are permitted to stay along the Lufupa river and catch fish using traditional methods. However, the number of people occupying such camps has risen dramatically in recent years and people are often present in all months.

■ **Information for visitors**

A number of lodges and camps operate in and around the park. A few of these (near the main roads and in Itezhi-Tezhi) are open throughout the year. However most are seasonal as the majority of roads become impassable during the rains. Just west of the main Kafue bridge on the tarmac Lusaka-Mongu road (M9), such a seasonal dirt track leads north to the Busanga plains and also provides access to most of the northern sector's camps. The northern gate at Kabanga and one or two other camps can be reached from the Mumbwa-Kasempa road (D181) in the north-east and the adventurous can reach the Busanga area on the western boundary road via Lushimba usually until the end of December. The southern sector of the park can be approached either via Itezhi-Tezhi or from Kalomo on the Livingstone-Lusaka road (T1). In addition to all the seasonal game-viewing tracks, an all-weather cattle cordon road connects Itezhi-Tezhi with the park's southern boundary. Most roads require a vehicle with high clearance and visitors exploring the more remote areas are advised to carry extra fuel. There are several airstrips in the park and some safari operators will organise air transfers.

Leopard (Andrea Leonard)

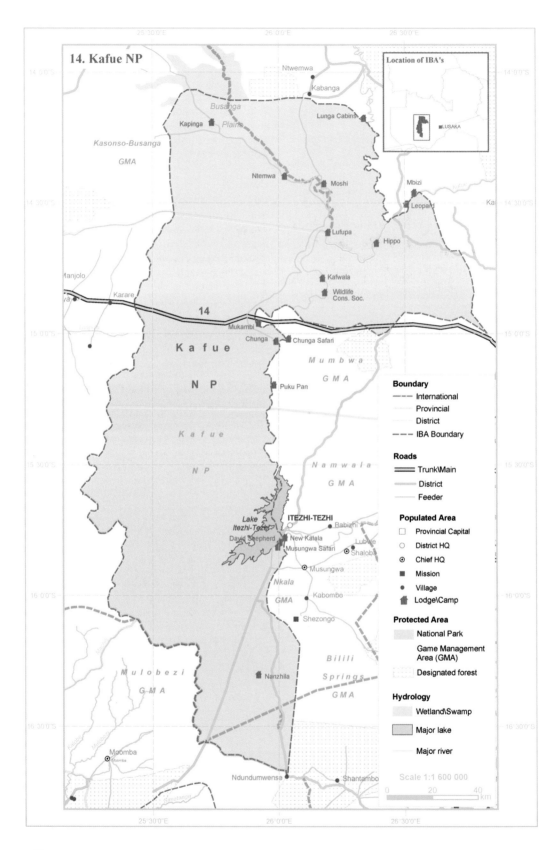

14. Kafue NP

Ntwemwa
Kabanga

Busanga
Kapinga *Plains*
Lunga Cabins

Kasonso-Busanga
GMA

Ntemwa
Moshi
Mbizi

Leopard
Ka

Lufupa
Hippo

Kafwala
Wildlife
Cons. Soc.

Manjolo
Karare
14
Mukambi
Chunga   Chunga Safari
Mumbwa

Kafue
GMA

Puku Pan

Kafue

Namwala
NP
GMA

Lake
Itezhi-Tezhi   **ITEZHI-TEZHI**   Babizhi
David Shepherd   New Kalala   Lubwe
Musungwa Safari   Shaloba

Musungwa

Nkala
GMA   Kabombo

Shezongo

Bilili

Mulobezi   *Springs*
GMA   Nanzhila   *GMA*

Moomba

Ndundumwensa   Shantambo

Location of IBA's

■ LUSAKA

Boundary
––– International
Provincial
District
––– IBA Boundary

Roads
═══ Trunk\Main
Distict
Feeder

Populated Area
☐ Provincial Capital
○ District HQ
⊙ Chief HQ
■ Mission
• Village
🏠 Lodge\Camp

Protected Area
National Park
Game Management
Area (GMA)
Designated forest

Hydrology
Wetland\Swamp
Major lake
Major river

Scale 1:1 600 000
0   20   40
km

15 Kafue Flats

Admin region: Namwala, Itezhi-tezhi, Mumbwa, Mazabuka and Monze Districts, Central and Southern Provinces
Co-ordinates: 15°23'-16°05'S 26°45'-27°57'E
Area: 650,500ha (Lochinvar NP: 41,000ha; Blue Lagoon NP: 42,000ha; GMA: 517,500ha; MCA: c.50,000ha)   **Altitude:** 980-1065m
Status: National Parks, Game Management, Ramsar Site, National Monuments, private conservation area
Categories: Globally threatened species, Biome-restricted species, Globally important congregations
International site code: ZM011   **Map:** p 89

■ Site description

After flowing south along a relatively narrow and well-defined course through Kafue NP (IBA 14), the Kafue River swings to the east at Itezhi-Tezhi and meanders for some 250km across an enormous floodplain known as the Kafue Flats, before plunging down the Kafue Gorge to join the Zambezi river. The IBA encompasses the greater proportion of the Kafue Flats, which is famous for its large herds of Kafue Lechwe *Kobus leche kafuensis* and concentrations of waterbirds.

The main river channel is bordered by levees, lagoons, oxbows and smaller channels, some of which support much aquatic vegetation, such as water lilies *Nymphaea*. Permanent swamp occurs in depressions and is dominated by reed mace *Typha* with some papyrus and *Phragmites*, but most of the area comprises vast stretches of seasonally inundated floodplain, dominated by a variety of grass species. When wet, the alluvial 'black cotton' clay renders much of the area inaccessible to vehicles and extensive cracks form on drying. At its widest point, the area liable to flooding is some 60km across. The floodplains are bordered by termitaria, scrub, munga woodland and scattered patches of palm savanna (*Hyphaene* and *Borassus*).

Water levels on the Flats are regulated by dams built in the 1970s, both up-stream (Itezhi-Tezhi) and down-stream (Kafue Gorge), as part of a hydropower project. Under natural conditions, flood levels began to rise in December and the flood peak passed slowly downstream between March and May; in most years, the floodplain would be dry once more by September. Regulation

has reduced the extent of flooding and raised minimum water levels, so that the area of floodplain has decreased and the area of termitaria and scrub in the upper floodplain, and permanent swamp and lagoon in lower-lying areas has increased. The hydropower project operates with no environmental constraints and proposed water management rules, including releases from Itezhi-tezhi to simulate the natural flood and benefit the wildlife and fishery on the Flats, have not been implemented. In recent years, flood levels have begun to increase in August, well before the end of the dry season and four months earlier than under natural conditions.

Within the site are two national parks (Lochinvar and Blue Lagoon) and together these comprise a designated Ramsar Site. Both were formerly cattle ranches. Lochinvar is better known and at its northern end lies the largest stretch of open water on the flats, the Chunga Lagoon. A geological fault runs through the south of the park and associated with this are hot springs and a large deposit of gypsum. Also in this area are two archaeological sites that have earned National Monument status. Sebanzi Hill is the site of an Iron Age village whilst Gwisho Hot Springs was occupied by Late Stone Age people in the second and third millennia BC. At the south-eastern end of the IBA lies the Mwanachingwala Conservation Area (MCA), owned by Zambia Sugar. This private initiative has already established a degree of protection and in time it is hoped that several species of large mammal will be reintroduced. The remainder of the IBA comprises the Kafue Flats GMA (No. 11). This is populated by cattle-herding Ila-Tonga and many fishermen (often immigrants) who live on the numerous small islands in the centre of the swamps and in villages of varying permanence elsewhere (Jeffery 1992).

■ Birds

Very large concentrations of resident and migratory waterbirds occur and large breeding colonies can be found deep within the swamps. The species spectrum varies greatly depending on the season and the water level, but species which are often found in significant numbers include White Pelican, Common Squacco Heron, Cattle Egret, Black Egret, Openbill Stork, Glossy Ibis, Fulvous Whistling Duck, White-faced Whistling Duck, Egyptian Goose, Spur-winged Goose, Knob-billed Duck, Red-billed Teal, Southern Pochard, Red-knobbed Coot, Common Pratincole, Kittlitz's Plover, Caspian Plover, Blacksmith Plover and Ruff.

When dry, the floodplains and termitaria host a rather different selection of species and particularly numerous are Red-capped Lark, Chestnut-backed Sparrow-Lark, Grey-rumped Swallow, Richard's Pipit, Capped Wheatear and Quail Finch. At the other end of the scale, the permanent swamp holds species such as Greater Swamp Warbler and Swamp Flycatcher.

The flats, and Lochinvar in particular, are well known for their high diversity and high density of breeding raptors. Vultures are particularly numerous, as are African Fish Eagles and Tawny Eagles. African Marsh Harriers, although apparently declining elsewhere (Leonard & Colebrook-Robjent, in prep.) are still very common and the three Palearctic harriers are also regular.

The Kafue Flats are extremely important for Wattled Cranes. In the 1970s and 1980s, population estimates for the area were mostly between 2000-3000 (Douthwaite 1974, Howard & Aspinwall 1984, Dodman 1996b) but the latest surveys suggest that the species has declined and only about 1000 occur (Kamweneshe & Beilfuss 2002). Slaty Egret numbers have fluctuated, but recently they have been recorded regularly (up to 30 in a day, Oct-Nov 2001) and several juvenile and immature birds have been seen, suggestive of local breeding. Corn Crake and Great Snipe are both regular non-breeding visitors and undoubtedly under-recorded. For example, a crude attempt to gauge the density of the former in Lochinvar resulted in 5 birds being flushed in as many hectares (Leonard & Peters 1998). The status of African Skimmer is not clear, but flocks of several hundred birds have been recorded on several occasions (e.g. Leonard & Peters 1998).

See summary box for key species. Lochinvar is very well known, Blue Lagoon less so. Many other areas have received very little attention. Total number of species recorded to date: 463 (Lochinvar NP: 447, Blue Lagoon NP: 337, MCA: 365).

■ Other flora and fauna

A wide variety of mammals occur and most notably the Kafue Lechwe *Kobus leche kafuensis* (LR/cd), a subspecies endemic to the Kafue Flats. This is

White Pelicans at Lochinvar NP. (Andrea Leonard)

The partially inundated floodplain at Lochinvar NP, teeming with life. (Peter Leonard)

also the largest protected population of this species anywhere. Historically, lechwe were spread throughout the area and numbered at least 100,000, and probably much more (Kamweneshe *et al.* 2002). The most recent estimate puts the total population at about 42,000 and declining (*ibid.*) and these animals are now restricted to the core area of the two national parks and intervening GMA. The lechwe is a 'keystone' species in the ecology of the Flats. Grazing and trampling by lechwe as the floods rise alters the structure and floristic composition of the vegetation, benefiting a wide variety of fish and waterfowl. The tall, dense stands of grasses are opened up and replaced by unpalatable, heavily-seeding herbs and open water, attracting huge numbers of granivorous and piscivorous waterbirds.

There are large concentrations of Common Zebra *Equus (quagga) burchelli* and other mammals include Wildebeest *Connochaetes taurinus* (LR/cd)(on the south side of the Kafue only), Oribi *Ourebia ourebi* (LR/cd), Sitatunga *Tragelaphus spekei* (LR/cd) and African Buffalo *Syncerus caffer* (LR/cd). Spot-necked Otter *Lutra maculicollis* (VU) and Spring Hare *Pedetes capensis* (VU) are still regular and Aardwolf *Proteles cristatus* probably still occurs on the south bank and Lochinvar perhaps holds the only protected population of this species in Zambia. Bats known include *Eptesicus (Pipistrellus) rendalli, Pipistrellus rueppelli* and *Tadarida midas*. The reed frog *Hyperolius (parallelus) pyrrhodiction* is endemic and the wormlizard *Zygaspis kafuensis* almost so (Broadley & Broadley 1997).

■ **Conservation issues**

Regulation of water levels by hydro-electric dams has affected the extent and quality of wetland habitats with significant consequences for birds. The loss of a large part of the floodplain has reduced the number of some species whereas birds associated with permanent swamp appear to have increased. The creation of a permanent lagoon at Chunga in Lochinvar NP has displaced many of the lechwe and waterbirds to the east and west, outside the Park boundaries, where they receive less protection. Recently the artificial floods have not followed a natural pattern and changes in the ecosystem have accelerated. In some years water levels have suddenly risen towards the end of the dry season when they would normally be receding rapidly. In such instances the nests of species such as Kittlitz's Plover and Common Pratincole are destroyed. There have also been extended periods of relatively high water, spanning several seasons (pers. obs.) creating an unnaturally stable environment. Many birds have benefited from these conditions as extensive wetland habitat becomes available throughout the year, but the long term effects of this stability are probably cause for serious concern. During the same period *Mimosa pigra* (first recorded in the area in 1982 (Turner 1986)) has spread dramatically near Lochinvar's Chunga Lagoon and now forms huge, impenetrable thickets. If it continues to spread at the current rate, vast areas of floodplain and shoreline could soon be covered rendering it unsuitable for most waterbirds, the Kafue Lechwe, Ila-Tonga cattle grazing and tourism. Water hyacinth *Eichhornia crassipes* probably benefits from a stable aquatic environment as well and in recent years it has covered significant areas of open water on the lower portion of the Kafue Flats (including the MCA). This invasive alien weed also spreads rapidly and is difficult to control. It reduces pH and oxygen levels and thus threatens fish populations (Bolnick 1995). Its impact on the area's bird life has yet to be assessed but it would seem to be a potential threat to any species that requires open water. The controlled flooding has also reduced the number of very high floods and as a result the termitaria zone has spread. This gradually progresses to woodland, or in many places dense thickets of thorny trees such as *Dichrostachys cinerea*. Many floodplain plants are threatened by these altered flooding regimes, particularly at the western end where several endemic species occur. The spike rush *Eleocharis angulata* is one such vulnerable plant and its tubers form a major part of the Wattled Crane's diet. The erratic flooding has reduced the tuber production and this is probably a significant factor in the decline of the crane population (Beilfuss *et al.* in prep.).

The proximity of the Kafue Flats to Lusaka and its inherent demand for meat and fish has generated significant illegal hunting and fishing industries. Poaching camps are hidden in many parts of the swamp and also within the *Mimosa* thickets. Several species of large mammal are now extinct (R. Nefdt, *in litt.*) and both the lechwe and zebra populations continue to decline (Kamweneshe *et al.* 2002) threatening the whole floodplain ecology. Hippopotamuses *Hippopotamus amphibius* are persecuted by fisherman who see them as a danger. The fishery has been degraded by water level regulation and overfishing. There is no regard for fishing seasons and in many instances mosquito netting is used as fish of all sizes are utilised. Large numbers of moulting ducks and Darters were drowned in gill nets set illegally in Lochinvar

National Park in the 1970s (R. Douthwaite, *in litt.*) and it is assumed this situation still continues. Formerly common on the Flats, Darters are now seen only in small numbers.

The human population is increasing rapidly and each year the temporary fishing camps in the GMAs increase in number and size. The settlements on islands in the centre of the flats are better established and are also growing rapidly. In some areas permanent structures such as schools and clinics have been built. The pressure for firewood, building materials and dugout canoes is now so great that many trees which were known to hold nesting colonies of herons and storks have been felled. Further investigation is required to assess the potential threats to other colonies within the flats. Large areas of both floodplain and swamp vegetation are burnt each year and the impact of such fires on the ecosystem must be considerable.

■ Information for visitors

Lochinvar NP is the most frequently visited part of the Kafue Flats and it is still the best area in which to see large concentrations of waterbirds and lechwe. To reach the park, turn west at a sign onto the dirt road just north of Monze town. After about 15km turn right at another sign and after a further 11km turn left at another sign. From here the road twists and turns for about 16km until you reach the park gate. There are more signs, but if in doubt, ask for directions from local residents. At the time of writing the roads are in poor condition and high clearance is essential. The park is accessible for much of the year, though visits after heavy rain are

Kafue Lechwe spend much of their time in or near water. (Richard Beilfuss)

Wattled Crane (Wouter Peters)

strictly for the brave and well-equipped. There is a basic campsite, though camping is permitted anywhere. Currently, there is also a luxury tented camp on the shores of the Chunga lagoon. It is worth driving out to both the north-east and north-west sides of the lagoon to explore areas of either shallow, flooded grassland or mud flats depending on the season. If you are not confident about navi-

gating across these largely road-free areas, then ask at the headquarters if a game scout could accompany you. And, if it looks wet - don't drive further! The floodplain is pure black cotton clay and it is very easy to get stuck. Perhaps the most exciting time to visit is towards the end of the dry season (Sept-Oct) when the local birds are joined by vast numbers of migrant waders.

Blue Lagoon NP is poorly developed and not often visited yet it still offers good birding. From Lusaka, take the Great West Road and turn left after about 23km. After a further 20km continue straight where the main road swings left. The park gate is about another 65km from here. Ask to be directed to the old farmhouse and then on to the causeway that stretches out onto the floodplain. This will involve back-tracking from the park gate a few kilometres. There are no accommodation facilities so visitors must be entirely self-sufficient and should consult park staff about where to camp. Once again, road surfaces are poor and a high clearance vehicle is advisable.

Many other parts of the GMA are accessible during the dry season, though the roads are generally rough and navigation can be difficult. At present the MCA has no tourist facilities and access is restricted.

Globally threatened species		
Madagascar Squacco Heron	Vulnerable	rare visitor
Slaty Egret	Vulnerable	regular in small numbers, not yet known to breed but may do so
Lesser Flamingo	Near-threatened	rare visitor
Cape Vulture	Vulnerable	rare visitor
Lappet-faced Vulture	Vulnerable	common breeding resident
Pallid Harrier	Near-threatened	regular non-breeding visitor
Lesser Kestrel	Vulnerable	common passage migrant and non-breeding visitor
Corn Crake	Vulnerable	regular non-breeding visitor
Wattled Crane	Vulnerable	common breeding resident
Denham's Bustard	Near-threatened	regular breeding resident
Black-winged Pratincole	Data deficient	scarce non-breeding visitor
Great Snipe	Near-threatened	regular non-breeding visitor
African Skimmer	Near-threatened	regular, status unclear, may breed
Chaplin's Barbet	Near-threatened	localised breeding resident
Biome-restricted species		
Eastern	-	2 near-endemics
Zambezian	9 endemics	9 near-endemics

Globally important congregations

(i) regularly holds >1% of biogeographic population of a congregatory waterbird

Reed Cormorant	>12,000 (1950s)
White Pelican	3,086 (Jul 1994), >6000 (Nov 1971)
Black Egret	2,933 (Jan 2000)
Openbill Stork	15,000-20,000 (Oct 1999), 500,000 (Nov 1970)
African Spoonbill	1,595 (Jan 2001)
Fulvous Whistling Duck	58,385 (Jan 1994)
White-faced Whistling Duck	17,900 (Jul 2001), 24,000 (Sep 1971)
White-backed Duck	500 (May-Jun 1971, Jun 1973)
Egyptian Goose	5,240 (Jul 2001)
Spur-winged Goose	4,398 (Jan 2002), >100,000 (Nov 1972), 90,000 (Jun 1973)
Knob-billed Duck	20,698 (Jan 1994)
African Pygmy Goose	10-15,000 (Apr-May 1972)
Red-billed Teal	10,407 (Jul 1999), >29,000 (Aug 1971)
Hottentot Teal	3,930 (Jan 2001)
Southern Pochard	3,068 (Jan 2000), >5,000 (Jan 1973), 6,550 (Jun 1973)
Wattled Crane	1,171 (Jan 1995), 1,500 (Mar 1980), 1,800 (Mar 1973)
Common Pratincole	17,070 (Jul 2000), >50,000 (Apr 1972, May 1980)
Kittlitz's Plover	5,000-6,000 (Oct 2000)
Caspian Plover	30,000-35,000 (Nov 1995)
Long-toed Plover	1,395 (Jan 2001)
Black-tailed Godwit	4300 (Oct 2000)
Little Stint	>10,000 (Nov, several years)
Curlew Sandpiper	>10,000 (Sep 1969)
Ruff	71,285 (Jan 2001)
Whiskered Tern	1,226 (Jul 1997)

(iii) regularly holds >20,000 waterbirds

Species of regional conservation concern

Common Bittern	rare, status unclear, may breed
Goliath Heron	common breeding resident
Saddle-billed Stork	regular breeding resident
Bateleur	fairly common, a few breed
African Marsh Harrier	common breeding resident
Southern Crowned Crane	localised but regular breeding resident
White-bellied Bustard	not recorded for many years, probably extinct
Yellow-throated Sandgrouse	common breeding resident
Southern Ground Hornbill	common breeding resident
Yellow-billed Oxpecker	status not known, no recent records
Red-billed Oxpecker	status not known, very few recent records

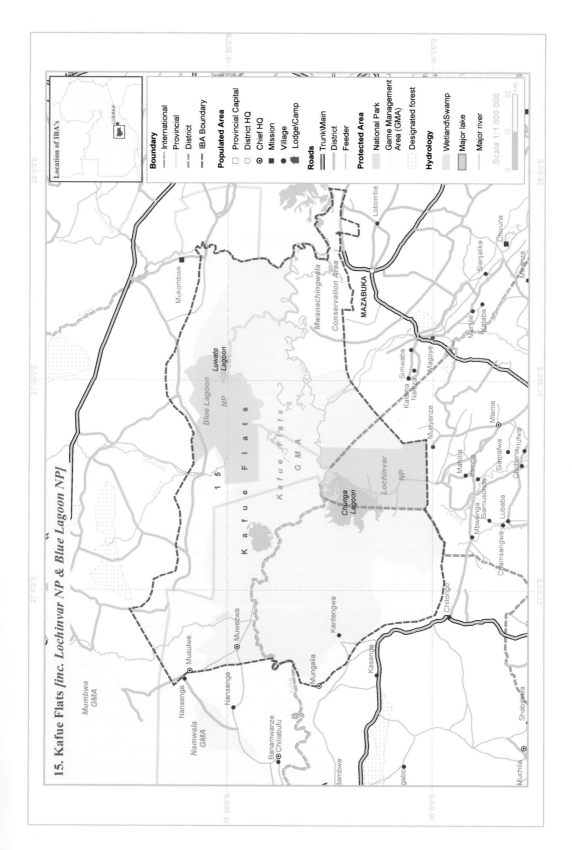

15. Kafue Flats [inc. Lochinvar NP & Blue Lagoon NP]

Boundary
- —··— International
- ——— Provincial
- —·—·— District
- —··—··— IBA Boundary

Populated Area
- □ Provincial Capital
- ○ District HQ
- ◉ Chief HQ
- ■ Mission
- ● Village
- ♦ Lodge/Camp

Roads
- ═══ Trunk/Main
- ─── District
- ─── Feeder

Protected Area
- National Park
- Game Management Area (GMA)
- Designated forest

Hydrology
- Wetland/Swamp
- Major lake
- Major river

Scale 1:1 000 000

0   10   20 Km

Mumbwa GMA

Namwala GMA

Banamwanze
◉ Chilalabufu

Bambwe

gabo

Muchila ◉

Shabalwa

Nansenga
◉ Musulwe

Nansenga

Muwezwa

Mungaila ◉

Kantengwa ●

Kasenga

Chitongo ◉

Mukombwe ■

Blue Lagoon NP

Luwato Lagoon

Kafue Flats

15

Kafue Flats GMA

Chunga Lagoon

Lochinvar NP

Mwanachingwala Conservation Area

MAZABUKA

Lobomba ●

Kalama Simwaba
Naleza
Magoye

Munyenze ●

Mahiba
Itembi
Siamusonde
Mbwenga Siamusonde
Lubaba ●
Chamsangwa ●

Chamsangwa

Chivuna ■

Sianjalika ●

Mwanza ●

Mungile
Kataba ●

Mteme ◉

Siachafwa
Chobana Hufwa

27°00'E   27°30'E   28°00'E

15°30'S   16°00'S

89

16 Nkanga River Conservation Area

Admin region: Choma District, Southern Province
Co-ordinates: 16°38'S 27°02'E
Area: 9700ha   **Altitude:** 1180-1280m
Status: private farms
Categories: Globally threatened species, Biome-restricted species
International site code: ZM010   **Map:** p 92

■ Site description

The site is situated on the Southern Province Plateau, about 20km north of Choma. It comprises a cluster of private farms (Nos. 59a, 60a, 63a, 180a, 2813) that are managed according to a conservation policy devised by the owners. The area has no legal status in this respect, but it has been actively protected for many years by the Bruce-Miller family and their neighbours. Several hundred hectares are regularly cultivated (mainly tobacco and maize) but much of the area is relatively undisturbed and used as pasture for cattle, sheep and game ranching. Game animals, both indigenous and introduced, are common and generate a proportion of the operation's income. The habitat is a mosaic of miombo and munga woodland, interspersed with dambos and several open grassy plains. Three seasonal rivers run through the site, including the rocky Nkanga, and these are flanked by riparian thicket. There are also a few extensive patches of deciduous thicket away from the drainage lines. A number of dams have been constructed and there are also some permanent hot springs and scattered kopjes.

■ Birds

The area is very well known and a holds a very broad range of species. Chaplin's Barbet is common in its favoured habitat of open savanna woodland with high densities of Sycamore Figs *Ficus sycomorus*. A good number of Zambezian endemics and near-endemics occur, particularly in the miombo, such as Racket-tailed Roller, Miombo Pied Barbet, Arnot's Chat, Miombo Grey Tit and Black-eared Seed-eater. The localised Green Indigobird is regular in small numbers in the thickets where its host, Red-throated Twinspot is common. When in leaf, the thickets also support many migrants such as Emerald Cuckoo, Narina Trogon, Red-capped Robin, River Warbler and Marsh Warbler. The equally seasonal dambos reg-

Chaplin's Barbets (Claire Spottiswoode)

ularly hold good numbers of Streaky-breasted Flufftail and African Black Coucal during the rains. Six species of francolin occur (Coqui, Crested, Shelley's, Natal, Swainson's and Red-necked) as well as a wide variety of raptors, including African Cuckoo Hawk, Crowned Eagle and Secretary Bird. Around the onset of the rains, colossal roosts build up in the reed mace *Typha* around the hot springs. Tens, and sometimes hundreds of thousands of European Swallows constitute a large proportion of such roosts and there are often large numbers of weavers, bishops and whydahs and several thou-

Typical Chaplin's Barbet habitat at NRCA with a large Sycamore Fig tree. (Andrea Leonard)

Cabanis's Bunting

sand Parasitic Weavers. Recently, Red-billed Oxpecker has been recorded regularly in small numbers and there are hopes that it will recolonise the area naturally, having been wiped out by poisonous cattle dips in the past.

See summary box for key species. The area is very well known. Total number of species recorded to date: 437.

■ Other flora and fauna

Indigenous mammals include Chacma baboon *Papio ursinus*, Serval Cat *Felis serval*, Leopard *Panthera pardus*, Aardvark *Orycteropus afer*, Bush Pig *Potamochoerus larvatus*, Bushbuck *Tragelaphus scriptus*, Greater Kudu *T. strepsiceros* (LR/cd), Sharpe's Grysbok *Raphicercus sharpei* (LR/cd), Oribi *Ourebia ourebi* (LR/cd) and Southern Reedbuck *Redunca arundinum* (LR/cd).

■ Conservation issues

Despite continual poaching, the area has been actively protected for several decades and is rich in indigenous fauna. Gamebirds are shot, sometimes in considerable numbers (mainly Helmeted Guineafowl and francolins), but there is careful management to ensure sustainable take-off and there are probably no serious threats to the bird life. The area is one of the few in Zambia to have had resident ornithologists for many years and the resultant data are now helping to highlight the status of many species. For example, Goliath Heron, Yellow-billed Kite, Bateleur, African Marsh Harrier and Dark Chanting Goshawk were all once common breeding residents and now they are no more than rare visitors (Leonard & Colebrook-Robjent, in prep.).

■ Information for visitors

Tourists are welcome; there is a campsite with basic facilities as well as fully catered chalet accommodation either at the main farm house (Muckle Neuk) or Masuku Lodge. From Choma the site can be reached from two directions on gravel roads and is signed to 'Bruce-Miller'. Following the Namwala road from where it begins on Choma's eastern periphery, a signed right-turn is taken after about 19km to reach NRCA. Alternatively, a more interesting route leaves the tar about 3km east of Choma and a signed left turn is taken after about 19km. For more information or to make bookings contact nansai@zamnet.zm or tel: 032 20592 / 032 20621. For Masuku Lodge contact somerset@coppernet.zm, masuku@zamnet.zm or tel: 032 20225.

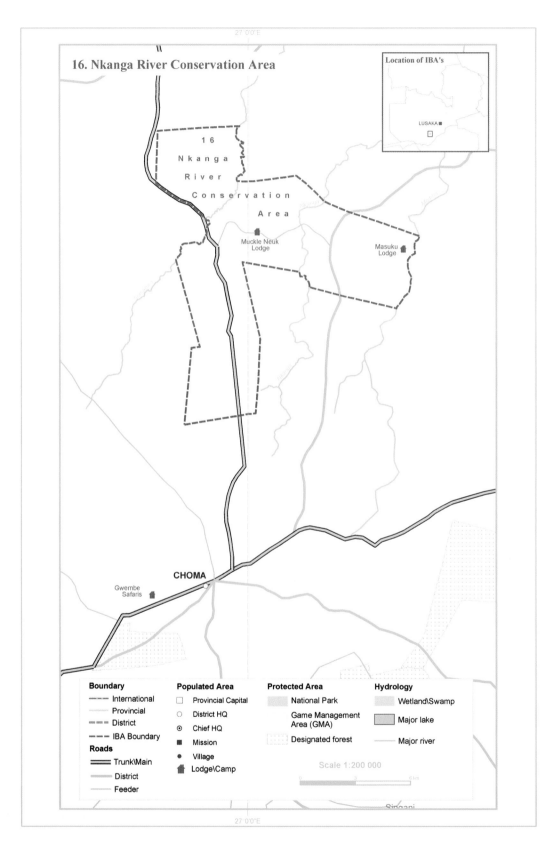

16. Nkanga River Conservation Area

Location of IBA's

LUSAKA ■

1 6

Nkanga

River

Conservation

Area

Muckle Neuk Lodge

Masuku Lodge

CHOMA

Gwembe Safaris

Boundary
- - - - International
Provincial
- - - District
- - - IBA Boundary

Roads
Trunk\Main
District
Feeder

Populated Area
□ Provincial Capital
○ District HQ
◉ Chief HQ
■ Mission
● Village
⌂ Lodge\Camp

Protected Area
National Park
Game Management Area (GMA)
Designated forest

Hydrology
Wetland\Swamp
Major lake
Major river

Scale 1:200 000

Singani

Globally threatened species		
Slaty Egret	Vulnerable	rare visitor
Lesser Flamingo	Near-threatened	rare visitor
Lappet-faced Vulture	Vulnerable	uncommon, may breed
Pallid Harrier	Near-threatened	uncommon passage migrant
Lesser Kestrel	Vulnerable	regular passage migrant
Corn Crake	Vulnerable	regular non-breeding visitor
Wattled Crane	Vulnerable	rare visitor
Denham's Bustard	Near-threatened	uncommon visitor
Black-winged Pratincole	Data deficient	rare passage migrant
Great Snipe	Near-threatened	uncommon non-breeding visitor
African Skimmer	Near-threatened	rare visitor
Chaplin's Barbet	Near-threatened	fairly common breeding resident

Biome-restricted species		
Eastern	-	1 near-endemic
Zambezian	11 endemics	11 near-endemics

Species of regional conservation concern	
Goliath Heron	rare visitor
Saddle-billed Stork	regular, may breed occasionally
Bateleur	uncommon visitor
African Marsh Harrier	rare visitor
Southern Crowned Crane	rare visitor
White-bellied Bustard	rare visitor
Yellow-throated Sandgrouse	occasional
Southern Ground Hornbill	uncommon, possibly resident
Red-billed Oxpecker	rare breeding resident

17 Mutulanganga

Admin region: Siavonga District, Southern Province
Co-ordinates: 16°15'S 28°44'E
Area: c.28,000ha (LF: c.10,000ha; unprotected: c.18,000ha)
Altitude: 400-700m
Status: Local Forest, unprotected
Categories: Globally threatened species, Biome-restricted species
International site code: --- **Map:** p 95

■ Site description

Probably the largest remaining block of undisturbed lowland deciduous thicket in Zambia. The site straddles the Chirundu-Siavonga road and is defined, in part, by the Mutulanganga Local Forest (No. 183). Further work is required to define the southern and eastern boundaries. The area is drained by the highly seasonal Mutulanganga and Mbendele rivers which flow eastwards into the Zambezi after heavy rain. There are stretches of mopane and other types of dry woodland with baobabs *Adansonia digitata*, but most of the area is cloaked in dense deciduous thicket. Here the core dominant tree is probably *Xylia torreana* (*Mimosoideae*), a species typical of only the least disturbed thickets. The human population is patchy and only dense in some places such as Lusitu, a somewhat dysfunctional settlement which houses many of the families moved from the area flooded by Lake Kariba in the late 1950s.

■ Birds

The area is perhaps best known as a regular breeding ground for the migratory African Pitta. Like most rains visitors, this elusive species is present between about late November and early April, although its distribution and the numbers present appear to change from year to year. Barred Long-tailed Cuckoo would appear to be seasonal as well and this is the only Zambian site from which the species is reported regularly. There are sight records of Dark-backed Weaver, here some distance from other parts of its Zambian range. These birds have yet to be identified racially but are possibly the eastern subspecies *stictifrons* which occurs further down the Zambezi Valley in Zimbabwe and Mozambique. Palearctic migrants are well represented and three that occur in significant numbers are Thrush-Nightingale, River Warbler and Marsh Warbler. Both Mottled and Bat-like Spinetails occur, the former usually breeding in hollow baobabs. Other species of interest that are typical include Western Banded Snake Eagle, Crested Guineafowl, Purple-crested Turaco, African Broadbill, Sombre Bulbul, White-throated Nicator and Livingstone's Flycatcher.

See summary box for key species. The areas close to the main road have been well explored. Other areas have received almost no attention from

African Pitta

ornithologists. Total number of species recorded to date: 198.

■ Other flora and fauna

There are few large mammals in the area, but African Elephants *Loxodonta africana* (EN) wander through the area from time to time. The egg-eating snake *Dasypeltis medici* occurs here at the very western end of its range.

■ Conservation issues

A somewhat controversial issue is the destruction caused by an increasing elephant population. Most areas of lowland deciduous thicket in Zimbabwe have been seriously degraded in this way (A. J. Tree *in litt.*) and although not currently a problem in Zambia, it may become so in the future. At present human disturbance would not appear to be a major issue but it requires very careful monitoring and surrounding areas already suffer from extremely bad soil erosion. Comparable thickets in the Chiawa area just north of Chirundu have been almost completely destroyed to make way for commercial farming thus stressing the conservation

River Warbler (Peter Leonard)

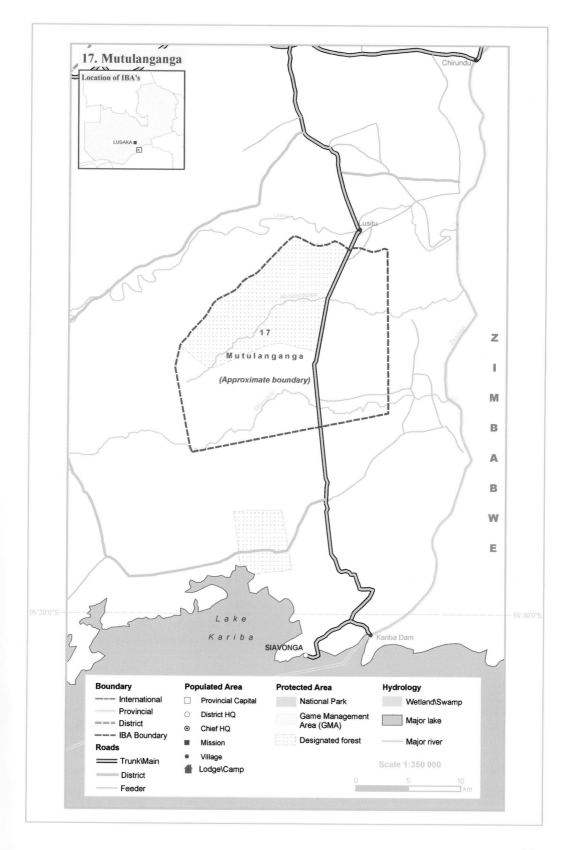

importance of the Mutulanganga thickets still further.

■ Information for visitors

The site is easily reached on the tarmac Chirundu-Siavonga road, but access to areas away from the road is very difficult. Many visitors make day trips from Siavonga or even Lusaka and the most popular starting points are the bridges over the Mutulanganga and Mbendele rivers, the former beside some large baobabs. Even exploring the thickets on foot can be hard and walking along one of the dry riverbeds is often the best way of getting

around. This also makes navigation easier. Some people prefer to walk along the road as traffic is usually sparse, but once the sun gets high it can become extremely hot and this route offers very little shade. It is possible to camp in the general area but there are no facilities. In a few spots there are vague and often overgrown tracks that lead a little way into the thickets. Functional camps can be pitched here and a panga (machete) or similar tool is invaluable if this option is chosen. African Pittas can be frustratingly elusive and are best located by call between late November and January. They tend to be most vocal after heavy rain.

Globally threatened species		
Lappet-faced Vulture	Vulnerable	occasional visitor
Lesser Kestrel	Vulnerable	scarce passage migrant
Biome-restricted species		
Eastern	-	4 near-endemics
Zambezian	1 endemic	4 near-endemics
Species of regional conservation concern		
Bateleur	fairly regular, may breed	
Southern Ground Hornbill	uncommon resident	

18 Lower Zambezi National Park

Admin region: Chongwe, Luangwa Districts, Lusaka Province
Co-ordinates: 15°10'- 15°42'S 29°10'-30°13'E
Area: c.440,000ha   **Altitude:** 350-1488m
Status: National Park
Categories: Globally threatened species, Biome-restricted species
International site code: ZM018   **Map:** p 99

■ Site description

A large and very varied area lying about 100km east of Lusaka. The Zambezi marks the southern boundary (as well as the Zimbabwean border) and the dramatic Zambezi escarpment bisects the park from south-west to north-east. The north-western half lies on the plateau and reaches altitudes of over 1400m; it is mainly miombo, with some munga and occasional strips of riparian forest. The escarpment is very steep in places, generally inaccessible and

thus little explored. At its lowest point the valley floor is only 350m a.s.l.. It is covered by a mosaic of mopane, deciduous thicket and palm savanna (*Hyphaene ventricosa*). Closer to the river are stretches of park-like woodland on alluvial soils consisting of imposing trees that are too large to be destroyed by elephants. Typical species include *Acacia albida, Trichilia emetica, Kigelia africana* and *Diospyros mespiliformis*. The Zambezi is a broad, but well-defined river along this stretch with varying numbers of sandbars and small islands depending on the water level. There are patches of riparian forest, many ox-bow lakes and a few areas of *Phragmites* swamp. There are floodplains on heavy clays in some areas, the largest section of which is known as Jeki Plain, about half way along the length of the park. At the eastern end of the park the river runs through the spectacular Mpata Gorge.

Until recently the area has been very inaccessible, initially due to lack of infrastructure and later because of the Rhodesian war. It was declared a national park in 1983, but the former president Kenneth Kaunda used the eastern half as a private hunting area and the road networks were still very poor. In the early 1990s when Kaunda left power the park began to open up. There is now considerable tourist activity and many camps and lodges have been built both inside and outside the park. The site lies adjacent to the Zimbabwean IBA ZW012: Middle Zambezi valley (Childes & Mundy 2001) which includes Mana Pools National Park.

■ Birds

Large numbers of waterbirds may congregate, especially at drying ox-bows. Other typical wetland birds found throughout the year include Egyptian Goose, African Fish Eagle, Water Dikkop and White-crowned Plover. Although never common, both Goliath Heron and Saddle-billed Stork occur in good numbers and African Skimmer regularly breeds on sandbars, possibly in numbers exceeding its 1% threshold.

The sand cliffs are home to enormous colonies of Southern Carmine Bee-eaters in the hot, dry season. It is likely that numbers exceed the 1% threshold, although no thorough counts have been carried out on the Zambian side. Colonies on the Zimbabwean side hold 10,500 individuals (Childes & Mundy 2001). Sharing this habitat are White-fronted Bee-eater, Horus Swift and African Sand Martin.

When flowering, the trees and mistletoes *Loranthus* in the alluvial woodland attract many sunbirds. Purple-banded can be abundant at times and Shelley's is occasionally recorded wandering from its miombo breeding habitat. Inhabitants of the deciduous thickets include Crested Guineafowl, White-throated Nicator, Black-throated Wattle-eye and Livingstone's Flycatcher and African Pitta is an unpredictable rains visitor. The mopane holds a wide array of characteristic species including large

numbers of Lilian's Lovebirds. The miombo has been poorly explored but the little fieldwork that has been carried out has revealed a good number of Zambezian endemics.

See summary box for key species. The areas close to the river are well known, but much of the rest of the park is very poorly known. Total number of species recorded to date: 378.

■ Other flora and fauna

A wide variety of large animals occur. African Elephants *Loxodonta africana* (EN) and African Buffalo *Syncerus caffer* (LR/cd) are common and often found in very large herds and Hippopotamus *Hippopotamus amphibius* and Nile Crocodile *Crocodylus niloticus* are numerous in the river. Predators include good numbers of Lion *Panthera leo* (VU) and a few Wild Dog *Lycaon pictus* (EN). Common antelope include Bushbuck *Tragelaphus scriptus*, Greater Kudu *T. strepsiceros* (LR/cd), Impala *Aepyceros melampus* (LR/cd) and Waterbuck *Kobus ellipsiprymnus* (LR/cd). Black Rhinoceros *Diceros bicornis* (CR) has been extinct since the 1980s. Although there are no recent records, Gentle (Blue) Monkey *Cercopithecus mitis* may still occur and the mouse *Mus neavei* is found, here at the very western end of its range. The flora is not well known, but *Adenium obesum* and *Selaginella imbricata* are recorded from the Mpata gorge and both have very restricted ranges in Zambia (M. Bingham *in litt.*).

■ Conservation issues

At present game numbers continue to increase and now there are healthy populations of several

Crested Guineafowl

Spotted Hyaena (Andrea Leonard)

species as noted above. In fact it has been suggested that overgrazing and elephant damage are becoming serious issues. Poaching continues to be a problem but the ever increasing presence of the tourist industry helps to protect the park. As ever, over-burning is a constant threat. The effects of a dramatic increase in water hyacinth *Eichhornia crassipes* require investigation as does a proposed dam at the Mpata gorge (Tumbare 2000) which could seriously affect the hydrology of the area.

■ Information for visitors

There are now numerous tourist facilities in the Lower Zambezi area catering for visitors on every

level. Camps are mainly seasonal as most roads become impassable during the rains. The main route into the park is via Chirundu. A few kilometres from here there is a pontoon across the Kafue after which the road runs parallel to the Zambezi, via Chiawa, until reaching the ford across the Chongwe (the park boundary) and the park gate. Once inside the park, the main track continues to run parallel to the Zambezi, but not always close to it. However, a network of game-viewing loops allows visitors to explore the areas between the road and river which is the most productive for animals. In theory, there are other routes into the park (two are marked on the map from the east and the north-west), but in practice they tend to be poorly maintained and sometimes completely impassable. Some camps also arrange transfers by boat from near the Kafue pontoon and it is possible to fly to airstrips both outside (near Royal Zambezi) and inside the park (at Jeki). If you are self-catering it is worth noting that very little in the way of supplies can be obtained in Chirundu. To reach the Mpata Gorge it is best to travel by boat. Several companies arrange canoe safaris which reach this point and it is also possible to visit from one or two lodges near Luangwa. It is rarely cold in the valley and towards the end of the dry season it can be extremely hot.

Globally threatened species		
Slaty Egret	Vulnerable	rare visitor
Lappet-faced Vulture	Vulnerable	uncommon breeding resident
Pallid Harrier	Near-threatened	rare non-breeding visitor
Lesser Kestrel	Vulnerable	rare passage migrant
African Skimmer	Near-threatened	regular breeding visitor
Biome-restricted species		
Eastern	-	4 near-endemics
Zambezian	10 endemics	9 near-endemics
Species of regional conservation concern		
Goliath Heron	breeding resident	
Saddle-billed Stork	breeding resident	
Bateleur	fairly common breeding resident	
African Marsh Harrier	occasional	
Southern Ground Hornbill	fairly common breeding resident	
Yellow-billed Oxpecker	a very rare vagrant	
Red-billed Oxpecker	fairly common breeding resident	

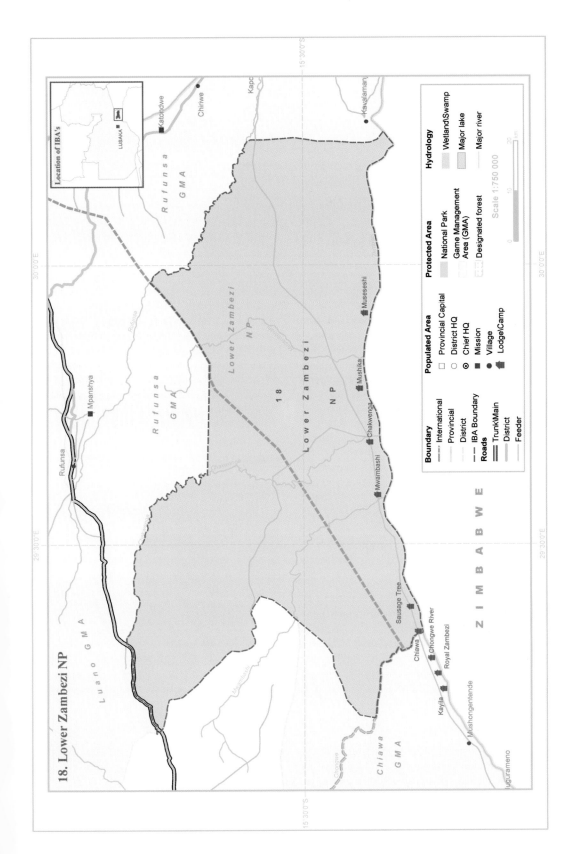

18. Lower Zambezi NP

Location of IBA's

LUSAKA

Scale 1:750 000

Boundary
International
Provincial
District
IBA Boundary
Roads
TrunkMain
District
Feeder

Populated Area
☐ Provincial Capital
○ District HQ
◉ Chief HQ
■ Mission
● Village
⌂ Lodge\Camp

Protected Area
National Park
Game Management
Area (GMA)
Designated forest

Hydrology
Wetland\Swamp
Major lake
Major river

Rufunsa GMA

Rufunsa GMA

Luano GMA

Lower Zambezi NP

18 Lower Zambezi NP

Chiawa GMA

ZIMBABWE

Latondwe
Chinwe
Kapo
Kawalaman
Museseshi
Mushika
Chakwenga
Mwambashi
Sausage Tree
Chongwe River
Chiawa
Royal Zambezi
Kayila
Mushongentende
Jugurameno
Mpanshya
Rufunsa

19 Chisamba

Admin region: Chibombo District, Central Province
Co-ordinates: 15°00'S 28°15'E
Area: 52,000ha (NF & LF: c.11,000; private farms: c.40,000ha;
unprotected: c.1000ha)
Altitude: c.1100m
Status: private farms, National and Local Forests, unprotected
Categories: Globally threatened species, Biome-restricted species
International site code: ZM017   **Map:** p 102

▪ Site description

Most of the site lies between the main Lusaka-Kabwe road and Chisamba town. It encompasses several private farms as well as Chisamba National Forest (No. 29) and Mwamboshi Local Forest (No. 30). It lies on the Lukanga-Luano watershed and the terrain is varied. Much of the area is flat sand-veld with miombo and well developed dambos. Frequently associated with such areas are massive sheets of lateritic ironstone. The laterite is mostly subsurface and has a major impact on the lateral subsurface movement of water, interrupting the flow and holding it back. In such areas the miombo is interspersed with patches of dry-evergreen forest. There are also thickets in which the emergent *Entandrophragma delevoyi* is characteristic, as well as *Brachystegia spiciformis* and *B. taxifolia*. Many areas of the miombo are also dominated by large and sprawling examples of *B. spiciformis* giving it an almost park-like quality. There are also patches of munga, strips of riparian forest and several rocky hills. In the farmed areas there is cleared pasture, arable land and there are numerous dams. At least two of the farms now operate game ranches and in addition to the direct ecological benefits, such areas also receive better protection. Within the National Forest are several sites of archaeological interest, including some very well preserved Iron Age furnaces and several Stone Age sites.

▪ Birds

The area is most important for its population of Chaplin's Barbets. These are most common in farmland with scattered Sycamore Figs *Ficus sycomorus*, particularly around the eastern end of the Chisamba road. Although many of the farm dams

attract good numbers of waterbirds, the most interesting wetlands are within Huntley Farm, to the west of the main road. Birds such as Darter, Great White Egret, White-faced Whistling Duck and African Jacana are common and in some years Slaty Egret has been regular. Little Bittern, African Water Rail and Purple Gallinule are all regular in patches of swamp and during the rains both Lesser Gallinule and Lesser Moorhen can be abundant. Rarer migrants include Corn Crake, Spotted and Striped Crakes and several species of wader. Up to

Chaplin's Barbet (Mike Harrison)

8 species of *Euplectes* can be found including Yellow-crowned Bishop, here on the edge of its range and where swamp meets forest Thick-billed Weavers can be common. The miombo holds a large number of Zambezian endemics and the more open formations seem particularly suited to species such as Racket-tailed Roller and Pale-billed Hornbill. Crowned Eagle is known to nest in several places and Thick-billed Cuckoo is regularly reported, particularly from Nyoni Farm.

See summary box for key species. The area is well known. Total number of species recorded to date: 404.

■ Other flora and fauna

A small number of large indigenous mammals occur and many others have been introduced on the game ranches. The herb *Monadenium friesii* is a local endemic found in the miombo and the thickets hold a number of rare tree species such as *Cassia angolensis*, *Diospyros abyssinica* and *Canthium longipedicellata* (M. Bingham in litt.).

■ Conservation issues

The greatest potential threat to Chaplin's Barbet would seem to be loss of Sycamore Figs and it is therefore vital that landowners remain aware of this tree's importance and that they are persuaded to conserve them. The protected status and condition of the National and Local Forests require monitoring. Brown-necked Parrots are trapped with lime in large numbers and sold illegally as cagebirds beside the main road. It is likely that many other species are trapped and discarded or eaten during this process and it is possible that Chaplin's Barbets are vulnerable.

■ Information for visitors

The IBA is within easy reach of Lusaka and is a popular destination for Zambian Ornithological Society (ZOS) field meetings. Both Chisamba Safari Lodge and Fringilla B&B and campsite have accommodation and restaurants and both are set in grounds suitable for birding. The private farms, such as Huntley, Nyoni, Sable and Lemba can all be visited by prior arrangement and details can been obtained from ZOS (see contact details in section 7).

Lesser Gallinule

101

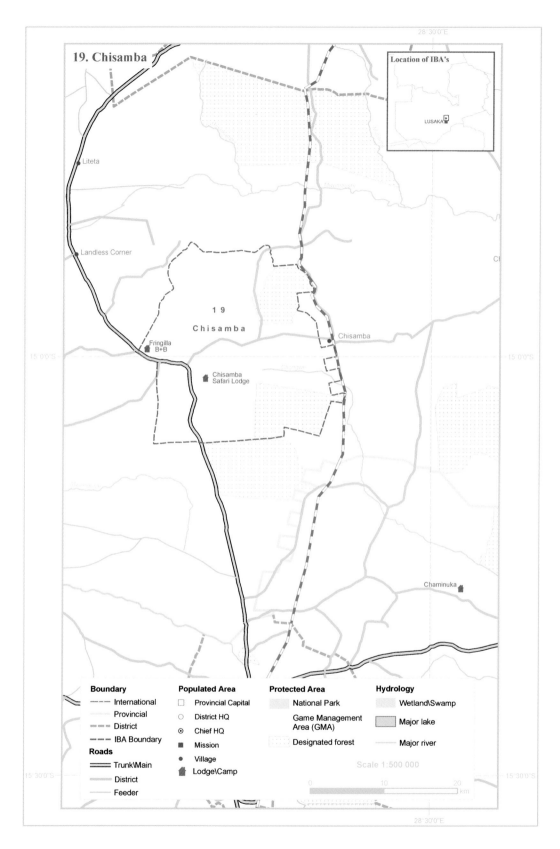

19. Chisamba

Location of IBA's

LUSAKA

Liteta

Landless Corner

1 9
Chisamba

Fringilla
B+B

Chisamba Safari Lodge

Chisamba

Chaminuka

Boundary		Populated Area		Protected Area		Hydrology	
-----	International	☐	Provincial Capital		National Park		Wetland\Swamp
	Provincial	○	District HQ		Game Management Area (GMA)		Major lake
--- ---	District	⊙	Chief HQ		Designated forest		Major river
--- ---	IBA Boundary	■	Mission				
Roads		●	Village				
▬▬▬	Trunk\Main	⌂	Lodge\Camp				
▬▬▬	District						
▬▬▬	Feeder						

Scale 1:500 000

0   10   20
km

Globally threatened species		
Slaty Egret	Vulnerable	occasional visitor
Lappet-faced Vulture	Vulnerable	occasional visitor
Pallid Harrier	Near-threatened	fairly regular passage migrant and non-breeding visitor
Lesser Kestrel	Vulnerable	regular passage migrant
Corn Crake	Vulnerable	occasional non-breeding visitor, probably overlooked
Black-winged Pratincole	Data deficient	rare visitor, small groups have occasionally wintered
Great Snipe	Near-threatened	regular non-breeding visitor
African Skimmer	Near-threatened	occasional visitor
Chaplin's Barbet	Near-threatened	common but localised breeding resident

Biome-restricted species		
Zambezian	13 endemics	13 near-endemics

Species of regional conservation concern	
Goliath Heron	scarce visitor
Saddle-billed Stork	fairly regular visitor
Bateleur	occasional, may breed
African Marsh Harrier	fairly regular, probably breeds
Yellow-throated Sandgrouse	fairly regular visitor
Southern Ground Hornbill	uncommon resident

20 Lukanga Swamp

Admin region: Chibombo, Kapiri Mposhi Districts, Central Province
Co-ordinates: 14°05'-14°38'S 27°25'-28°E
Area: 330,000ha   **Altitude:** 1100m
Status: unprotected
Categories: Globally threatened species, Biome-restricted species, Globally important congregations
International site code: ZM016   **Map:** p 105

■ Site description

Despite its proximity to the main line of rail, this enormous wetland remains one of Zambia's least explored areas. It comprises swamp, open lagoons and seasonally inundated floodplain and access is difficult. Permanent swamp covers about half the area and is dominated by *Phragmites australis* and *Cyperus papyrus* (Kamweneshe & Beilfuss 2002). There are many small areas of open water and a few larger expanses such as Lakes Suye and Chiposhya. Typical aquatic plants include *Aeschynomene fluitans* and *Nymphaea* spp.. Bordering the swamp is a band of floodplain and termitaria covering about 50,000ha. Rivers such as the Lukanga have smaller floodplains as well as

levees and oxbows and in places there is riparian forest and some mushitu.

The area is part of the Kafue drainage system and when the floods begin to rise they spill from the Kafue and fill the Lukanga basin leaving an area of shallow inundation that may be 70-80km wide. As the water levels in the Kafue drop, the Lukanga basin then drains back into it.

The human population is high in certain areas around the swamps and on some of the larger islands such as Chilwa and Chiboshe. People survive on subsistence agriculture, cattle herding, charcoal production, fuel wood cutting, hunting and some mat and basket production. There is also

A seasonal fishing settlement in the heart of the Lukanga swamps. (Richard Beilfuss)

African Pygmy Goose (Peter Leonard)

much small-scale fishing, though the fishermen tend to be immigrants from Western and Luapula Province (Kamweneshe & Beilfuss 2002).

■ Birds

The swamps are very poorly known, but the sparse data suggest they are rich in waterbirds such as White Pelican, Common Squacco Heron and Openbill Stork (Kamweneshe & Beilfuss 2002). It seems likely that following further survey work, more species will be shown to exceed their 1% threshold. There are also likely to be enormous numbers of secretive swamp inhabitants such as Red-chested Flufftail, Black Crake and Purple

Gallinule as well as passerines such as Greater Swamp Warbler and Swamp Flycatcher, both of which are somewhat localised in central Zambia.

There is a small but stable breeding population of Wattled Cranes estimated to number about 50 (Kamweneshe & Beilfuss 2002, Douthwaite 1974) with the majority in western areas of the swamp and along the Lukanga river. The very localised Common Bittern (subspecies *capensis*) has been recorded but its status is not known. There are two sightings of Shoebill (Burton & Benson 1961, van Lavieren 1973) which probably refer to wandering individuals and not a resident population. The area

Long-toed Plovers

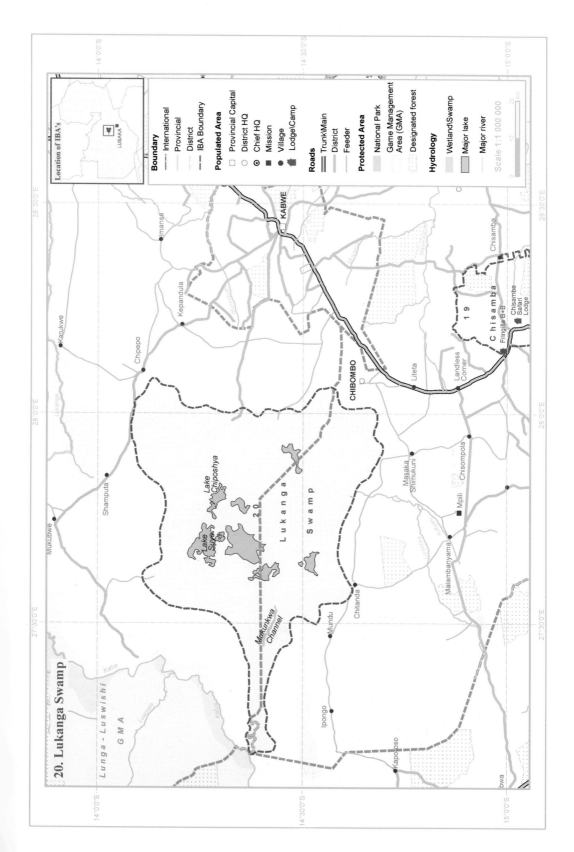

20. Lukanga Swamp

Boundary
International
Provincial
District
IBA Boundary

Populated Area
□ Provincial Capital
○ District HQ
⊙ Chief HQ
■ Mission
● Village
🏯 Lodge\Camp

Roads
Trunk\Main
District
Feeder

Protected Area
National Park
Game Management Area (GMA)
Designated forest

Hydrology
Wetland\Swamp
Major lake
Major river

Scale 1:1 000 000

Lunga - Luswishi
G M A

Mukubwe

Shamputa

Kaukwe

Chipepo

Kepandula

Ilmansa

KABWE

CHIBOMBO

Liteta

Landless Corner

Fringila B+B

Chisamba

Chisamba Safari Lodge

Masaka Shimukuni

Chisompola

Mpili

Malambanyama

Mundu

Chitanda

Ipongo

Kapotoso

Lake Chiposhya

Lake Suves

L u k a n g a   S w a m p

Mukunkwa Channel

around the confluence with the Kafue is slightly better known (Tree 1966a, b) and Chaplin's Barbet has been recorded near here. Birds of riparian forest include African Finfoot, Pel's Fishing Owl and Black-backed Barbets. A small number of Zambezian endemics occur such as Dickinson's Kestrel and Coppery-tailed Coucal. Further work is required to gauge the full importance of this site and to determine the status of many species.

See summary box for key species. The whole area is very poorly known. Total number of species recorded to date: 338.

■ Other flora and fauna

There is probably still a good population of Sitatunga *Tragelaphus spekei* (LR/cd) and recent survey work found 60 Oribi *Ourebia ourebi* (LR/cd) and a very small number of Red Lechwe *Kobus leche leche* (Kamweneshe & Beilfuss 2002). Whether or not other large mammals such as Hippopotamus *Hippopotamus amphibius* still

survive is not known. There are still good populations of Nile Crocodile *Crocodylus niloticus* and African Python *Python sebae*.

■ Conservation issues

The main threats caused by human disturbance are burning and hunting (including snaring, the use of dogs and nest-robbing at breeding colonies). Overfishing is also likely to be an issue as the off-season (December-February) is rarely observed or enforced.

■ Information for visitors

The area is most easily approached from Kabwe, Chibombo or Landless Corner. It is difficult to explore, but if a harbour is reached it is possible to negotiate the hiring of a fishing boat to gain access into the swamp. This is preferable to using your own craft as a hired boatman will also have vital navigational skills. This is an area that beckons to the adventurous.

Globally threatened species		
Shoebill	Near-threatened	rare visitor
Pallid Harrier	Near-threatened	passage migrant and non-breeding visitor, probably regular
Lesser Kestrel	Vulnerable	passage migrant, probably regular
Corn Crake	Vulnerable	non-breeding visitor, probably fairly common
Wattled Crane	Vulnerable	regular breeding resident
Great Snipe	Near-threatened	non-breeding visitor, probably fairly common
African Skimmer	Near-threatened	regular visitor, may breed
Chaplin's Barbet	Near-threatened	probably a scarce and localised resident

Biome-restricted species		
Zambezian	6 endemics	8 near-endemics

Globally important congregations		
(i) regularly holds >1% of biogeographic population of a congregatory waterbird		
Openbill Stork	>6,000 (Nov 2001)	

Species of regional conservation concern	
Common Bittern	status uncertain, possibly a breeding resident
Goliath Heron	uncommon breeding resident
Saddle-billed Stork	uncommon resident, probably breeds
Bateleur	regular, may breed
African Marsh Harrier	common breeding resident
Yellow-throated Sandgrouse	fairly common visitor, probably breeds
Southern Ground Hornbill	uncommon resident
Yellow-billed Oxpecker	status uncertain, no recent records
Red-billed Oxpecker	status uncertain, no recent records

21 Imanda

Admin region: Mpongwe District, Copperbelt Province
Co-ordinates: 13°29'S 27°56'E
Area: at least 1000ha   **Altitude:** 1180m
Status: unprotected
Categories: Biome-restricted species
International site code: ZM014   **Map:** p 108

■ Site description

Two large mushitus, about 25km west of Mpongwe and just south of St. Anthony's Mission. There are several such forests in the area growing on a limestone substrate that is prone to waterlogging and thus suitable for such vegetation. The main forest at Imanda represents one of the finest and largest examples of moist evergreen forest not only in this area, but also in the country as a whole. It is partly surrounded by a large dambo and also by some villages and cultivation. A number of poorly defined tracks run through the forest, but otherwise it remains relatively undisturbed. The second patch to the north-east is on the Bilima river and is less well known. Further work is required to establish a suitable boundary.

■ Birds

A wealth of mushitu species are to be found, several of which are Zambezian endemics. It is a well known site for Margaret's Batis which is fairly common. Other typical species include Lady Ross's Turaco, Cinnamon Dove, Eastern Least Honeyguide, Olive Woodpecker, Purple-throated Cuckoo-shrike, Bocage's Robin, Evergreen Forest Warbler, Laura's Warbler, Grey Apalis, Blue-mantled Flycatcher and Many-coloured Bush Shrike. Several species of raptor breed in the canopy such as Hooded Vulture, Ayres's Hawk Eagle and Crowned Eagle.

See summary box for key species. The main forest is well known, other areas much less so. Total number of species recorded to date: 221.

■ Other flora and fauna

There is a very rich diversity of forest plants, from the canopy trees to the herbaceous ground cover.

Bocage's Robin (Johann Grobbelaar)

Apart from the birds, the vertebrate fauna is not well known.

■ Conservation issues

Until recently people rarely ventured into the forests and they were only used for some subsistence hunting and occasional cutting of trees for building poles. However, as the woodland trees become depleted there is increasing pressure on the forests for firewood as well. Furthermore, near the villages, small gardens have been cut into the forest and such clearance requires careful monitoring. In dry years fire is a threat.

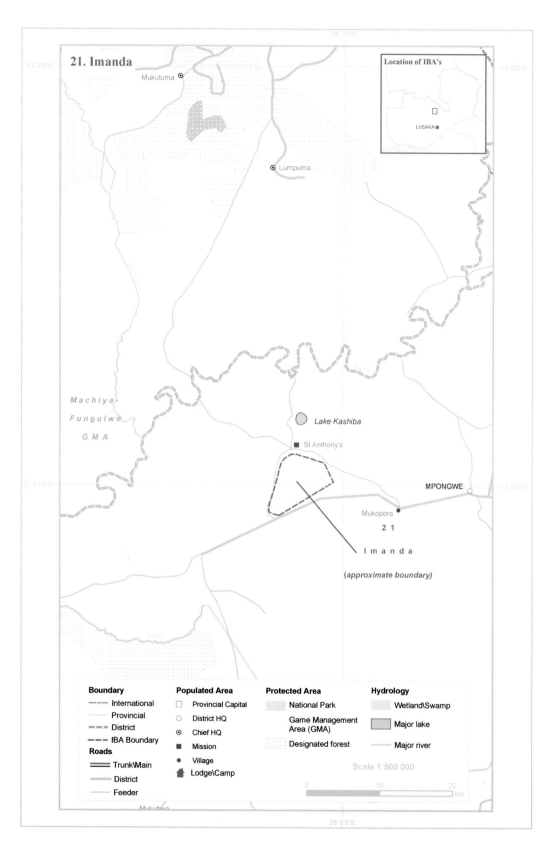

21. Imanda

Mukutuma ⊙

⊙ Lumpuma

Location of IBA's

LUSAKA ■

M a c h i y a -
F u n g u l w e
G M A

Lake Kashiba

■ St Anthony's

MPONGWE ⊙

Mukopora ●

2 1

I m a n d a

(approximate boundary)

Boundary	Populated Area	Protected Area	Hydrology
- - - - International	☐ Provincial Capital	National Park	Wetland\Swamp
Provincial	○ District HQ	Game Management Area (GMA)	Major lake
= = = District	⊙ Chief HQ	Designated forest	Major river
- - - IBA Boundary	■ Mission		
Roads	● Village		
Trunk\Main	🏠 Lodge\Camp	Scale 1:500 000	
District			
Feeder		0 10 20

Mukubwe

■ Information for visitors

Drive through Mpongwe to St. Anthony's Mission. The main forest at Imanda is most easily reached from the west side so from the mission follow a rough track heading south for about 5km to where the forest comes within about 100m of the track. There are a few small settlements along this stretch and local residents are usually happy to watch over

a vehicle (by arrangement) if left unattended. Several paths lead into or close to the forest and once inside it is not too difficult to move around, though it can be wet under foot, so gum-boots are advisable. Of interest nearby is Lake Kashiba; a very deep, natural sunken lake and a National Monument. It is surrounded by forest that also holds an interesting selection of birds.

Biome-restricted species		
Afromontane	-	4 near-endemics
Sub-Afromontane	1 endemic	-
Eastern	-	2 near-endemics
Zambezian	4 endemics	5 near-endemics

Species of regional conservation concern	
Bateleur	fairly common resident
African Marsh Harrier	regular
Southern Ground Hornbill	occasional
Margaret's Batis	fairly common resident

22 Chimfunshi

Admin region: Chingola District, Copperbelt Province
Co-ordinates: 12°20'S 27°31'E
Area: 9300ha   **Altitude:** 1280m
Status: private farm
Categories: Globally threatened species, Biome-restricted species
International site code: ZM013   **Map:** p 111

■ Site description

Just west of the Copperbelt, Chimfunshi Wildlife Orphanage is a large private farm on the banks of the Kafue river. At its heart is a long-established chim-panzee sanctuary which has received considerable attention from the international media. Chimpanzees are not indigenous to Zambia and most of the animals have either been confiscated from illegal traders or bred on site. At present they are kept in a variety of enclosures, the biggest of which encom-passes 1000ha of woodland. Additionally, 5300ha is being fenced to establish a game ranch and cattle are farmed on the remaining land. Much of the area is rich miombo woodland interspersed with dambos and a few patches of mushitu. Some sections of the

Kafue are fringed with tall riparian forest and others spread onto wide floodplains.

■ Birds

The miombo is rich in Zambezian endemics such as Pale-billed Hornbill, Whyte's Barbet, Miombo Pied Barbet, Central Bearded Scrub Robin, Black-collared Eremomela, Böhm's Flycatcher, Rufous-bellied Tit, Sousa's Shrike and Chestnut-mantled Sparrow-weaver. Sharp-tailed Starling is particu-larly common here. Regular species in the riparian forest include Lady Ross's Turaco, Golden-rumped Tinkerbird, Black-backed Barbet, Olive Woodpecker, Purple-throated Cuckoo-shrike, Yellow-throated Leaflove, Grey-olive Bulbul and

Red-capped Crombec

Grey Apalis. In richer mushitu, additional species include Bocage's Robin, Evergreen Forest Warbler, Laura's Warbler, White-chinned Prinia, Blue-mantled Flycatcher and Many-coloured Bush Shrike. The dambos hold species such as Fülleborn's and Rosy-breasted Longclaws, Marsh Whydah, Fawn-breasted Waxbill and Black-chinned Quailfinch.

See summary box for key species. The area is fairly well known. Total number of species recorded to date: 291.

■ Other flora and fauna

Although previously rich in large mammals most have been extirpated by illegal hunting. Small numbers of Gentle (Blue) Monkey *Cercopithecus mitis* and Sitatunga *Tragelaphus spekei* still occur in the mushitus and the occasional Hippopotamus *Hippopotamus amphibius* and Nile Crocodile *Crocodylus niloticus* is found in the main river.

■ Conservation issues

Most of the indigenous game had been hunted to extinction by the late 1970s but with increased pro-tection and restocking it is hoped that numbers will build up to their former levels. It is unlikely that there are any serious threats to the birds, though the trees and plants within the chimpanzee enclosures are gradually destroyed by these animals, despite the fact that they are fed daily.

■ Information for visitors

To reach Chimfunshi, drive through Chingola on the T5 and continue for 47.5km (4km past Munchinshi village) towards Solwezi. Turn right at the Chimfunshi signpost, then left at the second signpost 2km later, marked 'Chimfunshi 15km'. On site there is a campsite near the farm by the river and there are chalets at the main office. There is also an education centre on the far side of the property near the largest chimp enclosures. This is mainly for school parties, there are two big dormi-tories and full catering can be provided. Advance booking is recommended; see www.chimfunshi. org.za for details. There are also plans to build a lodge and an airstrip. Next to the Education Centre is a strip of gallery mushitu and if you follow this valley you reach a broad dambo with a large and very wet mushitu in its centre. This can be difficult to get into, but is easiest from the west side and gumboots are recommended. Once inside, it is not difficult to explore and it is home to a wealth of birdlife. It is possible to reach Chimfunshi in most vehicles, but as with most dirt roads, progress is much simpler with high clearance and conditions deteriorate during the rains. Contact details: Chimfunshi Wildlife Orphanage, P.O. Box 11190, Chingola, Tel/fax 00 260-2-311293.

Shikra (Neil Baker)

22. Chimfunshi Wildlife Orphanage

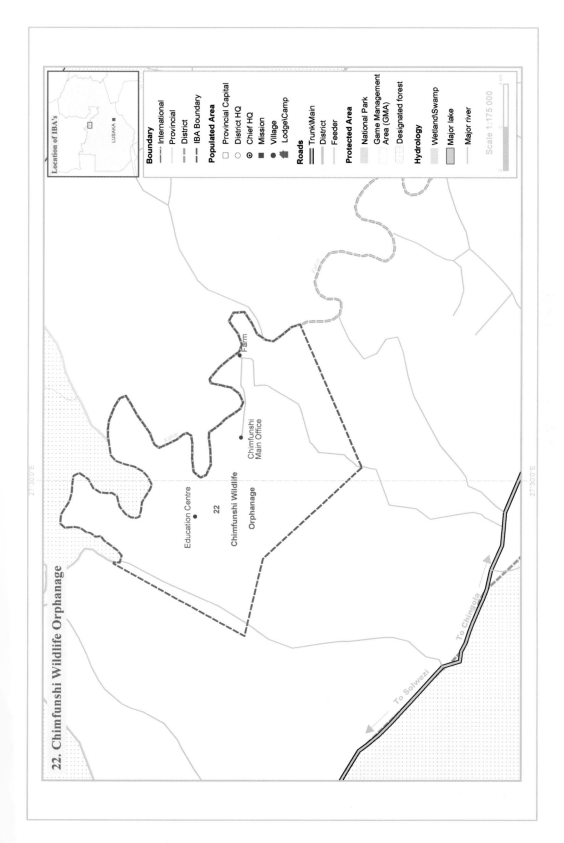

Globally threatened species		
Wattled Crane	Vulnerable	rare visitor
Denham's Bustard	Near-threatened	occasional visitor

Biome-restricted species		
Afromontane	-	3 near-endemics
Sub-Afromontane	1 endemic	-
Eastern	-	2 near-endemics
Guineo-Congolian	-	1 near-endemic
Zambezian	15 endemics	10 near-endemics

Species of regional conservation concern		
Goliath Heron	occasional	
Saddle-billed Stork	occasional	
Bateleur	fairly common resident	
African Marsh Harrier	regular	
Southern Ground Hornbill	fairly common resident	

23 North Swaka

Admin region: Mkushi District, Central Province
Co-ordinates: 13°13'-13°35'S 29°03'-29°41'E
Area: 108,000ha   **Altitude:** 1230-1893m
Status: National Forests, National Monument
Categories: Biome-restricted species
International site code: ZM015   **Map:** p 114

■ Site description

Two large and rather poorly known National Forests on the D.R.C. border, north of Mkushi town (North Swaka Block B National Forest No. 46, Mkushi Headwaters National Forest No. 115). Much of the area lies between 1250-1450m and comprises tall, rich miombo and broad headwater dambos. There are also extensive rocky ridges and hills, the highest of which is Mount Mumpu at 1893m. In such areas, the various headwaters of the Lunsemfwa system have carved gorges in the hills where waterfalls and strips of sub-montane forest can be found. On the ridge marking the eastern boundary is a National Monument called Fort Elwes. This structure was built in 1896-7 by European gold prospectors as a refuge in times of conflict. A series of very large dry stone walls remain, some of which are over two metres thick (Phillipson & Katanekwa, 1992).

■ Birds

The area is very rich in Zambezian endemics and near-endemics. In the miombo, these include Pale-billed Hornbill, Anchieta's Barbet, Black-collared Eremomela, Böhm's Flycatcher, Red-and-blue Sunbird, Sousa's Shrike, Chestnut-mantled Sparrow-weaver and Bar-winged Weaver. Other interesting woodland species include Thick-billed Cuckoo, White-tailed Blue Flycatcher and Stripe-breasted Seed-eater. The dambos hold Long-toed Flufftail, Fülleborn's Longclaw, Stout Cisticola and Marsh Whydah and along the streams can be found African Black Duck, Half-collared Kingfisher and Mountain Wagtail. Where such streams support gallery forest, Grey-olive Bulbul can be common and other species include Bocage's Robin, Laura's Warbler, Green-headed Sunbird and Black-bellied Seed-cracker. In the rocky hills are species such as Augur Buzzard, Black Eagle,

The enormous walls of Fort Elwes on a ridge overlooking the broad dambos of North Swaka. (Peter Leonard)

Mocking Chat and Rock-loving Cisticola.

See summary box for key species. The area is fairly well known. Total number of species recorded to date: 280.

■ Other flora and fauna

Not well known, though few large mammals remain. Gentle (Blue) Monkey *Cercopithecus mitis* is still occasionally reported. The area has a very rich flora with an interesting sub-montane element.

■ Conservation issues

There is some subsistence hunting, burning and grazing of cattle but there is very little settlement within the area at present. However, the populations of adjacent areas are growing rapidly and human encroachment needs careful monitoring. Tree-cutting is certainly becoming more of a problem.

■ Information for visitors

The quickest and easiest area to reach is the western half, through which the Mkushi-Musofu

Rufous-bellied Tit (Johann Grobbelaar)

113

23. North Swaka

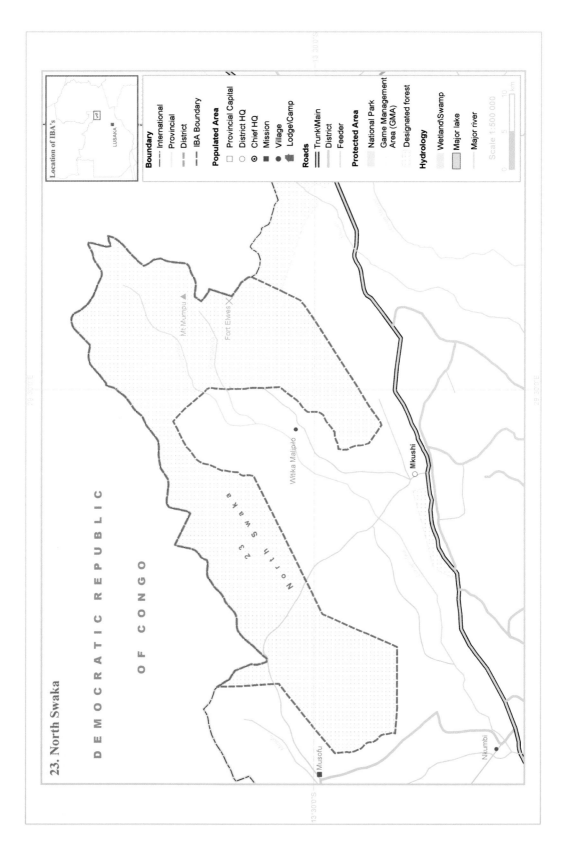

road runs. This portion of the site holds some of the richest miombo. However, most visitors choose to venture out to the eastern parts where the scenery is more spectacular. There is a very basic campsite near the series of waterfalls on the Changwena River (about 40km from Mkushi) and from here you can walk to Fort Elwes and Mount Mumpu. To reach the campsite from Mkushi, turn right 0.7km beyond the filling station, cross a small river and take the next left through the market. After another 14km fork right, enter the National Forest after a further 12km, bear right after another 7km and

reach the Changwena after another 4km. A high clearance vehicle is necessary, though four wheel drive is generally only needed after very heavy rain. Visitors should be fully self-sufficient. There are various unmarked tracks and paths traversing the area, but most walking is through undisturbed bush where a map is important and a GPS helpful. The terrain is rugged and a round trip to either Fort Elwes or Mount Mumpu is a relatively demanding walk, particularly if it is hot. There are occasional reports of petty theft from vehicles and tents left unattended.

Biome-restricted specie		
Afromontane	1 endemic	4 near-endemics
Sub-Afromontane	1 endemic	-
Eastern	-	2 near-endemics
Zambezian	15 endemics	17 near-endemics

Species of regional conservation concern	
Bateleur	fairly common resident
African Marsh Harrier	regular
Southern Ground Hornbill	fairly common resident
Bar-winged Weaver	fairly common, but localised, breeding resident

24 Wonder Gorge

Admin region: Kapiri Mposhi, Mkushi Districts, Central Province
Co-ordinates: 14°37'S 29°07'E
Area: at least 10,000ha   **Altitude:** 500-1150m
Status: unprotected, National Monument
Categories: Globally threatened species, Biome-restricted species
International site code: --- **Map:** p 117

■ Site description

Where the Lunsemfwa river descends the Muchinga escarpment it has carved a spectacular gorge into the sedimentary rock, several kilometres long. It is extremely steep, relatively narrow and about 300m deep. About halfway along its length it is joined from the north-east by the Mkushi river in an equally impressive gorge. Directly above the confluence is Bell Point, a viewpoint that has been awarded National Monument status due to its outstanding natural beauty (Phillipson & Katanekwa 1992). Bell Point was named after Miss Grace Bell,

a friend of E. Knowles Jordan who was probably the first European to reach the area in about 1913. The gorge is surrounded by rolling terrain covered with miombo, it is remote and sparsely populated. Further fieldwork is required to establish a suitable boundary. Ideally, this should remain a considerable distance from the gorge and thus aim to protect the surrounding miombo as well.

■ Birds

Very little fieldwork has been carried out, but there are at least two records of Taita Falcon and it seems

Central Bearded Scrub Robin (Warwick Tarboton)

likely that this localised species is a breeding resident. Many birds that are typical of rocky habitats occur, such as Black Eagle, Mocking Chat, Rock-loving Cisticola, Striped Pipit and Red-winged Starling. The surrounding miombo holds a good number of Zambezian endemics and near-endemics such as Pale-billed Hornbill, Miombo Rock Thrush, Central Bearded Scrub Robin, Arnot's Chat, Red-capped Crombec, Rufous-bellied Tit and Sousa's Shrike.

See summary box for key species. The area is very poorly known. Total number of species recorded to date: 134.

Orange-winged Pytilia

■ Other flora and fauna

Not known.

■ Conservation issues

At present there are no known threats and the remoteness and inaccessibility of the site seem to protect it. However, if the surrounding miombo was cleared this could pose a serious threat to species sensitive to disturbance such as Taita Falcon.

■ Information for visitors

Bell Point is the easiest area to reach. From Kabwe, drive to Lunsemfwa via Mulungushi and Kampumba. From Lunsemfwa follow the RD204 to Old Mkushi and turn right after c.20km. From here it is about 35km to Bell Point. Take the right fork after 1km and keep following the main track and after 21km turn left. Four wheel drive is probably not necessary, but high clearance is important. There are no facilities at Bell Point but it is possible to camp and travellers should be self-sufficient. There are no obvious paths, but the walking options are good for the adventurous and fit. It is possible to drive to near the mouth of the gorge on the western side by following the Luano Valley road. This branches off the Mulungushi-Lunsemfwa road just south of Kampumba. Vague tracks leaving this road lead very close to the gorge, but a sturdy off-road vehicle and navigational aids are important.

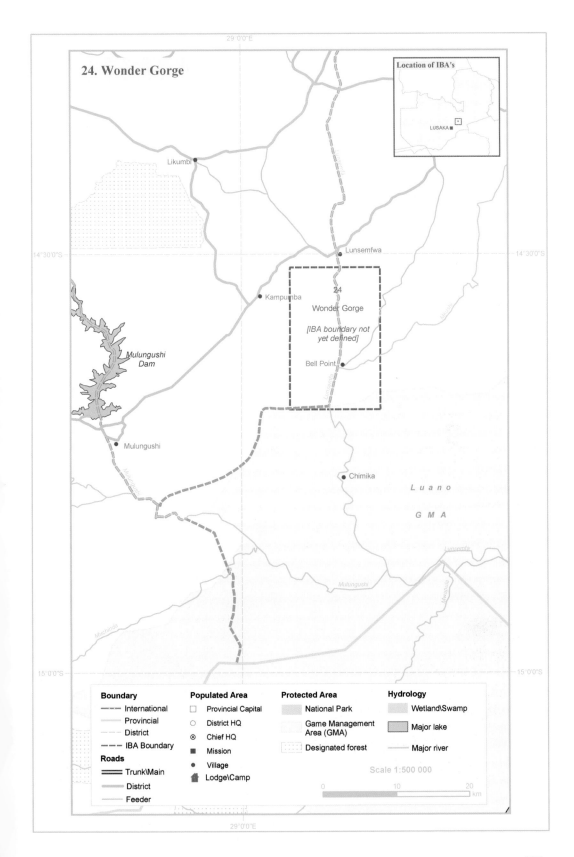

24. Wonder Gorge

Location of IBA's

LUSAKA ■

Likumbi

Lunsemfwa

24
Wonder Gorge

[IBA boundary not yet defined]

Kampumba

Mulungushi
Dam

Bell Point

Mulungushi

Chimika

L u a n o

G M A

Lunsemfwa

Mulungushi

Boundary	Populated Area	Protected Area	Hydrology
--- - International	☐ Provincial Capital	National Park	Wetland\Swamp
Provincial	○ District HQ	Game Management Area (GMA)	Major lake
District	◉ Chief HQ	Designated forest	Major river
--- - IBA Boundary	■ Mission		
Roads	● Village		Scale 1:500 000
Trunk\Main	🏠 Lodge\Camp		
District			0 10 20
Feeder			km

Globally threatened species		
Taita Falcon	Near-threatened	probably regular breeding resident

Biome-restricted species		
Zambezian	6 endemics	8 near-endemics

Species of regional conservation concern		
Bateleur	regular, probably breeds	

25 Kasanka National Park

Admin region: Serenje District, Central Province
Co-ordinates: 12°24'-12°39'S 30°03'-30°23'E
Area: 39,000ha   **Altitude:** c.1200m
Status: National Park
Categories: Globally threatened species, Biome-restricted species
International site code: ZM025   **Map:** p 121

■ Site description

Run by the Kasanka Trust, this is the only Zambian national park to be privately managed and is entirely reliant on independent funding. The park lies on the edge of Bangweulu basin to the west of the Serenje-Samfya road. It is dominated by woodland and has a great variety of miombo formations including some interesting areas of dwarf *Brachystegia stipulata* over deposits of bauxite. There are also areas of lake basin chipya and small patches of dry evergreen forest in which typical species are *Dialium angolense*, *Embelia schmitzii*, *Strychnos matopensis*, *Parinari excelsa* and *Entandrophragma delevoyi*. There is some particularly rich riparian forest and mushitu with trees such as *Parkia filicoidea*, *Diospyros mespiliformis* and some exceptionally large specimens of *Erythrophleum suaveolens* and *Khaya (nyasica) anthotheca*. The swamp and riverine vegetation is rich in wetland grasses and sedges. The area has an unusually high number of pans as well as some papyrus swamp, dambos and floodplains which attract high densities of game animals.

The Kasanka Trust (first registered in 1987) has responsibility for park management, community development, and tourism and it promotes education and research in wildlife conservation. The funding for these activities comes from a number of sources, including foreign governments, charities, individual supporters and tourists.

■ Birds

The miombo holds a large number of Zambezian endemics such as Miombo Pied Barbet, Black-

Böhm's Bee-eater (Mike Harrison)

118

Straw-coloured Fruit Bats roosting at very high density.
(Peter Leonard)

Straw-coloured Fruit Bats leaving their roost.
(Edmund Farmer)

collared Eremomela, Böhm's Flycatcher and Red-and-blue Sunbird. Both Anchieta's and Whyte's Barbet are found, as is the long-tailed race of Neddicky *Cisticola fulvicapilla angusticauda*. Other interesting woodland birds include Thick-billed Cuckoo, Little Tawny Pipit and White-tailed Blue Flycatcher. Common forest species include Western Banded Snake Eagle, Lady Ross's Turaco, Böhm's Bee-eater, Black-backed Barbet, Purple-throated Cuckoo-shrike and Green-headed Sunbird. Along the rivers Pel's Fishing Owl, African Finfoot and Half-collared Kingfisher are all regular. A wide variety of wetland birds occur and typical species include Spur-winged Goose, African Pygmy Goose and African Jacana. There are also small but stable populations of both Saddle-billed Stork and Wattled Crane.

See summary box for key species. The area is very well known. Total number of species recorded to date: 417.

■ Other flora and fauna

In November and December, Kasanka hosts an enormous seasonal influx of migratory Straw-coloured Fruit Bats *Eidolon helvum*. An estimated 5 million come to roost in one small area of mushitu and this represents one of the largest and densest aggregations of mammals in world. About 100 other species of mammal have been recorded including Spot-necked Otter *Lutra maculicollis* (VU), Tree Hyrax *Dendrohyrax arboreus* (VU) and slowly increasing numbers of African Elephant

Loxodonta africana (EN). Puku *Kobus vardoni* (LR/cd) are abundant and there are also very good numbers of Sitatunga *Tragelaphus spekei* (LR/cd). In addition, recent survey work counted 2160 Warthog *Phacochoerus africanus*, 173 Roan Antelope *Hippotragus equinus* (LR/cd) and 967 Hartebeest *Alcelaphus buselaphus lichtensteinii* (LR/cd). Gentle (Blue) Monkey *Cercopithecus mitis mitis* is common in the mushitu. There is one old uncertain record of the subspecies *C. m. albogularis* in the west of the park, but there are no recent records. There have been some mammal reintroduction programmes and more are planned. 38 reptiles have been recorded, including Slender-snouted Crocodile *Crocodylus cataphractus* (DD) and also recorded in the park are 26 amphibians, 63 fish, 19 dragonflies, 51 butterflies and 37 spiders (Stuart & Stuart 2003b).

■ Conservation issues

Since being privately managed, the park has been actively protected and although poaching incidents are still regular, they are much reduced and many species are flourishing. Similar effort is put into controlling fires. There are probably no threats to the bird life.

■ Information for visitors

There are good tourist facilities including two well-equipped and very comfortable camps and a camp-site. As well as game-viewing by vehicle, the park's attractions include boating, fishing and walking safaris. There is also the Fibwe tree-hide built 18m up in a large mululu *Khaya anthotheca* and overlooking the Kapabi swamp. It was designed for viewing sitatunga and there is probably no better place to watch these secretive animals. It is sometimes possible to camp at the Fibwe hide and visitors wishing to do so should make enquiries to park staff. The roost of Straw-coloured Fruit Bats in November and December is an incredible wildlife spectacle. Visitors can take guided walks through the forest in the daytime to view the bats as they chatter, fly and crawl about their roost before watching them depart to their feeding grounds at dusk. Although the roads are generally good, few travellers attempt to visit Kasanka without high clearance. However, four wheel drive is needed only rarely during the rains. The nearest fuel is in Serenje and from there the park is easily reached and well signed on the Samfya road. For much more information on the park and other interesting areas nearby, visit: www.kasanka.com

The meandering Kasanka River. (Edmund Farmer)

Globally threatened species		
Shoebill	Near-threatened	very rare vagrant
Lappet-faced Vulture	Vulnerable	regular, may breed
Pallid Harrier	Near-threatened	scarce passage migrant and non-breeding visitor
Lesser Kestrel	Vulnerable	occasional passage migrant
Corn Crake	Vulnerable	occasional non-breeding visitor, probably under-recorded
Wattled Crane	Vulnerable	breeding resident
Denham's Bustard	Near-threatened	occasional visitor, may breed
Biome-restricted species		
Afromontane	-	2 near-endemics
Sub-Afromontane	1 endemic	-
Eastern	-	2 near-endemics
Zambezian	17 endemics	14 near-endemics
Species of regional conservation concern		
Goliath Heron	regular resident, probably breeds	
Saddle-billed Stork	resident, possibly breeds	
Bateleur	fairly common breeding resident	
African Marsh Harrier	fairly common breeding resident	
Southern Ground Hornbill	fairly common breeding resident	
Red-billed Oxpecker	scarce visitor	

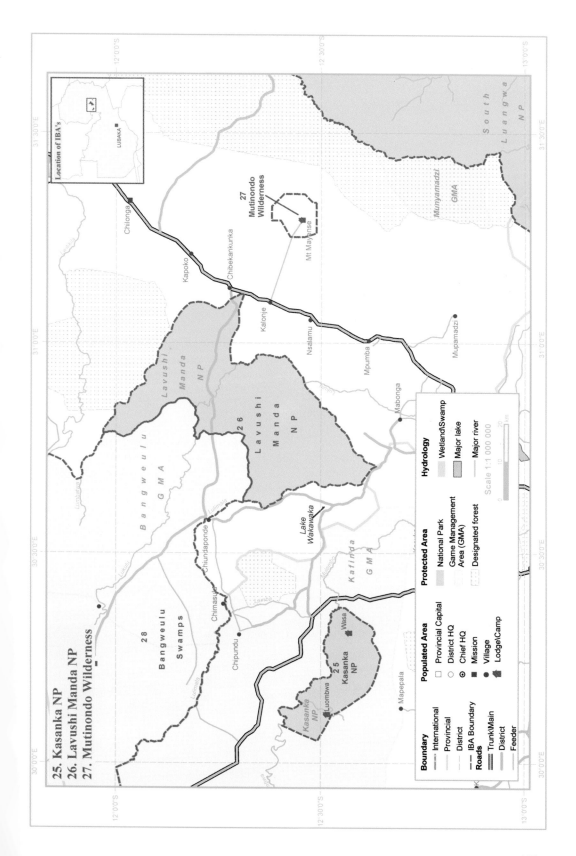

25. Kasanka NP
26. Lavushi Manda NP
27. Mutinondo Wilderness

26 Lavushi Manda National Park

Admin region: Mpika District, Northern Province
Co-ordinates: 11°58'-12°38'S 30°36'-31°05'E
Area: 150,000ha   **Altitude:** 1100-1808m
Status: National Park
Categories: Globally threatened species, Biome-restricted species
International site code: ZM024   **Map:** p 121

The Lavushi Manda Hills (Edmund Farmer)

■ Site description

This rather poorly known national park is situated to the west of the Great North Road between Serenje and Mpika. The terrain is gently rolling and lies mainly between 1200-1400m, although the Lavushi Manda Hills exceed 1800m in places. This scenic range extends for about 40km and runs parallel to the south-eastern boundary of the park. In the hills are some deep canyons and precipitous rock faces and cliffs (Clarke & Loe 1974). The habitat is predominantly mature miombo, but the park encompasses the headwaters of numerous small rivers along which run strips of forest or dambos. These then drain into the Bangweulu basin. The park is bisected from west to east by a single dirt road, but access to most of the area is very difficult and much of it remains little unexplored.

■ Birds

The miombo supports a wide variety of Zambezian endemics and near-endemics such as Pale-billed Hornbill, Anchieta's Barbet, Miombo Rock Thrush, Black-collared Eremomela and Böhm's Flycatcher. Collared Flycatcher can be a very common non-breeding visitor. In and around the riparian forest are Black Goshawk, African Finfoot, Lady Ross's Turaco, Pel's Fishing Owl, Böhm's Bee-eater, Grey-olive Bulbul, Bar-throated Apalis and Black-tailed Grey Waxbill whilst the dambos hold Fülleborn's Longclaw, Marsh Whydah and Locust Finch. Inhabiting the rocky areas are Augur Buzzard, Black Eagle, Freckled Rock Nightjar, Striped Pipit, Mocking Chat and Red-winged Starling.

See summary box for key species. The area is fairly well known, but many areas away from the main road deserve further exploration. Total number of species recorded to date: 203.

Sable are typical miombo antelope. (Andrea Leonard)

Collared Flycatcher

■ Other flora and fauna

Large mammal populations have been much reduced by poaching but species recorded recently in small numbers include African Elephant *Loxodonta africana* (EN), African Buffalo *Syncerus caffer* (LR/cd), Roan *Hippotragus equinus* (LR/cd) and Sable *H. niger* (LR/cd) antelopes, Southern Reedbuck *Redunca arundinum* (LR/cd), Sharpe's Grysbok *Raphicercus sharpei* (LR/cd), Klipspringer *Oreotragus oreotragus*

(LR/cd), Hartebeest *Alcelaphus buselaphus lichtensteinii* (LR/cd), Bush Duiker *Sylvicapra grimmia* and Warthog *Phacochoerus africanus*.

■ Conservation issues

Poaching has been a problem for many years and both fire and tree-cutting are likely to be threats. Many areas surrounding the park are only sparsely populated, but human encroachment needs to be assessed and monitored.

■ Information for visitors

There are no tourist facilities and most visitors tend to be in transit either to or from Bangweulu. However, hikers and campers will find it a rewarding area and those wishing to spend more time should check with ZAWA staff about where camping is permitted. The only road runs along a wooded watershed and it is generally more rewarding to explore the area on foot. Hikers should be equipped with a good map, a compass and ideally a GPS, as there are very few paths. The road runs from the Great North road (about 70km south of Mpika) to Chiundaponde, just west of the park and from here most travellers head south to Lake Wakawaka before bearing west towards Kasanka. The roads are rough. High clearance is important and four wheel drive necessary during the rains. The Kasanka Trust (see IBA 25) already has permission to operate safaris in the park and it is also keen to become involved in its management.

Globally threatened species		
Denham's Bustard	Near-threatened	status uncertain, probably regular
Great Snipe	Near-threatened	probably a regular non-breeding visitor
Biome-restricted species		
Afromontane	-	2 near-endemics
Eastern	-	1 near-endemic
Zambezian	12 endemics	9 near-endemics
Species of regional conservation concern		
Bateleur	fairly common breeding resident	
African Marsh Harrier	occasional	
Southern Ground Hornbill	fairly common resident	
Yellow-billed Oxpecker	status uncertain, probably scarce	

27 Mutinondo Wilderness

Admin region: Mpika District, Northern Province
Co-ordinates: 12°27'S 31°18'E
Area: 10,000ha   **Altitude:** 1360-1685m
Status: private conservation area
Categories: Globally threatened species, Biome-restricted species
International site code: --- **Map:** p 121

■ Site description

This private conservation area protects a beautiful tract of wild and undisturbed terrain south of Mpika, lying between the Great North Road and the Muchinga Escarpment. The vegetation is predominantly miombo (covering c.80% of the site) with a particularly high incidence of *Proteas*, epiphytic orchids and lichens such as *Usnea*. However, the area is characterised by granite whaleback inselbergs. Particularly numerous within the IBA, these cover about 7.5% of the area and range from small outcrops to imposing mountains. The tallest, at 1685m, is Mount Mayense which sits in the south-eastern corner of the property. Mutinondo's inselbergs have their own vegetation, dominated by *Xerophyta equisetoides* and shrubs such as *Vernonia bellinghamii, Ozoroa reticulata subsp. insignis* and *Iboza riparia*. Characteristic species of the rock surface are *Myrothamnus flabellifolius,* the mat-forming sedge *Coleochloa setifera*, and tussock grasses such as *Microchloa indica* and *Loudetia simplex*. Inselberg seepage sites include ferns, sedges and semi-aquatics such as *Drosera spp.* and *Xyris spp.* (Smith 2003). There are many dambos (covering about 9.4% of the site), some rather dry with numerous small *Cubitermes* termite mounds and others spongy and permanently wet. These drain into several rivers along which there are waterfalls, thin strips of riparian forest and occasional patches of mushitu. Such forest covers about 3.1% of the area and dominant trees include *Syzygium cordatum, Agauria salicifolia* and *Uapaca lissopyrena*. The botanical diversity is high and initial surveys have recorded more than 400 species (Smith *ibid.*). An enormous area of similarly undisturbed country surrounds the site and neighbouring local residents have expressed an interest in creating a much larger conservation area around the IBA.

■ Birds

Many Zambezian endemics and near-endemics occur in the miombo such as Miombo Rock Thrush and Sousa's Shrike and other interesting species include Thick-billed Cuckoo and Green-backed Honeyguide. Anchieta's and Whyte's Barbets can both be found, Bar-winged Weaver is relatively common and Stripe-breasted Seed-eater remarkably abundant. Ten species of sunbird have been recorded and particularly common are Red-and-blue, Violet-backed and Miombo Double-collared. Around the inselbergs are Freckled Rock Nightjar, Mocking Chat and Rock-loving Cisticola. The Muchinga Escarpment would appear to be an important flight path for migratory birds and species such as White Stork, Lesser Spotted Eagle and Steppe Eagle are regular during passage periods. Many other raptors have been recorded including Martial Eagle and African Hobby. European and African Marsh Harriers are both frequent over the dambos where other typical species include Blue Quail, Long-toed Flufftail, Natal

Bar-winged Weaver (Mike Harrison)

Red-and-blue Sunbird (Johann Grobbelaar)

Nightjar, Broad-tailed Warbler, Stout Cisticola, Marsh Whydah and Locust Finch. African Black Duck, African Finfoot, Half-collared Kingfisher and Mountain Wagtail are resident along the rivers and Grey-olive Bulbul and Bar-throated Apalis are found in the thin riparian forest. Mushitu species include Bocage's Robin, White-tailed Crested Flycatcher and Green Twinspot. There are old records of Taita Falcon from areas nearby but there are no records from the IBA.

See summary box for key species. The area is fairly well known. Total number of species recorded to date: 298.

■ Other flora and fauna

A wide variety of mammals have been recorded, although numbers remain relatively low. The area surrounding the IBA is equally undisturbed and it is hoped that many animals will recolonise (particularly from the Luangwa Valley in the east) without the need for restocking or fencing. Species that appear to be resident include Roan *Hippotragus equinus* (LR/cd) and Sable Antelopes *H. niger* (LR/cd), Southern Reedbuck *Redunca arundinum* (LR/cd), Klipspringer *Oreotragus oreotragus* (LR/cd), Sharpe's Grysbok

One of Mutinondo's many granite inselbergs. (Peter Leonard)

Raphicercus sharpei (LR/cd), Hartebeest *Alcelaphus buselaphus lichtensteinii* (LR/cd), Sitatunga *Tragelaphus spekei* (LR/cd), Leopard *Panthera pardus*, Caracal *Felis caracal*, Bush Pig *Potamochoerus larvatus* and Warthog *Phacochoerus africanus*. Smith's Red Rock Hare *Pronolagus rupestris* and Chequered Elephant Shrew *Rhynchocyon cirnei* (VU) have been reported on several occasions and both are on the very edge of their range here. 126 species of butterfly have been recorded to date including poorly known species such as *Abantis bamptoni* and *Kedestes lema*, the very localised *Zeritis sorhagenii*, the only Zambian record of *Pilodeudorix bemba* and an undescribed species of *Charaxes* (C. Congdon & I. Bampton, *in litt.*). The recent find of a single specimen of Cycad *Encephalartos schmitzii* represents a considerable extension of the known range in Zambia (Smith 2003).

■ Conservation issues

Poaching is a continual problem throughout the area and commercial poachers pass through it to reach the Luangwa Valley. Although not a problem within the IBA, chitemene farming methods are still practised widely in adjacent areas and this is reducing the quality of the surrounding woodland. Poachers, honey-gatherers and chitemene farmers are also thought to be responsible for the uncontrolled burning of large areas each year. This leads to soil erosion in the peaty dambos and subsequent water shortages in dry season. Many community based projects have been implemented in an attempt to improve these problems (such as agricultural support and education programmes, the development of local arts and crafts and various incentive schemes) but so far progress has been slow.

■ Information for visitors

The road to Mutinondo leads east off the Great North Road about 164km north of Serenje and 72km south of Mpika. The turn is about 500m south of Kalonje Railway Station. All but the lowest vehicles can use the track and from the tar it is 25km to the main camp. There is chalet accommodation and a campsite and full catering is available for either. The area is ideal for walking and a wide range of other activities is offered such as swimming, boating and horse-riding. Visitors, particularly campers, should keep food packed away or risk losing it to the cunning White-necked Ravens.

Visit: www.mutinondozambia.com or contact Mutinondo directly on 2MWL@bushmail.net or by post at P.O. Box 450126, Mpika.

Globally threatened species		
Lappet-faced Vulture	Vulnerable	occasional visitor
Lesser Kestrel	Vulnerable	occasional passage migrant
Biome-restricted species		
Afromontane	1 endemic	3 near-endemics
Sub-Afromontane	1 endemic	-
Eastern	-	1 near-endemic
Zambezian	14 endemics	11 near-endemics
Species of regional conservation concern		
Bateleur	regular, probably breeds	
African Marsh Harrier	regular, probably breeds	
Southern Ground Hornbill	uncommon resident	
Bar-winged Weaver	fairly common breeding resident	

28 Bangweulu Swamps (including Isangano NP)

Admin region: Samfya, Chilubi, Kasama, Mpika Districts, Luapula,
Northern Provinces
Co-ordinates: 11°03'-12°20'S 29°37'-30°50'E
Area: c.1,284,000ha (NP: 84,000ha; GMAs: c.750,000ha; unprotected:
c.450,000ha)
Altitude: 1100-1400m
Status: National Park, Game Management Area, unprotected
Categories: Globally threatened species, Biome-restricted species, Globally
important congregations
International site code: ZM026   **Map:** p 130

◼ Site description

A vast area of lakes, swamp, floodplain, termitaria and woodland in the Bangweulu basin. The site includes Isangano National Park, Bangweulu GMA (No. 26), Chambeshi GMA (No. 27) and Chikuni GMA (No. 34)(the latter a designated Ramsar site), the Kalasa Mokoso Flats GMA No 33 and the large area of unprotected swamps in the centre of the basin. The word Bangweulu means 'where the water meets the sky' and derives from the lake which is outside the IBA boundary. The basin drains into the Luapula River which eventually flows into the Congo.

The vegetation in the permanent swamps is dominated by *Cyperus, Phragmites, Typha, Limnophyton* and *Thalia* spp. and in the flooded grassland dominant genera include *Acroceras, Leersia, Sacciolepsis* and *Setaria*. During flood periods, thick mats of aquatic vegetation may form 'floating meadows'. The extent and timing of the annual flood depends on rainfall, but water levels usually begin to rise in January and reach their peak in March. From April onwards the water recedes and the floodplain tends to be dry by late May, although in wetter years pools may persist until August. Fringing the floodplain is termitaria and many trees and shrubs grow on the larger termite mounds thus creating a surprisingly rich ecosystem. Furthest from the wetland areas there is woodland of various types such as lake basin chipya dominated by *Erythrophleum, Parinari* and *Pterocarpus*. Isangano contains a lot of woodland, particularly in the east and there are also areas of watershed plain grassland. Further west are flood-plains and along the Chambeshi are patches of riparian forest.

The area supports a relatively high human population, with many permanent settlements on the margins of the wetland and on the larger islands. There are also numerous temporary dwellings within the swamps which are seasonal homes for fishermen. The area holds considerable numbers of large mammals and both ecotourism and trophy-hunting are fairly popular. Although much of the site falls within protected areas, in practice it receives very little protection. In the past there have been plans to gazette a new national park in the area (e.g. Ferrar 1998) but this has never come to fruition.

◼ Birds

The area is famous for its population of Shoebills, estimated to be about 200-300 (Howard & Aspinwall 1984, Kamweneshe & Beilfuss 2002). For much of the year birds are loosely concentrated near the main river channels, although when water levels are high there is much dispersal and individuals may be found at the very edges of the flood-plains. Wattled Cranes are often present in large numbers and Howard & Aspinwall (1984) estimated the population in the basin to be 1718. More recently, Kamweneshe & Beilfuss (2002) put the figure at 1030, but were quick to point out that this may reflect either the census methods or the seasonal distribution of the birds rather than an actual decline in numbers. Saddle-billed Storks are fairly common and Howard & Aspinwall (1984) logged

Shoebill with catfish (Richard Beilfuss)

more than 275. The basin may well represent one of the last strongholds of Common Bittern of the Afrotropical subspecies *capensis*. At times, Slaty Egret may occur in significant numbers as well, and in June 1981 it was 'very numerous' and 'in flocks'. However, more recently this species has been very uncommon in the area.

Some of the largest concentrations of herons, storks and wildfowl occur as flood waters recede and at this time large numbers of waterbirds are also breeding within the swamp. Few comprehensive waterfowl counts have been carried out and further work is likely to show that many species occur in numbers exceeding their 1% thresholds. Likely candidates include Black Egret, Yellow-billed Egret, White-backed Duck, Yellow-billed Duck, Hottentot Teal, Common Pratincole, Long-toed Plover, Ruff, Whiskered Tern and African Skimmer.

Denham's Bustard is common on the floodplain and during passage periods it is found alongside large numbers of Abdim's and White Storks. The three Palearctic harriers are all regular with Montagu's the most numerous. The permanent swamps hold enormous numbers of rallids and common swamp passerines include Greater Swamp Warbler, Chirping Cisticola, Swamp Flycatcher and 'Katanga' Masked Weaver *Ploceus velatus katangae*, the latter sometimes treated as a full

species. White-cheeked Bee-eater and White-rumped Babbler are distributed throughout the area and the plains hold an isolated population of Desert Cisticola alongside the rather localised Long-tailed Whydah. Fülleborn's Longclaw is common in places and Sharp-tailed Starling is regular in the woodland. An interesting change in status is that of Spur-winged Plover. This species was found for the first time in Zambia in 1999, but by 2002 it was being recorded with some regularity in Chikuni. Isangano is very poorly known, but a few species occur which have not been found elsewhere in the IBA. For example, White-backed Night Heron and Grey Apalis are known from the riparian forest and Grass Owl from thick grassland.

See summary box for key species. A few of the wetland areas are well explored, but much of the area remains very poorly known. Total number of species recorded to date: 390 (Isangano NP: 166).

■ Other flora and fauna

A wide variety of mammals occur including the endemic subspecies known as Black Lechwe *Kobus leche smithemani* (LR/cd). Over 100,000 live in the basin with the population centred on the floodplains of Chikuni GMA (Stuart & Stuart 2003a, Farmer & Jachmann *in litt.*). Large numbers of Sitatunga *Tragelaphus spekei* (LR/cd) occur in the swamps and about 7,500 Tsessebe *Damaliscus*

Black Lechwe (Mike Harrison)

lunatus (LR/cd) inhabit the plains, termitaria and open woodland (Farmer & Jachmann *in litt.*). Side-striped Jackal *Canis adustus* is particularly common and other mammals include Spot-necked Otter *Lutra maculicollis* (VU), Spotted Hyaena *Crocuta crocuta* (LR/cd), African Elephant *Loxodonta africana* (EN), Common Zebra *Equus (quagga) burchelli*, African Buffalo *Syncerus caffer* (LR/cd) and Oribi *Ourebia ourebi* (LR/cd). Reptiles include Slender-snouted Crocodile *Crocodylus cataphractus* (DD) but otherwise the herpetofauna is poorly known (D. Broadley *in litt.*).

■ Conservation issues

The swamps support a large human population and general disturbance is a continual threat to sensitive species such as Shoebills. Furthermore, nests of this species are raided and there have been reports of nests being actively destroyed by fishermen who consider the birds competitors. It has also been suggested that political problems have caused the birds to suffer with stories of fishermen killing Shoebills out of spite when promised revenue from ecotourism never materialised. It would appear that

Tsessebe in the termitaria. (Woody Cotterill)

small numbers of birds are still being caught for illegal live export. Large breeding colonies of other waterbirds may also be raided for food if found and a few species, particularly Spur-winged Geese are considered worth poaching with shotguns. Small numbers of birds are hunted under licence. Fires are widespread in the dry season and may thwart the breeding attempts of some species. Poaching of game animals and particularly Black Lechwe would appear to be a problem, particularly near the most densely populated areas. For example, the area around Mukuku Bridge, in the south-western corner of the IBA, still supported a healthy population in the early 1990s, yet there are now very few here. Mammal populations in Isangano are severely depleted and human encroachment is a threat in this area.

Flooded grassland in the Bangweulu basin.
(Richard Beilfuss)

■ Information for visitors

The Chikuni area is the most popular with visitors as it is the most accessible and it usually holds the highest numbers of animals and birds. Most visitors stay at Shoebill Island camp which is a short drive or boat ride from Chikuni Research Station. It is possible to fly into Chikuni, but many visitors drive via the village of Chiundaponde. The road is rough in places and the journey is not quick but it passes through some interesting terrain. A high clearance vehicle is important and four wheel drive recommended, particularly when some areas may still be wet around the end of the rains and the beginning of the dry season (April-July). This is undoubtedly

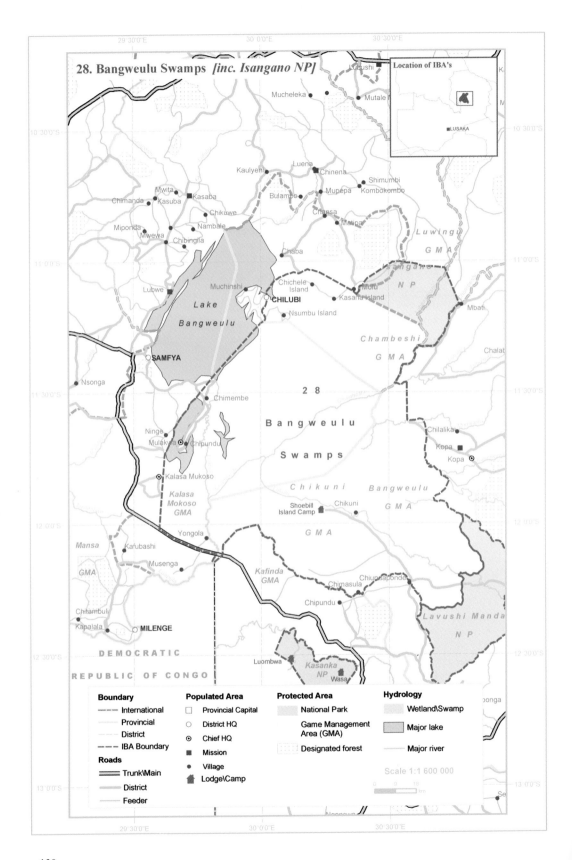

28. Bangweulu Swamps *[inc. Isangano NP]*

Location of IBA's

LUSAKA

Luwingu GMA

Isangano NP

Lubushi

Mucheleka

Mutale

Kaulyenhi

Luena

Chinena

Shimumbi

Kombokombo

Mwita

Kasaba

Chimanda

Kasuba

Bulambo

Mupepa

Chikuwe

Chansa

Matipa

Miponda

Nambale

Mwewa

Chibingila

Chaba

Chichele Island

Chichi

Motu

Mbati

Lubwe

Muchinshi

CHILUBI

Kasana Island

Nsumbu Island

Chambeshi GMA

Chalab

SAMFYA

Lake Bangweulu

Nsonga

Chimembe

2 8

B a n g w e u l u

Chilalika

Ninge

Mulekwa

Chipundu

Kopa

Kopa

S w a m p s

Kalasa Mukoso

Chikuni

Bangweulu

Kalasa Mokoso GMA

Shoebill Island Camp

Chikuni

GMA

Yongola

GMA

Mansa

Kafubashi

Kafinda GMA

GMA

Musenga

Chimasula

Chiundaponde

Chipundu

Chitambuli

Kapalala

MILENGE

Lavushi Manda NP

D E M O C R A T I C

R E P U B L I C   O F   C O N G O

Luombwa

Kasanka NP

Wasa

Boundary	Populated Area	Protected Area	Hydrology
- - - International	□ Provincial Capital	National Park	Wetland\Swamp
Provincial	○ District HQ	Game Management Area (GMA)	Major lake
District	◉ Chief HQ		
- - - IBA Boundary	■ Mission	Designated forest	Major river
Roads	● Village		
Trunk\Main	Lodge\Camp	Scale 1:1 600 000	
District			
Feeder		0 0 10 km	

the best time to seek Shoebills when they have not yet retreated into the deeper swamps. Shoebill Island is run by the Kasanka Trust and more information can be found on www.kasanka.com. The area along the main Serenje-Samfya road where it crosses the Luapula River (Mukuku Bridge) provides an interesting and very accessible taste of the Bangweulu basin. It is particularly good for migrant harriers and Long-tailed Whydahs but you are unlikely to see Shoebills or many Black Lechwe in this area. Just south of the Chambeshi bridge on the Kasama road, a fairly good track leads to Mbati and from there it runs parallel to the river, on the opposite bank to Isangano NP. Fishing boats can be hired to cross the river if one wishes to explore the park on foot. There are also a number of tracks which lead to the northern side of the park from Luwingu.

Globally threatened species		
Slaty Egret	Vulnerable	scarce visitor, status uncertain but occasionally common
Shoebill	Near-threatened	uncommon breeding resident
Lesser Flamingo	Near-threatened	rare vagrant
Cape Vulture	Vulnerable	rare vagrant
Lappet-faced Vulture	Vulnerable	regular breeding resident
Pallid Harrier	Near-threatened	common non-breeding visitor
Lesser Kestrel	Vulnerable	regular passage migrant and occasional non-breeding visitor
Wattled Crane	Vulnerable	common breeding resident
Denham's Bustard	Near-threatened	fairly common breeding resident
Great Snipe	Near-threatened	common non-breeding visitor
African Skimmer	Near-threatened	regular visitor

Biome-restricted species		
Afromontane	-	1 near-endemic
Zambezian	9 endemics	9 near-endemics

Globally important congregations	
(i) regularly holds >1% of biogeographic population of a congregatory waterbird	
Reed Cormorant	>10,000 (1960s)
White Pelican	"thousands" (1940s)
Rufous-bellied Heron	>1000 (Feb 1968, inc. c.400 pairs nesting)
Openbill Stork	>30,000 (Jul 2002)
Spur-winged Goose	>5000 (Jul 2002)
Wattled Crane	1030 (Jul 2002)
Caspian Plover	>1000 (Nov 1995)
(iii) regularly holds >20,000 waterbirds	

Species of regional conservation concern	
Common Bittern	breeding resident, status poorly known
Goliath Heron	regular breeding resident
Saddle-billed Stork	uncommon breeding resident
Bateleur	regular breeding resident
African Marsh Harrier	common breeding resident
Southern Crowned Crane	scarce breeding resident
Southern Ground Hornbill	localised, but not uncommon resident
Yellow-billed Oxpecker	scarce breeding resident.

29 North Luangwa National Park

Admin region: Mpika District, Northern Province
Co-ordinates: 11°27'-12°20'S 31°48'-32°35'E
Area: 463,600ha   **Altitude:** 600-1313m
Status: National Park
Categories: Globally threatened species, Biome-restricted species
International site code: ZM020   **Map:** p 135

■ Site description

Situated on the west bank of the Luangwa River, the park lies upstream from South Luangwa NP (IBA 40) and is separated from it by a corridor 30-40km wide (Munyamadzi GMA). The elevation varies greatly and as result the park encompasses a very wide range of habitats. About three quarters of the park lies between 600-900m and is dominated by a mosaic of mopane and savanna woodland. Large stretches of the mopane have been significantly modified by elephants, partly in times when poaching pressure caused them to concentrate in safe areas. Along the main river are groves of *Acacia albida, Trichilia emetica, Kigelia africana* and *Diospyros mespiliformis* interspersed with pockets of riparian thicket. Away from the river, the park climbs the first gentle ridges of the Muchinga Escarpment and about a quarter of the park lies between 900-1200m. Here, the better-drained soils support miombo and the streams are lined with riparian gallery forest. The park is very rich fossil deposits. In the past the park has suffered from neglect and intense poaching but since the mid 1980s it has received a lot more attention, protection and investment. The North Luangwa Conservation Project is funded by the Frankfurt Zoological Society.

■ Birds

The avifauna is very similar to that of the very well known south park (IBA 40). Typical birds along the river are Egyptian Goose, African Fish Eagle, Water Dikkop and White-crowned Plover. Both White-fronted and Southern Carmine Bee-eaters nest in the sand cliffs and the latter may exceed its 1% threshold. Adjacent riparian habitats are home to birds such as African Mourning Dove, Pel's Fishing Owl, Bat-like Spinetail and Lilian's Lovebird. The last is also regular in the mopane

where characteristic species include Red-billed Hornbill, Southern Long-tailed Starling and White-browed Sparrow-weaver. The area is rich in raptors such as Tawny and Martial Eagles.

The miombo holds many Zambezian endemics and near-endemics such as Racket-tailed Roller and Pale-billed Hornbill and the diversity increases with altitude. Typical of escarpment miombo are Shelley's Sunbird and Chestnut-mantled Sparrow-weaver and of particular interest is the rather localised White-winged Starling which is not uncommon here. In the richest miombo along the western boundary, species such as Central Bearded Scrub Robin, Trilling Cisticola, Böhm's Flycatcher and Red-and-blue Sunbird can be found.

The diversity of riparian forest birds also increases at plateau altitudes and along the upper Mwaleshi are species such as Hildebrandt's Francolin, Lady Ross's Turaco, Black-backed Barbet, Laura's Warbler, Green Twinspot and Black-tailed Grey Waxbill. Both Augur Buzzard and Peregrine Falcon probably breed in the Mwaleshi Gorge and Mountain Wagtail is regular along the river here.

See summary box for key species. The area is fairly

White-crowned Plovers

well known, although some quite large areas have yet to be explored by ornithologists. Total number of species recorded to date: 345.

■ Other flora and fauna

A wide variety of mammals is known to occur. The park is probably now the stronghold of the Wildebeest subspecies *Connochaetes taurinus cooksoni* which is endemic to the Luangwa Valley and the population is estimated to be almost 2000 (R. Tether *in litt.*). Other species include Lion *Panthera leo* (VU), Spotted Hyaena *Crocuta crocuta* (LR/cd), Bushy-tailed Mongoose *Bdeogale crassicauda*, African Elephants *Loxodonta africana* (EN), Bushbuck *Tragelaphus scriptus*, Greater Kudu *T. strepsiceros* (LR/cd), Eland *Taurotragus oryx* (LR/cd), Sharpe's Grysbok *Raphicercus sharpei* (LR/cd), Puku *Kobus vardoni* (LR/cd), Waterbuck *K. ellipsiprymnus* (LR/cd) and Impala *Aepyceros melampus* (LR/cd). African Buffalo *Syncerus caffer* (LR/cd) are found in particularly good numbers and towards the escarpment species such as Hartebeest *Alcelaphus buselaphus lichtensteinii* (LR/cd), Roan *Hippotragus equinus* (LR/cd) and Sable Antelopes *H. niger* (LR/cd) are found. Black Rhinoceros *Diceros bicornis* (CR)

Lions (Andrea Leonard)

was effectively exterminated in the 1980s, but the North Luangwa Conservation Project has recently embarked on an ambitious reintroduction programme.

■ Conservation issues

Although the area has suffered in the past it is now probably the best-protected park in the country.

The Mwaleshi River meandering across the floor of the Luangwa Valley, with the Muchinga Escarpment on the horizon. (Elsabe van der Westhuizen)

Poaching and burning have been brought under control, the game numbers are increasing and much of the damaged vegetation (primarily mopane) is regrowing fast. Most of the park is uninhabited and human encroachment is minimal but nevertheless carefully monitored.

■ Information for visitors

The park was once very difficult to visit but in recent years this has all changed. It is still nowhere near as developed as the South park, but many people see this as an advantage. There are currently three safari camps on the Mwaleshi river and a campsite near the Mano entrance gate. The road network is not extensive, but the camps operate many walking safaris. Although most animals concentrate near the Mwaleshi on the valley floor, the escarpment and features such as the Mwaleshi Falls are well worth exploring. Visitors often arrive by air, but the road access is relatively simple. In contrast to the South park, the main access is from the west. A signed dirt road leaves the Great North Road about 64km north of Mpika. From here it is about 40km to the Mano Gate. Four wheel drive is rarely needed, but high clearance is advisable. For a short period towards the end of the dry season it becomes possible to ford the Luangwa River and drive to South Luangwa NP via Luambe NP. Furthermore, at the time of writing a pontoon is being constructed here which would operate from June to October and make such a trip simpler. Much of the park becomes inaccessible during the rains.

Globally threatened species		
Lesser Flamingo	Near-threatened	rare vagrant
Lappet-faced Vulture	Vulnerable	regular breeding resident
Denham's Bustard	Near-threatened	rare visitor
African Skimmer	Near-threatened	regular breeding visitor
Greater Spotted Eagle	Vulnerable	very rare non-breeding visitor

Biome-restricted species		
Afromontane	-	1 near-endemic
Eastern	-	2 near-endemics
Zambezian	12 endemics	9 near-endemics

Species of regional conservation concern	
Goliath Heron	regular breeding resident
Saddle-billed Stork	regular breeding resident
Bateleur	common breeding resident
African Marsh Harrier	rare visitor
Southern Crowned Crane	regular breeding resident
Southern Ground Hornbill	common breeding resident
Yellow-billed Oxpecker	common breeding resident
Red-billed Oxpecker	common breeding resident

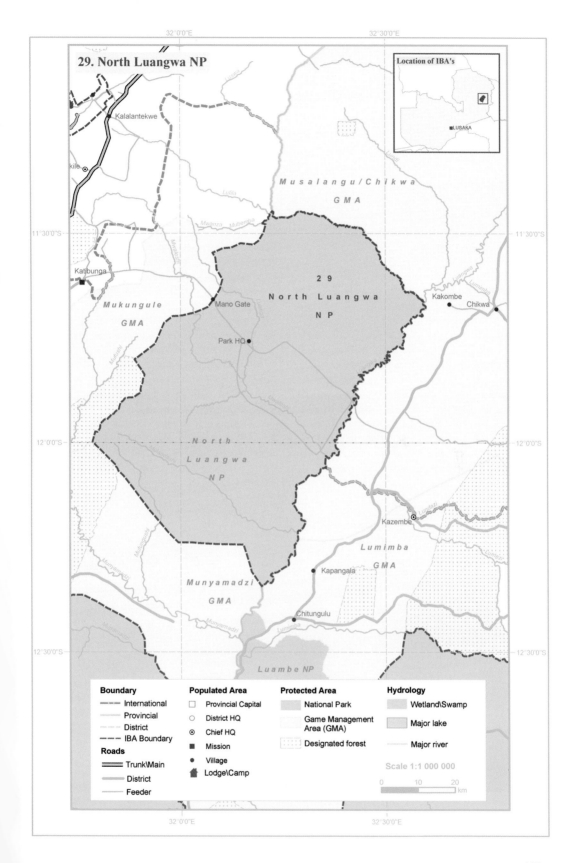

29. North Luangwa NP

Location of IBA's

■LUSAKA

Musalangu / Chikwa
GMA

2 9
North Luangwa
N P

Kalalantekwe

kile

Katibunga

Mukungule
GMA

Mano Gate

Park HQ

North
Luangwa
N P

Kakombe   Chikwa

Kazembe

Lumimba
GMA

Munyamadzi
GMA

Kapangala

Chitungulu

Luambe NP

Boundary	Populated Area	Protected Area	Hydrology
----- International	□ Provincial Capital	National Park	Wetland\Swamp
Provincial	○ District HQ	Game Management Area (GMA)	Major lake
District	⊙ Chief HQ	Designated forest	Major river
--- IBA Boundary	■ Mission		
Roads	● Village		
Trunk\Main	🏠 Lodge\Camp		
District		Scale 1:1 000 000	
Feeder		0 10 20 km	

30 Shiwa Ng'andu

Admin region: Chinsali District, Northern Province
Co-ordinates: 11°12'S 31°45'E
Area: 9000ha   **Altitude:** 1460-1760m
Status: private estate
Categories: Globally threatened species, Biome-restricted species
International site code: ZM023   **Map:** p 138

■ Site description

An unusual but well known private estate with its roots in Zambia's colonial past. At its heart is an enormous manor house around which has grown a thriving community with its own school, post office and clinic. There is also a sizeable lake and a dramatic mountainous backdrop. It lies at submontane levels and as a result the climate is relatively cool and the rainfall high. The name of the estate derives from the lake, known as Ishiba Ng'andu, which translates as 'lake of the royal crocodile'. It is a natural waterbody and thus a somewhat rare plateau habitat with fringing reedbeds and papyrus swamp. Elsewhere the terrain is dominated by miombo of various formations. On the rocky hills it

is somewhat stunted and in other areas it has been invaded by exotic species and *Eucalyptus* in particular. There are numerous broad and very wet dambos, some riparian forest and thickets, bracken-briar and several patches of tall mushitu. Interestingly, there are also some small patches of Afromontane forest comprising trees such as *Croton macrostachyus*, *Ficalhoa laurifolia*, *Olea capensis*, *Podocarpus latifolius* and *Polyscias fulva* (Dowsett-Lemaire *in* Dowsett *et al.* in prep.). The soils are poor and besides cattle there has been some production of essential oils. However, it is hoped that more revenue will now be generated by wildlife and tourism. Recently, the house has been restored and the entire estate has been game-fenced. It is known as the

The manor house at Shiwa. (Chris McIntyre/Sunvil Africa)

Miombo Grey Tit (Warwick Tarboton)

Mansha River Wildlife and Flora Management Area, a restocking programme has begun and many new conservation measures have been implemented.

■ Birds

With its wide range of habitats, the site supports a considerable diversity of bird life. Waterbirds are well represented with a wide variety of herons, storks and wildfowl recorded. Osprey is regular around the lake, Greater Swamp Warbler inhabits the papyrus and both African Finfoot and Half-collared Kingfisher can be found along the rivers. Palm-nut Vulture is regular, especially around the lake and near *Raphia farinifera* palms. The dambos are rich and characteristic species include Black-rumped Buttonquail, Long-toed Flufftail, Great Snipe, Grass Owl, White-cheeked Bee-eater, Rosy-breasted Longclaw, Broad-tailed Warbler, Black-chinned Quailfinch, Stout and Lesser Black-backed Cisticolas. Mushitu birds include Golden-rumped Tinkerbird, Splendid Starling and Black-bellied Seed-cracker as well as a number of Afromontane species including Cinnamon Dove, Bocage's Robin, Evergreen Forest Warbler, Bar-throated Apalis and White-tailed Crested Flycatcher. Often

near forest, but also in the woodland is White-headed Saw-wing and other miombo birds include breeding Dusky Larks and Bar-winged Weavers at the very eastern edge of their range. In rocky areas are Mocking Chat and Rock-loving Cisticola.

See summary box for key species. The area is well known. Total number of species recorded to date: 373.

■ Other flora and fauna

Fourteen species of mammal have been introduced, most of which were known from the area previously. Other indigenous animals include Yellow Baboon *Papio cynocephalus*, Cape Clawless Otter *Aonyx capensis*, Sitatunga *Tragelaphus spekei* (LR/cd), Blue Duiker *Cephalophus monticola*, Klipspringer *Oreotragus oreotragus* (LR/cd) and Nile Crocodile *Crocodylus niloticus*. There are rich wetland, hill and gorge floras. The cycad *Encephalartos schmitzii* occurs in the hills and it is one of the few localities in Zambia from which the montane *Ocotea usambarensis* is known.

■ Conservation issues

The area is now well protected and patrolled by game scouts. A fishing season is now enforced and netting has been banned. Several projects have been started to encourage sustainable development including small scale fish-farming, honey production and a bio-gas project to reduce the need for wood fuel.

■ Information for visitors

Shiwa is easy to reach by road. Follow the Great North Road towards Isoka and 94km beyond Mpika take a well-signed left turn. The entrance gate is reached after 2km and the main house after a further 11km. The journey from Lusaka takes approximately 9 hours. Four wheel drive is not needed, but the dirt roads require reasonable clearance. There is an airstrip for those travelling by plane. Visitors may stay in the luxurious main house or a further 19km down the road is Kapishya Hot Springs where there is chalet accommodation and a campsite beside a wonderful spring that is the perfect temperature for bathing in. Hiking, horse-riding, game-viewing and boating are all available. The birding is good throughout the area with some of the best mushitu just below

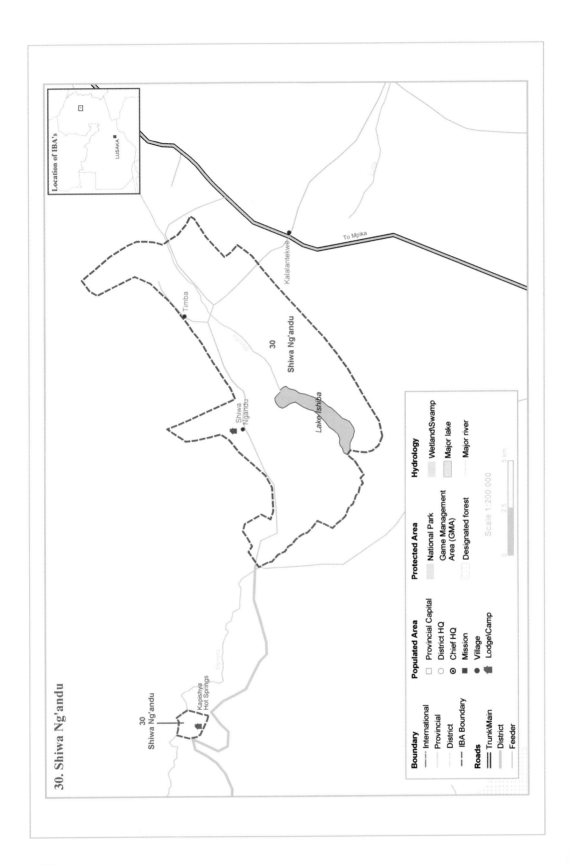

30. Shiwa Ng'andu

Location of IBA's

LUSAKA ■

To Mpika

Kalalantekwe

Timba

30

Shiwa Ng'andu

Lake Ishiba

Shiwa
Ngandu

Kapishya
Hot Springs

30
Shiwa Ng'andu

Kwenze

Boundary
International
Provincial
District
IBA Boundary

Roads
Trunk\Main
District
Feeder

Populated Area
□ Provincial Capital
○ District HQ
◉ Chief HQ
■ Mission
● Village
Lodge\Camp

Protected Area
National Park
Game Management
Area (GMA)
Designated forest

Hydrology
Wetland\Swamp
Major lake
Major river

Scale 1:200 000

0   2.5   5 km

the main house. Here, causeways have been constructed through the swampy forest and provide very easy access to this often inaccessible habitat. Visit www.shiwangandu.com for more information.

Globally threatened species		
Madagascar Squacco Heron	Vulnerable	rare visitor
Lappet-faced Vulture	Vulnerable	occasional visitor
Denham's Bustard	Near-threatened	occasional, may breed
Great Snipe	Near-threatened	common non-breeding visitor
African Skimmer	Near-threatened	occasional visitor
Biome-restricted species		
Afromontane	1 endemic	6 near-endemics
Sub-Afromontane	1 endemic	-
Eastern	-	1 near-endemic
Zambezian	17 endemics	12 near-endemics
Species of regional conservation concern		
Goliath Heron	occasional, may breed	
Saddle-billed Stork	occasional visitor	
Bateleur	fairly common breeding resident	
African Marsh Harrier	common breeding resident	
Southern Ground Hornbill	uncommon resident	
Bar-winged Weaver	localised breeding resident	

Honey Buzzard

31 Luapula Mouth

Admin region: Nchelenge, Kawambwa Districts, Luapula Province
Co-ordinates: 9°25'-10°05'S 28°31'-28°45'E
Area: c.90,000ha   **Altitude:** c.900m
Status: unprotected
Categories: Globally threatened species, Biome-restricted species, Globally important congregations
International site code: ZM027   **Map:** p 141

■ Site description

A large area of dense papyrus swamp in the lowest reaches of the Luapula River as it fans out to meet Lake Mweru. The main river channel marks the site's western boundary as well as the Congolese border and in the east the wetland has a well-defined edge. The tarmac Mansa-Nchelenge road runs a little way above and parallel to the shoreline and this area is fairly densely populated. Within the swamp are scattered open lagoons and a network of small channels, kept navigable by fishermen and inhabitants of the larger islands. There is some scrub and a few small pockets of forest along the swamp margins.

■ Birds

The site is most important for its very isolated (or 'satellite') populations of two species near-endemic to the Lake Victoria Basin biome. Papyrus Yellow Warbler is widespread and not uncommon although it is easily overlooked. Birds belong to the subspecies *bensoni* which is endemic to these swamps. White-winged Warbler was only discovered in 1996 but it is common throughout the site. In time, this population may also prove to be a distinctive subspecies (Leonard & Beel 1999). Other characteristic swamp birds include Red-chested Flufftail, African Water Rail, Purple Gallinule, White-cheeked Bee-eater, Little Rush Warbler, Lesser and Greater Swamp Warblers, Chirping Cisticola, Swamp Flycatcher, Marsh Tchagra, Red-shouldered Whydah, Slender-billed, Yellow-backed and 'Katanga' Masked Weaver *Ploceus velatus katangae*. More often around the edges are Black-faced Canary, Brown Firefinch and White-rumped Babbler. Jacobin Cuckoo is regular in the swamp and appears to be breeding, but it is not clear which species it could be parasitising

Papyrus Yellow Warbler (Peter Leonard)

(Leonard 1999b). Lesser Black-backed Gull and White-winged Black Tern are both common on the open water and Palm-nut Vulture is regular in the general area. Madagascar Bee-eater may occasionally spend the non-breeding season in the area and Angola Swallow is a common breeding visitor.

See summary box for key species. The swamps are fairly well known in places, but large areas remain to be explored. Total number of species recorded to date: 212.

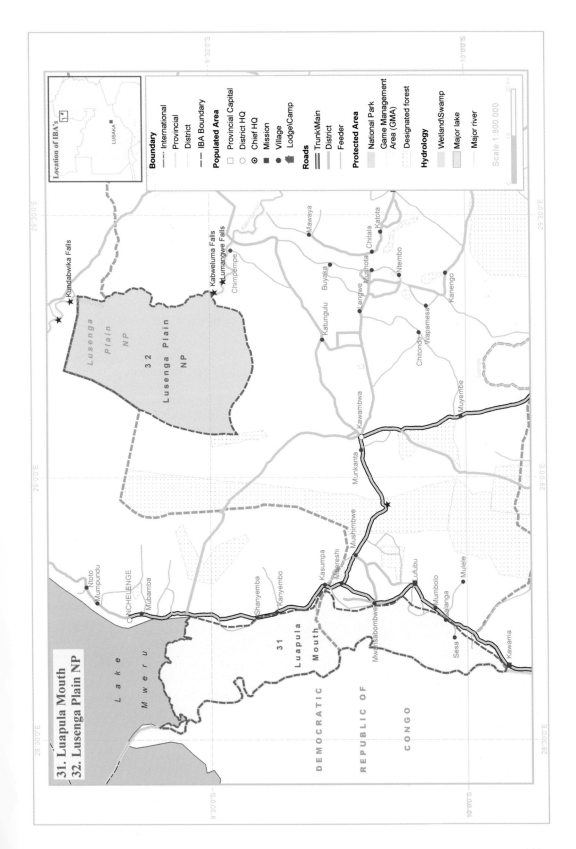

31. Luapula Mouth
32. Lusenga Plain NP

White-winged Warbler

■ Other flora and fauna

Poorly known. Sitatunga *Tragelaphus spekei* (LR/cd) has been recorded recently but its status is not known. The only Zambian records of the bats *Taphozous perforatus* and *Miniopterus inflatus* come from Kilwa Island which lies close to the site. Slender-snouted Crocodile *Crocodylus cataphractus* (DD) has been recorded in the past.

■ Conservation issues

A major threat to the swamp is fire. Whereas most swamp-dwelling species will tolerate a lack of water it may take months before birds return to areas that have been burnt. There is also widespread trapping and snaring and large numbers of birds are sold at nearby markets.

■ Information for visitors

The site is very easy to reach from the tarmac Mansa-Nchelenge road. Perhaps the best area from which to explore the papyrus is the harbour at Chabilikila, some 20km south of Nchelenge and the point from which boats leave for Chisenga Island. A track beside Chabilikila Primary School leads to the swamp edge and here it is possible to walk along the shoreline, or hire a boat to get further into the swamp. Between Mbereshi and Nchelenge, the main road crosses causeways over the Lunde and Nshinda rivers but although these hold a lot of papyrus, the density of birds seems to be lower. Finding suitable campsites can be difficult, but there are several functional rest-houses in Nchelenge and Mbereshi.

Globally threatened species		
Lesser Kestrel	Vulnerable	regular passage migrant
Papyrus Yellow Warbler	Vulnerable	not uncommon breeding resident
Biome-restricted species		
Afromontane	-	1 near-endemic
Lake Victoria Basin	-	2 near-endemics
Zambezian	3 endemics	4 near-endemics
Globally important congregations		
(i) regularly holds >1% of biogeographic population of a congregatory waterbird		
Southern Pochard	1000 (Oct 1954)	
Species of regional conservation concern		
Bateleur	regular	
African Marsh Harrier	fairly common breeding resident	

32 Lusenga Plain NP

Admin region: Kawambwa District, Luapula Province
Co-ordinates: 9°13'-9°35'S and 29°03'-29°20'E
Area: 88,000ha   **Altitude:** 980-1374m
Status: National Park
Categories: Globally threatened species, Biome-restricted species
International site code: --- **Map:** p 141

■ Site description

This remote and somewhat forgotten park lies on the north-western corner of the Northern Province plateau and its eastern boundary is the Kalungwishi River. The plain after which the park is named is in the south-western corner; it is oval-shaped and measures about 7km x 5km. It was formed by the weathering of an old volcanic plug dome. The grassland of the plain is typical of upland dambos in northern Zambia and towards the centre there are some very wet, swampy areas. Along the small drainage lines entering the plain are patches of mushitu and set back from the plain are scattered patches of dry evergreen *Marquesia* forest. Many of the park's rivers support strips of rich gallery mushitu but the vast majority of the area is covered by woodland. This is predominantly miombo of various formations ranging from tall, dense types on flatter terrain, to more open and sometimes stunted types on the steep and rocky ground. On alluvial soils there are patches of *Pteleopsis anisoptera* and at lower altitudes the woodland is somewhat drier. The Kalungwishi is a sizeable river with a variety of waterfalls and rocky rapids as well as quiet backwaters lined with riparian forest.

■ Birds

The park has seen only one short ornithological survey (Leonard in prep.), but this revealed a rich variety of birds including a good number of Zambezian endemics. The plain is home to Wattled Crane, Blue Quail, Coppery-tailed Coucal, White-cheeked Bee-eater, Banded Martin, Fülleborn's and Rosy-breasted Longclaws, Broad-tailed Warbler, Stout Cisticola, Marsh Whydah, Parasitic Weaver and Black-chinned Quailfinch. Mushitu birds include Western Banded Snake Eagle, Lady Ross's Turaco, Purple-throated Cuckoo-shrike,

Kabweluma Falls (Peter Leonard)

Cabanis's Greenbul, Bocage's Robin, Evergreen Forest Warbler, Laura's Warbler, Many-coloured Bush Shrike, Square-tailed Drongo and Splendid Glossy Starling. Common miombo species include Pale-billed Hornbill, Whyte's Barbet, Black-collared Eremomela, Red-capped Crombec, 'Long-tailed' Neddicky *Cisticola fulvicapilla angusticauda* and Red-and-blue Sunbird. Violet-backed Sunbird is unusually numerous. Amongst the species found along the Kalungwishi are Rock Pratincole and Half-collared Kingfisher and the

143

A female Violet-backed Sunbird at her nest. (Warwick Tarboton)

park's single Guineo-Congolian species, Cassin's Grey Flycatcher.

See summary box for key species. The area remains poorly known. Total number of species recorded to date: 214.

■ Other flora and fauna

Although clearly depleted, a number of large mammals remain. Species found on the recent survey include Yellow Baboon *Papio cynocephalus*, Vervet *Cercopithecus pygerythrus* and Gentle (Blue) Monkey *C. mitis*, Gambian Sun Squirrel *Heliosciurus gambianus*, Greater Galago *Otolemur crassicaudatus*, Bush Pig *Potamochoerus larvatus* and Southern Reedbuck *Redunca arundinum* (LR/cd). Other tracks found were identified as Bushbuck *Tragelaphus scriptus*, duikers *Sylvicapra/Cephalophus* spp., Hartebeest *Alcelaphus buselaphus lichtensteinii* (LR/cd) and Roan Antelope *Hippotragus equinus* (LR/cd). The discovery of the recently described *Brachystegia astlei* from the southern border of the park (M. Bingham *in litt.*) leaves little doubt that there is more to be discovered in the flora of this corner of the country.

■ Conservation issues

Small-scale subsistence hunting using traps and snares is regular, particularly in mushitu. Birds most at risk and clearly targeted by such methods were Helmeted Guineafowl and francolins. Tree cutting is currently not a problem and isolated incidences are probably for honey collection. Perhaps the most important conservation issue is the rigorous burning of large sections of the park, affecting all habitats.

■ Information for visitors

The park is almost never visited by tourists and no ZAWA scouts are posted here. There is virtually no internal road network, but the area is easily explored on foot and offers a huge tract of remote wilderness to the more adventurous and truly self-sufficient traveller. Access is difficult, but not impossible. The south-western corner of the park can be approached from Kawambwa on the D76 and after crossing the Mbereshi River a motorable track leads from Tambatamba village to the abandoned and derelict Mbeleshi Wildlife Camp. The track continues up and around the head of the Mbereshi dambo, in the centre of which is an extremely large mushitu. It enters the park at about 9°32'S 29°04'E and continues up its western edge for several kilometres. The plain can be reached on foot, although maps, a compass and a GPS are essential. There are three major waterfalls on the Kalungwishi all of which are well worth visiting. Camping is permitted and these sites could be used as starting points for further exploration of the park. Kundabwika Falls in the north-east and Lumangwe Falls in the south-east are both National Monuments. Kabweluma Falls is a short distance downstream from Lumangwe.

Black-collared Eremomela

Globally threatened species		
Lappet-faced Vulture	Vulnerable	status not known, possibly only a scarce visitor
Wattled Crane	Vulnerable	probably a breeding resident in small numbers

Biome-restricted species		
Afromontane	-	3 near-endemics
Sub-Afromontane	1 endemic	-
Eastern	-	1 near-endemic
Guineo-Congolian	-	1 near-endemic
Zambezian	12 endemics	8 near-endemics

Species of regional conservation concern	
Saddle-billed Stork	status not known, probably regular in small numbers
Bateleur	fairly common breeding resident
African Marsh Harrier	regular, probably breeds
Southern Crowned Crane	status not known
Southern Ground Hornbill	occasional, probably breeds
Yellow-billed Oxpecker	status not known, possibly no longer occurs

33 Kalungwishi

Admin region: Mporokoso District, Northern Province
Co-ordinates: 9°52'S 30°22'E
Area: c.15,000ha   **Altitude:** 1600-1650m
Status: unprotected
Categories: Globally threatened species, Biome-restricted species
International site code: ZM028   **Map:** p 146

■ Site description

The site was once a State Ranch, but it has been abandoned for many years. Many such ranches were established to protect the headwaters of major river systems and this site encompasses the entire headwaters of the Kalungwishi River. All except the western boundaries are defined by the Kalungwishi watershed and the eastern and southern boundaries are also followed by district roads. At its heart is one of the region's largest dambos, running from west to east. From this branch about nine tributary dambos and such habitat covers about 60% of the site. There are numerous patches of mushitu along the upper reaches of these drainage lines and the remaining area is predominantly miombo. It lies about 100km east-north-east of Kasama in one of the highest parts of the Northern Province. The general area is sparsely populated, undisturbed and suitable for IBA status.

■ Birds

Poorly known, but clearly holds a rich diversity of species owing to the variety and maturity of the habitat. Characteristic of the dambo are Blue Quail, Black-rumped Buttonquail, Long-toed Flufftail, Wattled Crane, Denham's Bustard, Great Snipe, Natal Nightjar, Black-and-rufous Swallow, Fülleborn's Longclaw, Rosy-breasted Longclaw, Stout, Chirping and Lesser Black-backed Cisticolas, Marsh Whydah, Parasitic Weaver, Fawn-breasted Waxbill and Black-chinned Quailfinch. Mushitu species known to occur include Bocage's Robin, Evergreen Forest Warbler, Laura's Warbler, Grey Apalis, Green-headed Sunbird, Many-coloured Bush Shrike and

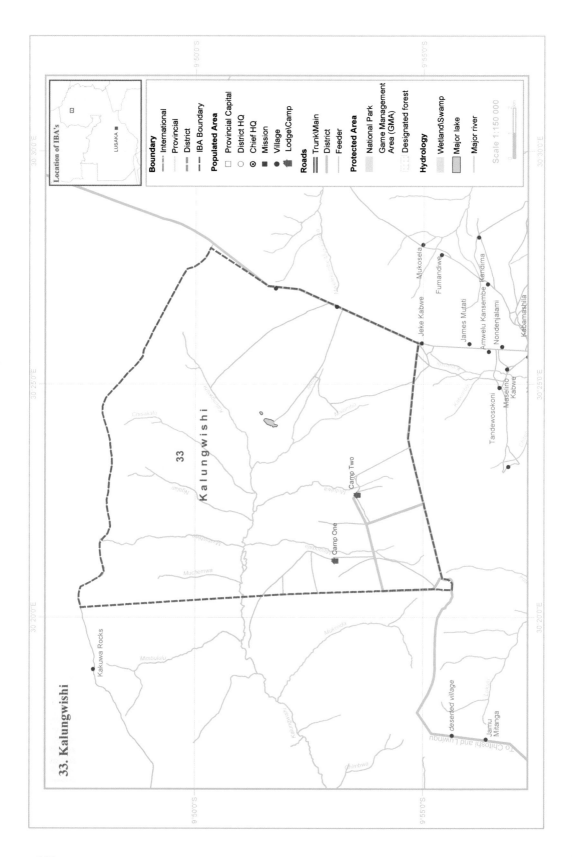

33. Kalungwishi

Long-toed Flufftail

White-tailed Crested Flycatcher. The miombo holds a large number of Zambezian endemics such as Arnot's Chat, Black-collared Eremomela, Böhm's Flycatcher, Sousa's Shrike, Red-and-blue Sunbird and Oustalet's White-bellied Sunbird.

See summary box for key species. The area remains rather poorly known. Total number of species recorded to date: 231.

■ Other flora and fauna

Very poorly known. The dambos are now amongst the most productive of the remaining sources of chikanda (edible orchid tubers) in the country. The endemic genus *Micrargiella* (*Scrophulariaceae*) appears to be common in the area (M. Bingham *in litt.*).

■ Conservation issues

At present the area is almost pristine and benefits from the very low density of human habitation. However, the site needs very careful monitoring, especially if it is fragmented for settlement as it could be very quickly destroyed.

■ Information for visitors

A remote area but one which is accessible throughout the year. From the Kasama-Luwingu road take the Chitoshi turn, about 40km east of Luwingu. About 20km beyond Chitoshi, this turns east abruptly as it meets the Kalungwishi watershed and from here it is about 5km to where an old ranch track leads north into the IBA. This track follows three sides of a square and rejoins the Chitoshi road a little further on. From it, other smaller tracks lead deeper into the area and there are two old farm settlements near the main dambo. The roads are all rough and high clearance is important. Four wheel drive is likely to be needed in the wet season. There are no facilities so visitors should be entirely self-sufficient.

White-cheeked Bee-eater (Edmund Farmer)

147

Globally threatened species		
Corn Crake	Vulnerable	non-breeding visitor, probably not uncommon
Wattled Crane	Vulnerable	breeding resident
Denham's Bustard	Near-threatened	breeding resident
Great Snipe	Near-threatened	common non-breeding visitor

Biome-restricted species		
Afromontane	1 endemic	4 near-endemics
Sub-Afromontane	1 endemic	-
Zambezian	17 endemics	13 near-endemics

Species of regional conservation concern		
Bateleur	common resident	
African Marsh Harrier	common resident	
Southern Ground Hornbill	regular resident	

34 Mweru Wantipa National Park

Admin region: Kaputa, Nchelenge Districts, Luapula, Northern Provinces
Co-ordinates: 8°27'-8°59'S 29°14'-29°59'E
Area: 313,400ha   **Altitude:** 900-1425m
Status: National Park
Categories: Globally threatened species, Biome-restricted species, Globally important congregations
International site code: ZM029   **Map:** p 151

■ Site description

Lying in the far north of the country between Lakes Mweru and Tanganyika, the park encompasses a third lake, from which it takes its name. Until recently the water level fluctuated both seasonally and over longer cycles and the area would change periodically from grassland and swamp to a large shallow lake. However, a dam has been built and much of the area now remains permanently flooded. The lake and surrounding areas lie at comparatively low altitude between 900-1000m and Itigi thicket is the dominant vegetation type. Itigi thicket is also found in small pockets in DRC and more extensively in Tanzania and characteristic plants include *Bussea massaiensis* subsp. *floribunda* (*Casesalpinioideae*), *Pseudoprosopis fischeri* (*Mimosoideae*) and *Burttia prunoides* (*Connaraceae*) (White 1983). Further west, the land gradually rises and a mosaic of miombo and dambos predominates. The terrain becomes increasingly rugged and hilly and it rises to over 1400m in places. A single road bisects the park running roughly north-south along the western shore of the lake.

■ Birds

Waterbirds can be numerous at times and the lake shore sometimes supports large numbers of migrant waders. The occurrence of Shoebills has always been irregular and associated with the condition of the wetland but it is not clear how the controlled hydrology has affected its status. In 1955, over 600 pairs of Lesser Flamingo nested, probably unsuccessfully, although the site lies on the periphery of this species' normal breeding range. Species characteristic of the Itigi thickets include Hildebrandt's Francolin, Green Coucal, African Pitta, White-throated Nicator, Many-coloured Bush Shrike, Dark-backed Weaver and Green Twinspot. The miombo holds good numbers of Zambezian

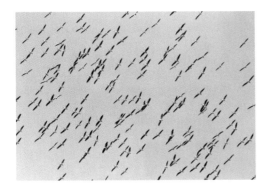

White Pelicans (Andrea Leonard)

endemics such as Pale-billed Hornbill, Black-collared Eremomela, Red-capped Crombec and Chestnut-mantled Sparrow-weaver. Bare-faced Go-away Bird occurs in the more open habitats and in the far north-west of the park Anchieta's Barbet and Grey-winged Robin can be found in the riparian forest, both on the edge of their range.

See summary box for key species. The thickets are fairly well explored, but large sections of the park have not been explored by ornithologists. Total number of species recorded to date: 283.

■ Other flora and fauna

A wide variety of mammals occur including Chequered Elephant Shrew *Rhynchocyon cirnei* (VU), Bushy-tailed Mongoose *Bdeogale crassi-*

cauda, Boehm's Squirrel *Paraxerus boehmi,* Sitatunga *Tragelaphus spekei* (LR/cd), Yellow-backed Duiker *Cephalophus silvicultor* (LR/nt) and Puku *Kobus vardoni* (LR/cd). Reptiles include Slender-snouted Crocodile *Crocodylus cataphractus* (DD). The woodland and savanna associated with Itigi thicket have species with restricted ranges such as the trees *Strophanthus eminii* and an undescribed species of *Stereospermum* (M. Bingham *in litt.*).

■ Conservation issues

Poaching has left the large mammal populations very depleted and the park still receives a very low level of protection. Threats to the birds and the vegetation are probably few but the effect of the dam requires further investigation as does the human encroachment in areas such as the eastern lake shore. The park is regularly affected by over-burning.

■ Information for visitors

The park is accessible throughout the year in a vehicle with high clearance but the single access road is currently in poor condition. This road runs between Nkoshya (east of Mununga on Lake Mweru) and Kaputa. There are no tourist facilities in, or even particularly close to the park so visitors wanting to explore should be self-sufficient campers. It is sometimes possible to camp within the park and enquiries should be made at the entrance gates. It is difficult, though not impossi-

A male Pennant-winged Nightjar. (Lizet Grobbelaar)

ble, to approach the park on foot from various points in the north and west and these areas provide some of the most rewarding hiking. There is now a good road linking Chiengi with Kaputa, along which lies some very interesting terrain. The gallery forests near Chitunda (Lambwe Chikwama) are the only Zambian locality from which Joyful Greenbul is known. It was last recorded with certainty on 12-12-83, but the forests are now very degraded and the bird probably no longer occurs. Bamboo Warbler is also known from the area and may still survive in the dense regrowth. West of Chiengi a road follows the northern shore of Lake Mweru and this area is the only part of Zambian in which Orange-cheeked Waxbill is common. A little further on, Spotted Thrush-Babbler occurs in the thickets along the Luao River.

Striped Crake

Globally threatened species

Shoebill	Near-threatened	status unknown
Lesser Flamingo	Near-threatened	rare visitor, has attempted to breed

Biome-restricted species

Eastern	-	1 near-endemic
Zambezian	9 endemics	4 near-endemics

Globally important congregations

(i) regularly holds >1% of biogeographic population of a congregatory waterbird	
White Pelican	>6000 (Oct 1954, inc. >1500 nestlings)

Species of regional conservation concern

Goliath Heron	common, probably breeds
Saddle-billed Stork	regular, probably breeds
Bateleur	common breeding resident
African Marsh Harrier	fairly common, probably breeds
Southern Crowned Crane	status unknown
Southern Ground Hornbill	fairly common, probably breeds
Yellow-billed Oxpecker	status unknown, probably a scarce breeding resident

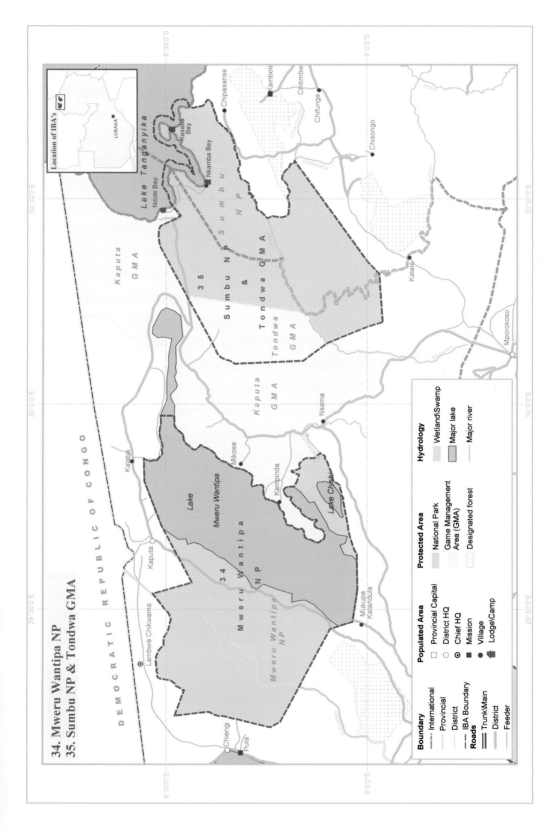

34. Mweru Wantipa NP
35. Sumbu NP & Tondwa GMA

Boundary
- International
- Provincial
- District
- IBA Boundary

Roads
- Trunk\Main
- District
- Feeder

Populated Area
- ☐ Provincial Capital
- ○ District HQ
- ◉ Chief HQ
- ■ Mission
- ● Village
- ⚑ Lodge\Camp

Protected Area
- National Park
- Game Management Area (GMA)
- Designated forest

Hydrology
- Wetland\Swamp
- Major lake
- Major river

Location of IBA's

LUSAKA

D E M O C R A T I C   R E P U B L I C   O F   C O N G O

Lake Tanganyika

Kaputa GMA

Ndole Bay

Kasaba Bay

Nkamba Bay

Chipasanse

Kambole

Chitimbwe

Chifunge

Chisongo

Sumbu N P

3 5

Sumbu NP & Tondwa GMA

Tondwa GMA

Kaputa GMA

Katele

Mporokoso

Nsama

Kalaba

Mikose

Kampinda

Lake Mweru Wantipa

Lake Chishi

Lambwe Chikwama

Kaputa

3 4

Mweru Wantipa N P

Mukupa Kalandula

Chiengi

Puta

151

35 Sumbu National Park and Tondwa GMA

Admin region: Kaputa, Mbala Districts, Northern Province
Co-ordinates: 8°27'-9°04'S 30°04'-30°45'E
Area: 256,000ha (NP: 202,000ha; GMA: 54,000ha)   **Altitude:** 773-1433m
Status: National Park, Game Management Area
Categories: Globally threatened species, Biome-restricted species, Globally
important congregations
International site code: --- **Map:** p 151

■ Site description

The park sits at the southern end of Lake Tanganyika and includes about 100km of its shore-line. This is a typical Rift Valley lake with dramatic steep sides for much of its length and a maximum depth of 1470m. In most places the shore is rocky but there are also sandy stretches. Other features of the lake shore are two promontories known as Cape Nundo and the Inangu Peninsula. The park is bisected from south-west to north-east by the Lufubu River in what's known as the Yendwe Valley. Where this and other similar valleys broaden and meet the lake there are groves of ripar-ian trees such as *Acacia albida* and *Trichilia emetica*. Elsewhere in the river valleys there is *Pteleopsis anisoptera* woodland and the remainder of the park comprises various woodland types (including miombo and areas dominated by *Pterocarpus angolensis*) and large stretches of Itigi thicket. Itigi thicket is also found in small pockets in DRC and more extensively in Tanzania and characteristic plants include *Bussea massaiensis* subsp. *floribunda* (*Casesalpinioideae*), *Pseudoprosopis fischeri* (*Mimosoideae*) and *Burttia prunoides* (*Connaraceae*) (White 1983).

Tondwa GMA (No. 29) lies immediately to the west of the park. It acts as a buffer zone and is also a relatively popular hunting area. At its heart is a very large pan which supports an abundance of wildlife and a rich diversity of aquatic vegetation. There is a small fishing settlement beside the pan.

■ Birds

The broad range of habitats holds a wide diversity of species, though the woodland has not been well explored. Many waterbirds can be found along the lake shore and both African Fish Eagle and Palm-nut Vulture are regular. Lesser Black-winged Plover is probably a regular breeding visitor and the first Zambian records of Spur-winged Plover came from the Kasaba Bay area in 1999 (Robinson *et al.* 2001). Pel's Fishing Owl is occasional in thick riparian vegetation and both species of oxpecker are regular. Typical birds of the Itigi thickets include Crested Guineafowl, Green Coucal, Böhm's Bee-eater, African Pitta, White-throated Nicator and Red-capped Robin.

Tondwa Pan supports enormous concentrations of waterbirds and species recently recorded in very large numbers include Little Grebe, White-backed Duck, African Pygmy Goose, Common and Lesser Moorhens, Red-knobbed Coot and Lesser Jacana (1000-2000 in Dec 1999). Saddle-billed Stork, Shoebill and Wattled Crane are probably all regular

African Spoonbill (Andrea Leonard)

Puku (Mike Harrison)

and Lesser Flamingo has occasionally occurred in good numbers.

See summary box for key species. The main areas are fairly well known, but large areas remain unexplored. Total number of species recorded to date: 348 (Sumbu NP: 295, Tondwa GMA: 217).

■ Other flora and fauna

Both areas support a wide variety of mammals, although populations are depleted. Puku *Kobus vardoni* (LR/cd) and Bushbuck *Tragelaphus scriptus* are common, Hartebeest *Alcelaphus buselaphus lichtensteinii* (LR/cd), Roan *Hippotragus equinus* (LR/cd), Sable *H. niger* (LR/cd) and Southern Reedbuck *Redunca arundinum* (LR/cd) are regular and several other species are recorded occasionally such as Sitatunga *Tragelaphus spekei* (LR/cd), Yellow-backed Duiker *Cephalophus silvicultor* (LR/nt) and Waterbuck *Kobus ellipsiprymnus* (LR/cd). Warthog *Phacochoerus africanus* are frequent and there are several large herds of African Buffalo *Syncerus cafer* (LR/cd). Other species occurring in small numbers include Lion *Panthera leo* (VU), African Elephant *Loxodonta africana* (EN), Common Zebra *Equus (quagga) burchelli*

and Spot-necked Otter *Lutra maculicollis* (VU). A very small number of Wild Dogs *Lycaon pictus* (EN) may still survive (Buk 1995). Reptiles include Lake Tanganyika Water Snake *Lycodonomorphus bicolor* and Water Cobra *Boulengerina annulata stormsi*, both endemic to Lake Tanganyika and Groove-crowned Bullfrog *Hoplodactylus occipitalis* at the very southern limit of its range. About 450 species of fish (mainly *Cichlidae*) have been recorded, many of which are endemic. The woodland and savanna associated with Itigi thicket have species with restricted ranges such as the trees *Strophanthus eminii* and an undescribed species of *Stereospermum* (M. Bingham *in litt.*).

■ Conservation issues

The area continues to suffer high levels of poaching. Despite a relatively strict licensing system, over-fishing remains a threat at Tondwa, as does general human encroachment. Fire is a problem throughout the area.

■ Information for visitors

There are currently three lodges along the lake shore (Ndole Bay ndolebay@coppernet.zm, Nkamba Bay and Kasaba Bay 2Kasaba@bushmail.net) and Ndole Bay also has a campsite. There is a fully tarred airstrip at Kasaba Bay and boat transfers can be arranged between here and other lodges or even from Mpulungu. By road the park can be reached via either Mporokoso or Kaputa, but these routes are rough and can be very difficult during the rains. There is also an overland route from Mbala, but this is only for the most adventurous travellers and local advice should be sought before attempting it. The access track to Tondwa leaves the Mporokoso road about 20km before the Sumbu park gate, close to the Mutundu Wildlife Checkpoint. This leads to the pan where there is a small settlement and from here a visitors can follow a network of rough tracks around the area. It can be very helpful to take a ZAWA scout who can act as a guide and they can be found either at the Sumbu gate or the checkpoint on the main road. Insect repellent will be invaluable to anyone wishing to explore the pan thoroughly. Motorists are advised to carry extra fuel as the supplies in this part of the country can be erratic. Visitors approaching by road from Mporokoso may wish to explore the stretch of miombo just north of Nsama which is a good site for White-winged Starling.

Globally threatened species		
Madagascar Squacco Heron	Vulnerable	vagrant
Shoebill	Near-threatened	occasional at Tondwa
Lesser Flamingo	Near-threatened	sporadic visitor
Lappet-faced Vulture	Vulnerable	fairly common resident, probably breeds
Wattled Crane	Vulnerable	regular at Tondwa, may breed
Denham's Bustard	Near-threatened	occasional
African Skimmer	Near-threatened	occasional

Biome-restricted species		
Afromontane	-	1 near-endemic
Eastern	-	1 near-endemic
Zambezian	8 endemics	4 near-endemics

Globally important congregations	
(i) regularly holds >1% of biogeographic population of a congregatory waterbird	
White-backed Duck	300 (Dec 1999)

Species of regional conservation concern	
Goliath Heron	occasional
Saddle-billed Stork	regular, may breed
Bateleur	fairly common breeding resident
African Marsh Harrier	fairly common, probably breeds
Southern Crowned Crane	occasional, may breed
Yellow-throated Sandgrouse	status uncertain, possibly regular in Tondwa GMA
Southern Ground Hornbill	fairly common breeding resident
Yellow-billed Oxpecker	regular breeding resident
Red-billed Oxpecker	regular breeding resident

36 Saise River

Admin region: Mbala District, Northern Province
Co-ordinates: 8°58'S 31°40'E
Area: c.4000ha   **Altitude:** 1525m
Status: unprotected
Categories: Globally threatened species, Restricted-range species, Biome-restricted species
International site code: ZM030   **Map:** p 156

■ Site description

The site is positioned about 20km east of Mbala beside the international boundary with Tanzania. It comprises an 8km section of the perennial Saise River and the surrounding dambo. The main channel contains some sizeable areas of papyrus swamp and there is a floodplain of varying width. Flanking this are broad stretches of typical dambo grassland with scattered areas of termitaria. In several places the termitaria is particularly well developed with a high density of large mounds, each supporting a wide variety of shrubs and trees. Beyond the grassland is scrub and degraded wood-

Lake Tanganyika Weaver (Peter Leonard)

land. Villages are scattered throughout the surrounding area, cattle are grazed on the floodplain and the river is heavily fished. The Saise River and its immediate tributaries constitute the only system which drains from Zambia into Tanzania and it eventually flows into Lake Rukwa.

■ Birds

A poorly known area, visited by ornithologists for the first time in 1996 when Lake Tanganyika Weaver was discovered in considerable numbers (Leonard & Beel 1996a, 1999). This remains the only Zambian site from which the species is known. Breeding has not been proved but the presence of large numbers of juveniles suggests that it is likely to occur either within or close to the site. Large flocks roost each night within the papyrus. Other swamp inhabitants include Red-chested Flufftail, African Water Rail, Purple Gallinule, Coppery-tailed Coucal, Greater Swamp Warbler and Chirping Cisticola. Common, Ethiopian and

Great Snipe have all been recorded in the flooded grassland. Other dambo birds include Fülleborn's Longclaw, Rosy-breasted Longclaw, Stout Cisticola, Red-headed Quelea, Parasitic Weaver and Locust Finch. Characteristic of the termitaria are Bare-faced Go-away Bird, Spot-flanked Barbet, White-rumped Babbler, Marico Sunbird, Brown Firefinch and good numbers of Palearctic warblers. More typical of the scrub and degraded woodland are Dickinson's Kestrel, Whinchat and Oustalet's White-bellied Sunbird.

See summary box for key species. Fairly poorly known. Total number of species recorded to date: 192.

■ Other flora and fauna

Not known.

■ Conservation issues

The habitat surrounding the site is somewhat degraded but the dambo remains relatively undisturbed. However, there is some hunting and trapping of small birds and fire is likely to be a problem in the dry season.

■ Information for visitors

The area is fairly easily reached either from the north via Kawimbe or from the south via the Mbala-Tunduma road. A high clearance vehicle is important but four wheel drive is rarely necessary. There are no facilities but self-sufficient travellers will not have difficulty finding somewhere to camp. Accommodation is available in Mbala.

Spot-flanked Barbet

155

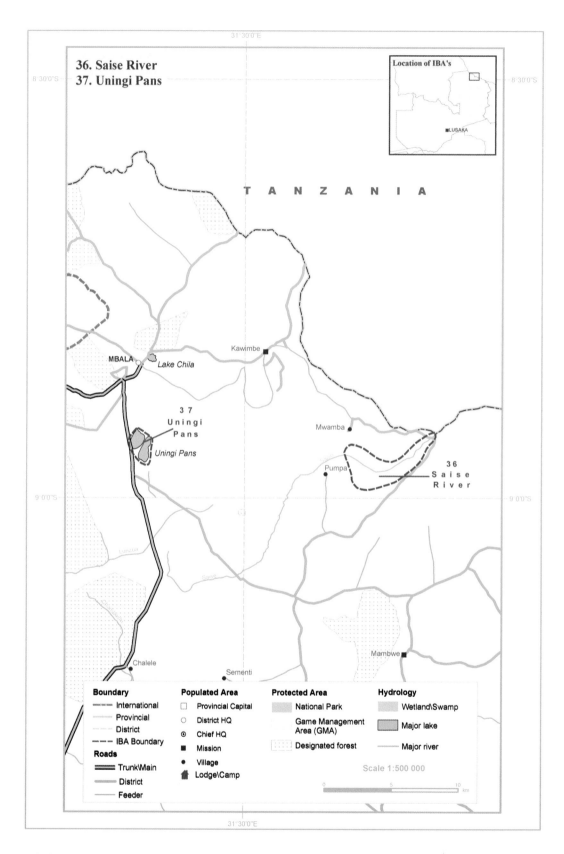

36. Saise River
37. Uningi Pans

Location of IBA's

■LUSAKA

T A N Z A N I A

Kawimbe ■

MBALA ○ Lake Chila

3 7
U n i n g i
P a n s

Uningi Pans

Mwamba ●

Pumpa ●

3 6
S a i s e
R i v e r

Lunzua

Saise

Chalele ●

Sementi ●

Mambwe ■

Boundary
- - - International
——— Provincial
· · · · District
– – – IBA Boundary

Roads
━━━ Trunk\Main
——— District
——— Feeder

Populated Area
□ Provincial Capital
○ District HQ
◉ Chief HQ
■ Mission
● Village
⛺ Lodge\Camp

Protected Area
National Park
Game Management Area (GMA)
Designated forest

Hydrology
Wetland\Swamp
Major lake
—— Major river

Scale 1:500 000

0   5   10
                km

156

Globally threatened species		
Great Snipe	Near-threatened	fairly common non-breeding visitor
Restricted-range species		
Lake Tanganyika Weaver	s055	common, probably breeds
Biome-restricted species		
Zambezian	6 endemics	2 near-endemics
Species of regional conservation concern		
Bateleur	regular	
African Marsh Harrier	common, probably breeds	
Southern Ground Hornbill	uncommon resident	

37 Uningi Pans

Admin region: Mbala District, Northern Province
Co-ordinates: 8°55'S 31°22'E
Area: c.1000ha **Altitude:** c.1800m
Status: unprotected
Categories: Globally threatened species, Biome-restricted species, Globally important congregations
International site code: --- **Map:** p 156

■ Site description

The site comprises two large pans separated by a narrow strip of land. The more westerly lies adjacent to the main Kasama-Mbala road, about 10km south of Mbala. They represent an unusual plateau habitat and hold a wide variety of aquatic vegetation. The water levels fluctuate greatly and when high the pans support large rafts of water lilies *Nymphaea* and patches of swamp dominated by reed mace *Typha* and various sedges *Cyperus* spp.. In drier periods the pan bases revert to grassland and occasionally one pan will dry out completely, but it is rare for both to do so. Fringing the pans are areas of scrub and degraded miombo, some farmland and a few patches of evergreen thicket. The area was once a part of the now abandoned Mbala State Ranch.

■ Birds

For some time Uningi has been the most important site in Zambia for Great Crested Grebes. Although also known from nearby Lake Chila (8°50'S

31°21'E) and a small area in Western Province, Uningi has provided the majority of recent records. However, since the mid 1990s and several consecutive dry years there have been no records. The pans have been visited frequently and explored thoroughly and it is unlikely that birds have been overlooked. Furthermore there have been no recent records from other Zambian localities so there is much concern over the species' status in Zambia (Van Daele & Leonard 2001). Whether or not the species is able to re-establish itself in the future

Marsh Owl

Lilac-breasted Roller (Mike Harrison)

remains to be seen, but the East African population is now considered to be 'critically endangered' (Bennun & Njoroge 1999). Other birds typical of the deep water pools include White-backed Duck, African Pygmy Goose, African and Lesser Jacanas. Many other waterbirds occur and characteristic birds include Rufous-bellied Heron, Great White Egret, Purple Heron, Saddle-billed Stork, Common, Ethiopian and Great Snipe. More typical of grassland are European Marsh Harrier, Corn Crake, Marsh Owl, Broad-tailed Warbler and Parasitic Weaver. Oustalet's White-bellied Sunbird is common in the scrub and degraded woodland and the patches of evergreen thicket attract Speckled Mousebird, Trumpeter Hornbill, Black-backed Barbet and Olive Woodpecker. The Afromontane near-endemic Baglafecht Weaver was recently discovered (Leonard & Van Daele 2001) highlighting the submontane altitude of the site and the only confirmed Zambian record of the vagrant White-throated Bee-eater comes from Uningi (Leonard *et al.* 2001b).

See summary box for key species. Fairly well known. Total number of species recorded to date: 215.

■ Other flora and fauna

Not known.

■ Conservation issues

Whether there are any human factors that have influenced the decline of the Great Crested Grebe is

Globally threatened species		
Lesser Kestrel	Vulnerable	regular passage migrant
Corn Crake	Vulnerable	occasional non-breeding visitor
Great Snipe	Near-threatened	fairly common non-breeding visitor

Biome-restricted species		
Afromontane	-	3 near-endemics
Zambezian	8 endemics	4 near-endemics

Globally important congregations	
(i) regularly holds >1% of biogeographic population of a congregatory waterbird	
Great Crested Grebe	42 (Sep 1972) but see text

Species of regional conservation concern	
Great Crested Grebe	once a common breeding resident and visitor, now status uncertain and no records since 1994
Goliath Heron	uncommon
Saddle-billed Stork	regular visitor
Bateleur	fairly common visitor
African Marsh Harrier	common, probably breeds
Southern Ground Hornbill	uncommon

not known. There is some trapping and snaring of birds and fire becomes a problem when the pans dry out. The surrounding area has become increasingly degraded as the human population has increased in recent years.

■ Information for visitors

The site is very easy to reach in any vehicle or by public transport as it lies beside the main Kasama-Mbala road. There are no facilities, but Mbala has accommodation and self-sufficient travellers should find somewhere to pitch camp. Lake Chila is often worth visiting and lies just beyond Mbala on the Kawimbe road. Also accessible from here are the spectacular Kalambo Falls about 35km north of Mbala. The falls are a National Monument and, at 221m, one of the highest in the world.

38 Nyika National Park

Admin region: Chama District, Eastern Province
Co-ordinates: 10°38'S 33°38'E
Area: 8000ha   **Altitude:** 1300-2225m
Status: National Park
Categories: Globally threatened species, Restricted-range species, Biome-restricted species
International site code: ZM022   **Map:** p 162

■ Site description

This relatively small park lies along the Malawi border in the far north-east of the country. The site lies adjacent to the much larger Malawian national park of the same name (IBA MW002, Dowsett-Lemaire *et al.* 2001). Nyika is one of only three truly montane areas in Zambia; the Mafinga Mountains (IBA 39) lie about 80km to the north and the Makutu Mountains are half way between the two. Together they constitute Zambia's eastern highlands. There are a few rocky outcrops on the plateau, but most of Nyika's terrain is gently undulating and dominated by *Loudetia-Andropogon* grassland, often with pockets of *Protea* and *Erica*. There are scattered patches of montane forest, often in depressions or along streams. The largest of these are Chowo (90ha) and Manyanjere (75ha) which have a tall, closed canopy 25-30m high, with emergents reaching 35-40 m. The floristic composition of the forests has been studied in detail (Dowsett-Lemaire 1985). *Afrocrania (Cornus) volkensii, Croton macrostachyus, Podocarpus latifolius* and *Polyscias fulva* are important fruit trees. Typical emergents include *Aningeria adolfi-friedericii, Entandrophragma excelsum* and *Olea capensis*. Most forests and some streams are bordered by dense bracken-briar, a transitional vegetation type typical of areas where forest has been burnt. Along the western side of the park runs a precipitous escarpment which, in places, supports miombo. At higher levels, this woodland becomes somewhat stunted. In general, the flora contains many species of limited distribution elsewhere in Zambia and the area is particularly rich in orchids (La Croix *et al.* 1991). The eastern highlands are generally cool and wet and they are an important catchment area within which several large rivers rise.

■ Birds

Over 40 species on the Zambian list are restricted to the eastern highlands. Many of these are restricted to Nyika alone and most belong to the Afromontane biome. True forest species include Rameron Pigeon, Bar-tailed Trogon, Moustached Green Tinkerbird, Eastern Mountain Greenbul, Yellow-streaked Bulbul, Olive Thrush, White-chested Alethe, Olive-flanked Robin, Chestnut-headed Apalis, White-tailed Crested Flycatcher, African Hill Babbler, Eastern Double-collared Sunbird, Fülleborn's Black Boubou, Waller's Red-winged Starling and Red-faced Crimsonwing. Some species, such as Starred Robin and Cape Batis, inhabit forest patches of all sizes, whereas others, such as Orange Thrush and Sharpe's Akalat,

Bar-tailed Trogon

tend to remain within the more extensive tracts. Scarce Swift also typically feeds over the larger forests. This is one of the few localities in Zambia where good numbers of Blackcaps occur as non-breeding visitors. Silvery-cheeked Hornbill, however, is only a scarce and erratic visitor. Birds more typical of forest edge and bracken-briar include Red-breasted Sparrowhawk, Hildebrandt's Francolin, Pink-breasted Turtle Dove, Mountain Nightjar, Cape Robin, Cinnamon Bracken Warbler, Mountain Yellow Warbler, Black-lored Cisticola, Slaty Flycatcher, Bronze Sunbird, Baglafecht and Bertram's Weavers, Swee Waxbill, Cape Canary,

African Citril and Streaky Seed-eater. Wandering groups of Slender-billed Chestnut-winged Starling are perhaps most often found in this habitat. Brown Parisoma is rather specialised and is found almost exclusively in the dense canopies of *Acacia abyssinica* trees. Often associated with *Proteas* and other small flowering shrubs are Yellow-tufted Malachite, Scarlet-tufted Malachite and Greater Double-collared Sunbirds. Birds characteristic of the grassland include Pallid and Montagu's Harriers, Red-winged Francolin, Common Quail (subspecies *erlangeri*), Red-tailed Flufftail, Wattled Crane, Denham's Bustard, Grass Owl, Blue Swallow, Wing-snapping, Wailing and Churring Cisticolas and Mountain Marsh Whydah. The rocky western escarpment supports a number of other species such as Augur Buzzard, Red-rumped Swallow, Mottled and African Black Swifts.

See summary box for key species. Very well known. Total number of species recorded to date: 224 (plateau as a whole, including Malawi: 428).

■ Other flora and fauna

A wide variety of mammals known including Chequered Elephant Shrew *Rhynchocyon cirnei* (VU), Tanganyika Mountain Squirrel *Paraxerus lucifer,* the groove-toothed rats *Otomys typus* and *O. denti,* Four-striped Grass Mouse *Rhabdomys*

A typical view over the Nyika plateau with rolling grassland and patches of forest in the drainage lines. (Bob Medland)

pumilio, African Palm Civet *Nandinia binotata* (very rare), Leopard *Panthera pardus,* African Elephants *Loxodonta africana* (EN), Eland *Taurotragus oryx* (LR/cd)(rare), Natal Duiker *Cephalophus natalensis* (LR/cd), Klipspringer *Oreotragus oreotragus* (LR/cd), Southern Reedbuck *Redunca arundinum* (LR/cd), Roan *Hippotragus equinus* (LR/cd) and the dwarf galago *Galagoides zanzibaricus* (Ansell & Dowsett 1988). The chameleon *Chamaeleo* (*goetzei*) *nyikae,* the toad *Bufo nyikae* and the reed frog *Hyperolius* (*quinquevittatus*) *mertensi* are endemic to the plateau (Critchlow 2001) and at the southern limit of their ranges are the bush viper *Atheris rungweensis,* the toad *Bufo loennbergi* and the reed frog *H. pictus.* There are many butterflies unknown elsewhere in the country, including *Axiocerces nyika, Iolaus helenae, Lepidochrysops handmani, L. chalceus* and *L. nyika* all of which are (on present evidence) endemic to the Nyika. Other species known from nowhere else in Zambia include: *Neptis nina, Cymothoe cottrelli, Charaxes nyikensis* and *Uranothauma williamsi.*

■ Conservation issues

Poaching has reduced the populations of large mammals and meat-drying racks have been found within the park. Fire is a threat to all habitats and the fire-breaks around the forest patches have not been maintained in recent years. Within Zambia, the total area of mature montane forest is c.200ha, so the many species restricted to this habitat are very vulnerable on a national scale.

■ Information for visitors

The park is not accessible by road within Zambia and must be approached from Malawi. Most visitors travel via Mzuzu and Rumpi from where the park is signed. The road is rough in places and a high clearance vehicle is needed. There are currently no facilities within the Zambian park, although some visitors camp near the dilapidated resthouse where clean water can be obtained. The Malawian park has several accommodation options.

Globally threatened species		
Lappet-faced Vulture	Vulnerable	scarce visitor
Pallid Harrier	Near-threatened	regular non-breeding visitor
Lesser Kestrel	Vulnerable	regular passage migrant
Corn Crake	Vulnerable	regular non-breeding visitor
Wattled Crane	Vulnerable	uncommon, breeds on Malawi side
Denham's Bustard	Near-threatened	regular, breeds on Malawi side
Blue Swallow	Vulnerable	breeding visitor in small numbers
Restricted-range species		
Sharpe's Akalat	EBA 105	localised resident
Churring Cisticola	EBA 105	common resident
Black-lored Cisticola	EBA 105	common resident
Chestnut-headed Apalis	EBA 105	common resident
Fülleborn's Black Boubou	EBA 105	common resident
Mountain Marsh Whydah	EBA 105	uncommon resident, more numerous on Malawi side
Biome-restricted species		
Afromontane	32 endemics	17 near-endemics
Zambezian	-	2 near-endemics
Species of regional conservation concern		
Bateleur	fairly common resident, probably breeds	
African Marsh Harrier	occasional visitor	
Southern Ground Hornbill	uncommon resident	

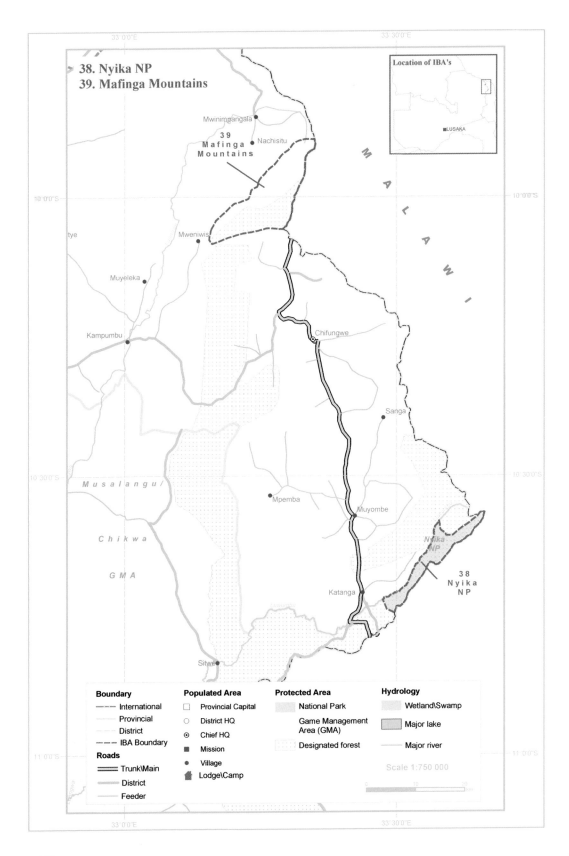

38. Nyika NP
39. Mafinga Mountains

Location of IBA's

LUSAKA

39
Mafinga
Mountains

Mwinimpangala

Nachisitu

MALAWI

Mweniwis

Muyeleka

Kampumbu

Chifungwe

Sanga

Musalangu

Mpemba

Muyombe

Chikwa

GMA

Nyika
NP

38
Nyika
NP

Katanga

Sitwe

Boundary
- - - International
—— Provincial
- - - District
- - - IBA Boundary

Roads
═══ Trunk\Main
—— District
—— Feeder

Populated Area
☐ Provincial Capital
○ District HQ
◉ Chief HQ
■ Mission
● Village
⌂ Lodge\Camp

Protected Area
National Park
Game Management
Area (GMA)
Designated forest

Hydrology
Wetland\Swamp
Major lake
—— Major river

Scale 1:750 000

39 Mafinga Mountains

Admin region: Isoka District, Northern Province
Co-ordinates: 9°55'-10°06'S 33°15'-33°20'E
Area: c.13,000ha (NF: c.7000ha; unprotected: c.6000ha)
Altitude: 1200-2200m
Status: unprotected, National Forest
Categories: Restricted-range species, Biome-restricted species
International site code: --- **Map:** p 162

■ Site description

The most northerly block of mountains within Zambia's eastern highlands. As with the Nyika Plateau (IBA 38), the Mafingas straddle the international boundary with Malawi. As well as Mafinga National Forest (No. 296) in the south of the area, the site encompasses all the land above about the 1500m contour which is largely uninhabited and rarely even visited. Miombo covers most of the lower slopes and in several places it reaches unusually high altitudes of over 2000m. In some areas this woodland is dominated by masuku trees *Uapaca* spp. Broken rocky terrain and scree cover large parts of the higher ground and there are small stretches of montane grassland and *Protea* scrub. Along the streams are patches of riparian forest, often in precipitous gullies, but there is only one large patch (40ha) of montane forest known as Mulangale (9°59'S 33°18'E). Most forest is bordered by bracken briar. The Mafingas are an important catchment area and they contain the source of the Luangwa.

■ Birds

Several taxa are known only from the Mafingas within Zambia. These include Yellow-throated Warbler and the race of Cabanis's Greenbul *Phyllastrephus cabanisi placidus* which is sometimes treated as a full species. Although they may be non-breeding wanderers, Silvery-cheeked Hornbills occur more regularly here than at any other Zambian site. Typical forest birds include Rameron Pigeon, Cinnamon Dove, Bar-tailed Trogon, Moustached Green Tinkerbird, Eastern Mountain Greenbul, Yellow-streaked Bulbul, Olive Thrush, White-chested Alethe, Chestnut-

A typical view over the Mafinga Mountains with extensive rocky terrain and strips of forest in the valleys.
(Peter Leonard)

Silvery-cheeked Hornbills

headed Apalis, Cape Batis, White-tailed Crested Flycatcher, Eastern Double-collared Sunbird and Many-coloured Bush Shrike. Birds found along the forest edge and in the bracken briar and scrub include Hildebrandt's Francolin, Mountain Nightjar, Cape Robin, Slaty Flycatcher, Bronze Sunbird, Bertram's Weaver, Swee Waxbill, Cape Canary, African Citril and Streaky Seed-eater. Wailing Cisticola and Yellow-tufted Malachite Sunbird are characteristic of the grassland and in rocky areas are species such as Common Kestrel, Red-rumped Swallow, Mottled and African Black Swifts. Zambezian endemics and near-endemics found in the miombo include Red-capped

Sharpe's Akalat

Crombec, Miombo Double-collared Sunbird, Black-eared Seed-eater, Miombo Grey and Rufous-bellied Tits. Sharpe's Starling has recently been recorded (Dowsett *et al.* 2003) and this constitutes the first record for Zambia. This species is an Afromontane endemic, but it is unlikely to be resident on the Mafingas and such a record probably refers to non-breeding wanderers.

See summary box for key species. The forest has been well explored, other areas much less so. Total number of species recorded to date: 144.

■ Other flora and fauna

Not well known. Mammals include Chequered Elephant Shrew *Rhynchocyon cirnei* (VU) and Giant Mastiff Bat *Otomops martiensseni* (VU)(pers. obs., P. Van Daele *in litt.*). Others with limited Zambian distributions include Smith's Red Rock Hare *Pronolagus rupestris*, Lesser Pouched Rat *Beamys hindei* and Nyika Bush-rat *Aethomys nyikae*. Butterflies include the possibly endemic *Iolaus stewarti*, an isolated population of *Pilodeudorix zelomima*, and the very local *Iolaus pamelae*.

■ Conservation issues

The mountains are currently uninhabited above about 1600m and local residents visit the higher levels only very rarely. There is a small amount of subsistence hunting but perhaps the main threat is fire. This seems to reach the upper levels of the Mafingas regularly and it gradually destroys the forest.

■ Information for visitors

The area is remote, rugged and difficult to reach, but adventurous travellers who make the effort will be richly rewarded with some of Zambia's finest scenery and wildest terrain. Previous expeditions have usually relied on hiring local residents as guides and porters and all exploration of the area must be done on foot. Water is readily available, but all other supplies and equipment must be taken. A relatively simple and interesting route into the mountains is up the Zinsa Valley, starting from near Nsami Primary School (10°07'S 33°16'E). Along its upper reaches, the Zinsa valley supports some substantial blocks of riparian forest. The general area is not too difficult to reach coming from Isoka via Kampumbu, but it should be noted that even the track to Nsami will probably require high clearance and four wheel drive. It is also possible to approach from Malawi. The northern parts of the Zambian Mafingas are very poorly known.

Restricted-range species		
Sharpe's Akalat	EBA 105	very localised resident
Black-lored Cisticola	EBA 105	scarce resident
Chestnut-headed Apalis	EBA 105	common resident
Biome-restricted species		
Afromontane	18 endemics	12 near-endemics
Sub-Afromontane	1 endemic	-
Eastern	-	1 near-endemic
Zambezian	3 endemics	5 near-endemics

40 South Luangwa National Park

Admin region: Serenje, Mpika, Petauke, Chipata Districts, Central, Northern, Eastern Provinces
Co-ordinates: 12°20'-13°45'S 31°-32°08'E
Area: 905,000ha   **Altitude:** 500-1550m
Status: National Park
Categories: Globally threatened species, Biome-restricted species, Globally important congregations
International site code: ZM019   **Map:** p 170

■ Site description

The second largest and probably the most famous of Zambia's national parks. It encompasses a portion of the mid-Luangwa Valley and a 250km section of the Luangwa River. It lies mainly on the west bank of the river and stretches to the lower foothills of the Muchinga Escarpment. Most of the area lies between 500-900m, but the central part of the park's western boundary follows the lip of the escarpment where several areas reach 1000m and the highest is 1550m. The climate is hot and the rainfall relatively low.

The active, meandering river has created many ox-bow lakes and when the water level is low, sand cliffs and sand bars are a prominent feature of the main channel. Bordering the river is a mosaic of riparian habitats including levee thickets and areas of floodplain. There are also groves of woodland on alluvial soil characterised by trees such as *Diospyros mespiliformis, Acacia albida, Trichilia emetica, Kigelia africana* and *Khaya (nyasica) anthotheca.* Further from the river are large areas of drier thicket, scrub and woodland. Baobabs *Adansonia digitata* are numerous and there is some munga, but mopane is dominant and in the north it forms a wide belt, covering almost half the park's width. Beyond this, the land begins to rise gently and various miombo formations cover the majority of the remaining area, becoming richer at higher altitudes. Similarly, the riparian forest that lines many small streams verges on being mushitu in some of the higher gorges on the escarpment. Scattered grasslands are more common in the north, the largest being the Chifungwe Plain.

The first protected area in the Luangwa Valley was declared in 1904, but the current area was not declared a game reserve until 1938. It became a

Thornicroft's Giraffe - a subspecies endemic to the
Luangwa Valley. (Andrea Leonard)

National Park in 1972. The first tourist camp was
opened by Chief Nsefu in 1949 and over the following decades the tourist industry continued to
grow steadily. In 1975, tarmac roads had been constructed in several areas and an international airport
was opened in Mfuwe. Along with Livingstone and
the Victoria Falls, the park remains Zambia's most
popular tourist destination.

■ Birds

With abundant game, the area is a stronghold for
Yellow-billed and Red-billed Oxpeckers. There are
also large numbers of raptors and vultures in par-
ticular. Also numerous are gamebirds such as
Helmeted Guineafowl, Swainson's and Red-
necked Francolins. Typical of the river are Hadada,
Egyptian Goose, White-faced Whistling Duck,
Water Dikkop, White-fronted Sand Plover, White-
crowned Plover and Pied Kingfisher. African
Skimmers breed on sand bars and the number

occurring may exceed the 1% threshold. In the late
dry season, vast colonies of Southern Carmine Bee-
eaters breed in the sand cliffs along with Horus
Swift, White-fronted Bee-eater and African Sand
Martin. In the riparian forest are Western Banded
Snake Eagle and Pel's Fishing Owl. Large numbers
of waterbirds are attracted to the oxbows and particularly large concentrations occur as fish are
trapped in drying pools. Characteristic birds at such
'feeding frenzies' include White Pelican, Great
White Egret, Saddle-billed Stork, Marabou Stork
and African Fish Eagle. Many waterbirds breed
during the rains when water levels are high and the
most famous example is the huge Yellow-billed
Stork colony in the Nsefu Sector. The salt pan
nearby attracts good numbers of Southern Crowned
Crane (>500 in July 1988 and October 1992) and
Painted Snipe.

Mopane birds are very well represented and particularly numerous are Lilian's Lovebird, Red-billed
Hornbill, Southern Grey-headed Sparrow and
White-browed Sparrow-weaver. Red-billed
Buffalo Weaver is common but localised and often
nests in large trees such as baobabs. The scarce
Mottled Spinetail is also closely associated with
this tree, whereas Bat-like Spinetail is distributed
more generally. Alpine Swift can be a common,
though much overlooked, dry season visitor. The
few records of Madagascar Squacco Heron also fall
in this season though it may be no more than a
vagrant. Many migrants visit during the rains
including Dwarf Bittern and Lesser Gallinule
around the seasonal pools, Senegal Kingfisher and
Broad-billed Roller in the woodland and Cardinal
Quelea in areas of tall grass. Recently two separate
Greater Spotted Eagles have been tracked to the
area by satellite telemetry representing the first
records south of the equator and a huge leap in the

Hippopotami at dusk. (Andrea Leonard)

Elephant on the bank of the Luangwa River. (Chris McIntyre/Sunvil Africa)

species' known migratory range (Leonard 1998a).

The area around Kabvumbu Pans (Frank's Lakes) is an unusual valley habitat being two rather shallow pans supporting water lilies *Nymphaea* and various sedges *Cyperus* spp. and surrounded by dambo-like grassland. Several birds occur which are very rarely reported from elsewhere in the park such as White-backed Duck, Blue Quail, African Water Rail and Parasitic Weaver. Similarly, several areas along the western boundary lie at plateau altitudes between c.900-1550m and hold about 20 species unknown from the rest of the park, many of which are Zambezian endemics. These include miombo birds such as Red-capped Crombec, Sousa's Shrike and Bar-winged Weaver and forest species such as Eastern Least Honeyguide, Bocage's Robin, Evergreen Forest Warbler, Laura's Warbler and Black-bellied Seed-cracker. Red-winged Warbler is particularly common in long grass and rank growth and Swee Waxbill also occurs here, on the very edge of its range.

See summary box for key species. The main tourist areas are very well known. Away from the river,

there has been much less exploration. Total number of species recorded to date: 458.

■ Other flora and fauna

A wide variety of mammals known to occur, including Honey Badger *Mellivora capensis*, Bushy-tailed Mongoose *Bdeogale crassicauda,* Spotted Hyaena *Crocuta crocuta* (LR/cd), Lion *Panthera leo* (VU), African Elephants *Loxodonta africana* (EN), Common Zebra *Equus (quagga) burchelli*, Warthog *Phacochoerus africanus*, the endemic subspecies of Giraffe *Giraffa camelopardalis thornicrofti* (LR/cd), African Buffalo *Syncerus caffer* (LR/cd), Bushbuck *Tragelaphus scriptus*, Greater Kudu *T. strepsiceros* (LR/cd), Eland *Taurotragus oryx* (LR/cd), Sharpe's Grysbok *Raphicercus sharpei* (LR/cd), Puku *Kobus vardoni* (LR/cd), Waterbuck *K. ellipsiprymnus* (LR/cd), Impala *Aepyceros melampus* (LR/cd) and the endemic subspecies of Wildebeest *Connochaetes taurinus cooksoni* (LR/cd). The Wild Dog *Lycaon pictus* (EN) population is small, but apparently stable and possibly increasing after it suffered a severe outbreak of anthrax in the 1980s (Buk 1995). Riparian areas in the park support some of the highest densities of Leopard *Panthera*

Southern Carmine Bee-eaters breed in huge numbers in the banks of the Luangwa River. (Bob Medland)

pardus anywhere but Cheetah *Acinonyx jubatus* (VU) is extremely scarce. Black Rhinoceros *Diceros bicornis* (CR) is now almost certainly extinct. Hippopotamus *Hippopotamus amphibius* is abundant and huge concentrations build up when the river is low. Several species such as Roan *Hippotragus equinus* (LR/cd) and Sable *H. niger* (LR/cd) antelopes are more common in the west of the park away from the main tourist areas so they are not recorded so frequently. The slit-faced bat *Nycteris grandis* is known from the east bank of the river on the boundary of the IBA. The nettle *Pouzolzia bracteosa* remains known only from the type specimen which was collected in the area (Friis 1991).

■ Conservation issues

The area is relatively well protected and the high presence of the tourist industry also helps to deter poachers from much of the park. However, there is some illegal fishing and snaring and large-scale poaching remains a problem in the more remote areas. For example, it is known that organised groups of commercial poachers walk to the area from beyond the Muchinga Escarpment and tend to focus their efforts on the largest mammals (Elephant, Hippopotamus and Buffalo). Human encroachment is currently not a major problem, although its effects in the GMA around Mfuwe need to be assessed and monitored. As always, fire is a potential threat. Each year there is an official, though slightly controversial Hippopotamus cull. Many of the oxbows are full of the invasive alien weed Nile Cabbage *Pistia stratiotes*.

■ Information for visitors

There are numerous safari camps in and around the park catering for visitors on all levels. Many tourists fly to Mfuwe International Airport, but it is not difficult to drive to the park. The main route is via Chipata on a dirt road of variable quality. Although smaller cars do drive along this route, a vehicle with high clearance is still advisable. From Chipata the park is signed and it is approximately 115km to the park's main gate. Coming from Lusaka, turn left just before Chipata's memorial arch, left again after about 67km and again after a further 30km. Once at the tarmac road in Mfuwe, turn left for the airport or right for the park. Other routes to the area are more difficult, but often more scenic and interesting such as coming from Petauke via Sandwe. Towards the end of the dry season it is also possible to approach from Mpika either via North Luangwa NP (IBA 29) or the Nabwalya road through Munyamadzi GMA. However, local advice should be sought before embarking on such a trip. Most of the park's internal roads become impassable during the rains and only a small network around Mfuwe remains open at all times. Night drives are a major attraction to many of South Luangwa's visitors but it should be noted that only licensed vehicles are allowed to enter the park at this time so night drives must be booked with a local operator. Fuel is available in Mfuwe, but most other supplies will need to be bought in Chipata. For those wanting to explore the western escarpment areas, it is possible to reach the park from the Great North Road. About 67km beyond Serenje, turn right onto the tarmac D225 (signed to

Part of the Nsefu Sector Yellow-billed Stork colony in the wet season. (Chris McIntyre/Sunvil Africa)

Lusiwasi Dam) and fork left after 20km. Cross the Lusiwasi River after a further 30km, turn left after a further 3km and right after another 1km. After about another 8km the road enters the park a winds through an escarpment gorge. There may be signs to a safari camp which is planned in the area, but otherwise visitors should be self-sufficient and equipped for camping. Note that the lower sections of this road have been washed away and there is no access to the rest of the park from here.

Globally threatened species

Madagascar Squacco Heron	Vulnerable	rare, but regular vagrant
Lesser Flamingo	Near-threatened	very rare vagrant
Lappet-faced Vulture	Vulnerable	fairly common breeding resident
Pallid Harrier	Near-threatened	rare passage migrant and non-breeding visitor
Greater Spotted Eagle	Vulnerable	very rare non-breeding visitor
Lesser Kestrel	Vulnerable	rare passage migrant
Corn Crake	Vulnerable	scarce non-breeding visitor, probably overlooked
Wattled Crane	Vulnerable	vagrant
Denham's Bustard	Near-threatened	rare visitor
Great Snipe	Near-threatened	regular non-breeding visitor
African Skimmer	Near-threatened	common breeding visitor

Biome-restricted species

Afromontane	-	3 near-endemics
Sub-Afromontane	1 endemic	-
Eastern	-	4 near-endemics
Zambezian	13 endemics	13 near-endemics

Globally important congregations

(ii) regularly holds >1% global population of a terrestrial species

Southern Carmine Bee-eater	numerous colonies, some comprising as many as 2000 birds, though comprehensive data are lacking

Species of regional conservation concern

Goliath Heron	common breeding resident
Saddle-billed Stork	common breeding resident
Bateleur	common breeding resident
African Marsh Harrier	uncommon, may breed
Southern Crowned Crane	common breeding resident
Southern Ground Hornbill	common breeding resident
Bar-winged Weaver	very localised resident
Yellow-billed Oxpecker	common breeding resident
Red-billed Oxpecker	very common breeding resident

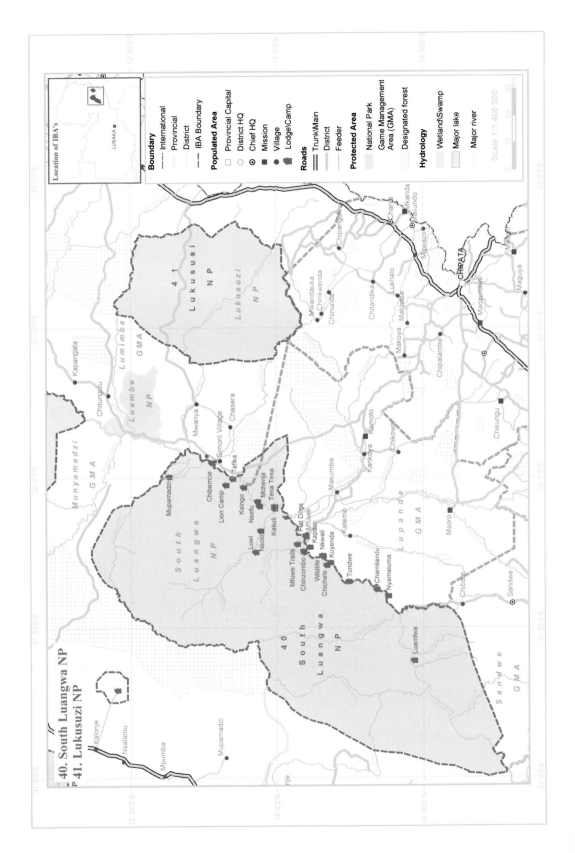

40. South Luangwa NP
P 41. Lukususzi NP

41 Lukususi National Park

Admin region: Lundazi District, Eastern Province
Co-ordinates: 12°28'-13°05'S 32°22'-32°50'E
Area: 272,000ha   **Altitude:** 650-1240m
Status: National Park
Categories: Globally threatened species, Biome-restricted species
International site code: ZM021   **Map:** p 170

■ Site description

This poorly known and neglected national park lies close to the Malawi border and about 70km north of Chipata. Most of the park lies on the plateau and is dominated by miombo. This woodland is richest in the east and there are numerous broad dambos. In the west is the gentle Luangwa Valley escarpment and as the elevation decreases, the woodland becomes thin or stunted. The drainage lines become well-defined rocky streams along which patches of riparian forest and thicket may be found. A small section of the park reaches the valley floor where there is some mopane. Granite outcrops can be found through much of the park, some of which are very large. There is a single road running from west to east from which one or two vague tracks have been made by aquamarine miners.

■ Birds

Poorly known, but a small amount of fieldwork has already revealed good numbers of Zambezian endemics. It is one of the few areas in Zambia from which Olive-headed Weaver is known, though this species would seem to be highly localised within the park (being dependent on significant quantities of the lichen *Usnea*). It is also known from several localities just beyond the park's eastern boundary, but none offers realistic long-term protection. The enigmatic White-winged Starling is common in places and other miombo birds recorded include Racket-tailed Roller, Pale-billed Hornbill, Miombo Pied Barbet, Little Spotted Woodpecker, Miombo Rock Thrush, Central Bearded Scrub Robin, Red-capped Crombec, Yellow-bellied Hyliota, Böhm's Flycatcher, Rufous-bellied Tit, Spotted Creeper, Violet-backed Sunbird, Miombo Double-collared Sunbird, Sousa's Shrike, Chestnut-mantled Sparrow-weaver and Black-eared Seed-eater. Yellow-throated Longclaw is restricted to Eastern Province in Zambia and is common in the dambos. African Black Duck and Half-collared Kingfisher are regular along the streams. Mocking Chat has been recorded from the kopjes, but otherwise this

Olive-headed Weaver

171

habitat has received little attention from ornithologists so far.

See summary box for key species. Poorly known. Total number of species recorded to date: 210.

■ Other flora and fauna

The large mammal populations are depleted. Klipspringer *Oreotragus oreotragus* (LR/cd), Hartebeest *Alcelaphus buselaphus lichtensteinii* (LR/cd) and Bush Duiker *Sylvicapra grimmia* have all been recorded recently and African Elephant *Loxodonta africana* (EN), Roan *Hippotragus equinus* (LR/cd) and Eland *Taurotragus oryx* (LR/cd) are occasionally reported.

■ Conservation issues

The legal mining of aquamarine has decreased as licence fees have risen, but illegal mining would appear to continue. The disturbance caused by such activity is not known and requires investigation. Large mammals are sparse and illegal hunting con-

White-winged Starling

tinues, though it seems unlikely that the bird life is at risk. There is some clearance of miombo in peripheral areas near villages and although the areas concerned are small, the problem requires investigation.

■ Information for visitors

A single road runs through the park from Mwanya in the west to the Chipata-Lundazi road in the east. Much of it is in poor condition and the escarpment sections have a particularly loose surface. A high clearance vehicle is necessary and it is probably unwise to drive beyond the plateau during the rains. The turning from the Lundazi road is about 115km north of Chipata. There are no facilities and visitors should be entirely self-sufficient. It is usually possible to camp within the park, though enquiries should be made at the park gate. The road runs along a wooded watershed and it is generally more rewarding to explore the area on foot. Hikers should be equipped with a good map, a compass and ideally a GPS, as there are very few paths. A few tracks approach the park's southern boundary and it is also possible to enter the park on foot from here.

Hartebeest (Mike Harrison)

Globally threatened species		
Lesser Kestrel	Vulnerable	occasional passage migrant
Olive-headed Weaver	Near-threatened	localised resident

Biome-restricted species		
Zambezian	12 endemics	9 near-endemics

Species of regional conservation concern	
Goliath Heron	occasional
Bateleur	fairly common, probably breeds
Southern Ground Hornbill	fairly common, probably breeds
Red-billed Oxpecker	status uncertain, probably rare

42 Nyanje Hills

Admin region: Petauke District, Eastern Province
Co-ordinates: 14°34'S 31°45'E
Area: c.5000ha   **Altitude:** c.1010-1410m
Status: unprotected
Categories: Globally threatened species, Biome-restricted species
International site code: --- **Map:** p 174

■ Site description

The area lies about 20km south of Sinda and it contains an unusually high density of granite inselbergs. These range from small kopjes to vast whaleback domes. Much of the surrounding area is degraded woodland and farmland supporting a relatively high human population. There are small patches of undisturbed habitat, particularly on and around the hills. At the eastern end is Nyanje Mission but the site is not yet well defined and further work is required to determine a practicable boundary. The site could possibly encompass Mchembwe (No. 118) and Chilowe (No. 119) Local Forests.

■ Birds

The site is most important for the localised and specialised Boulder Chat which can be found in the thickets at the bases of the hills. Other species characteristic of these kopjes include Black Stork, Augur Buzzard, Black Eagle, Lanner Falcon, Peregrine Falcon, Freckled Rock Nightjar, African Black Swift, African Rock Martin, Striped Pipit, Familiar Chat, Mocking Chat, Rock-loving

Black Stork

Cisticola, White-necked Raven, Red-winged Starling and Cinnamon-breasted Rock Bunting. Cape Bunting is extremely localised in Zambia and its status is uncertain, but there are several records from this area. A number of Zambezian endemics

173

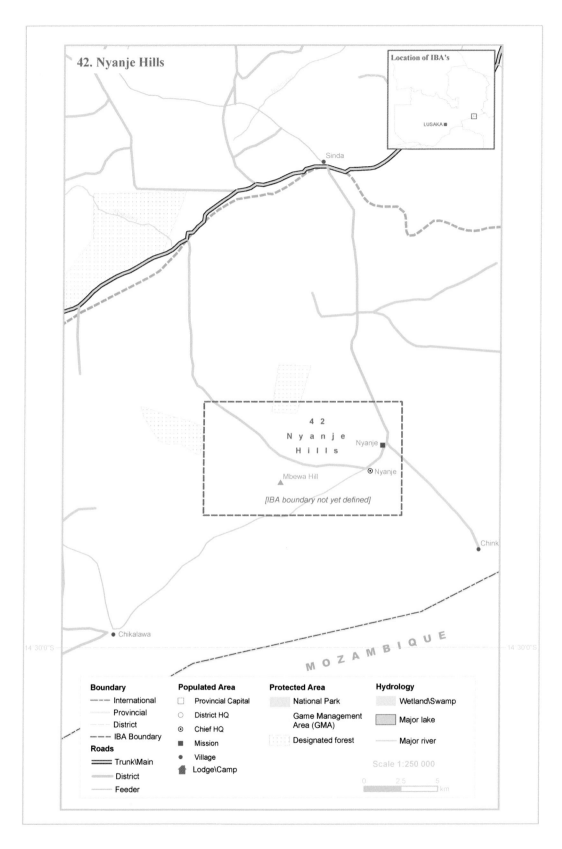

42. Nyanje Hills

Location of IBA's

LUSAKA ■

Sinda

4 2
N y a n j e
H i l l s

Nyanje ■

⊙ Nyanje

▲ Mbewa Hill

[IBA boundary not yet defined]

Chink

14 30'0"S

● Chikalawa

M O Z A M B I Q U E

14 30'0"S

Boundary	Populated Area	Protected Area	Hydrology
- - - International	☐ Provincial Capital	National Park	Wetland\Swamp
Provincial	○ District HQ	Game Management Area (GMA)	Major lake
District	⊙ Chief HQ		
- - - IBA Boundary	■ Mission	Designated forest	Major river
Roads	● Village		
Trunk\Main	🏠 Lodge\Camp		Scale 1:250 000
District			
Feeder			0 2.5 5 km

Gaboon Nightjar (Warwick Tarboton)

and near-endemics occur in the miombo including Racket-tailed Roller, Pale-billed Hornbill, Miombo Rock Thrush, Red-capped Crombec, Rufous-bellied Tit, Miombo Double-collared Sunbird, Broad-tailed Paradise Widow and Black-eared Seed-eater. The somewhat localised Red-winged Warbler has been found in areas of long grass with scrub and thicket.

See summary box for key species. Fairly well known, though less so away from the kopjes. Total number of species recorded to date: 222.

■ Other flora and fauna

Poorly known. The rock hyrax *Procavia johnstoni* is not uncommon and this is the only site from which it is currently known in Zambia.

Klipspringer *Oreotragus oreotragus* (LR/cd) is occasionally recorded.

■ Conservation issues

The hillside habitats would appear to be relatively undisturbed, but in many places the human encroachment is severe and woodland has been cut right up to the hill bases for both fuel and agriculture. Fire occasionally sweeps across the very fragile grasses on the hillsides and this sometimes destroys the thin peaty soils to which they cling. There is some subsistence hunting, particularly of birds.

■ Information for visitors

The area is easily reached throughout the year in any vehicle. A well maintained dirt road leads south from the Great East Road beside Sinda Motel which provides the closest accommodation. It is also possible to camp within the area if a private arrangement is made with a local farmer. It is about 20km from Sinda to Nyanje Mission beyond which a network of rough tracks make it possible to drive reasonably close to most hills in the area. The largest hill is known as Mbewa Hill (meaning rat or mouse) as it is said that local people once fled into the hills like rats to escape an attack on the area. It is worth noting that it is often more interesting and definitely safer to walk around some of these hills than to try climbing their sheer slopes.

Globally threatened species		
Lesser Kestrel	Vulnerable	occasional passage migrant
Biome-restricted species		
Zambezian	4 endemics	8 near-endemics
Species of regional conservation concern		
Bateleur	occasional, probably no longer breeds	
Southern Ground Hornbill	occasional	

5. References

Anon. 1977. Species notes. **Newsletter Zambian Orn. Soc.** 7 (11): 96 & 98.

Ansell W.F.H. 1978. **The Mammals of Zambia.** Chilanga, Zambia: The National Parks and Wildlife Service.

Ansell W.F.H. & Dowsett R.J. 1988. **Mammals of Malawi: an annotated checklist and atlas.** St. Ives, Cornwall, England: Trendrine Press.

Aspinwall D.R. 1976. Interesting localities: Northern Mwinilunga. **Newsletter Zambian Orn. Soc.** 6 (10): 114-115.

Aspinwall D.R., 1977. Black-winged Pratincoles *Glareola nordmanni* at Mwinilunga and Liuwa Plain. **Bull. Zambian Orn. Soc.** 9: 58-59.

Aspinwall D.R. 1979. Bird notes from Zambezi District, North-western Province. **Occ. Papers Zambian Orn. Soc.** 2: 1-60.

Aspinwall D.R. & Leonard P.M. 1998. ZOS Research Priorities. **Zambia Bird Report** 1997: 45-49.

Astle W.L. 1989. **South Luangwa National Park Map.** Oxford, U.K.: Lovell Johns Ltd.

Barnes K.N. (ed) 1998. **The Important Bird Areas of Southern Africa.** Johannesburg: BirdLife South Africa.

Beel C. 1995. Zambian Bird List becomes shorter - Mwinilunga specialities under threat. **Newsletter Zambian Orn. Soc.** 25 (8): 89-90.

Beel C. 1996. Species notes for September 1996. **Newsletter Zambian Orn. Soc.** 26 (9): 104-116.

Beilfuss R., Bento C., Hancock P., Kamweneshe B., McCann K. & Morrison K. (in prep.) Water, Wetlands, And Wattled Cranes: A Regional Monitoring And Conservation Program For Southern Africa.

Bennun L. & Njoroge P. (eds) 1996. Birds to watch in East Africa: A preliminary Red Data list. **Research reports for the Centre for Biodiversity, National Museums of Kenya: Ornithology** 23.

Bennun L. & Njoroge P. 1999. **Important Bird Areas in Kenya.** Nature Kenya (The East Africa Natural History Society): Nairobi.

Benson C.W. & Irwin M.P.S. 1965. A new species of tinker-barbet from Northern Rhodesia. **Bull. B.O.C.** 85: 5-9.

Benson C.W., Brooke R.K., Dowsett, R.J. and Irwin, M.P.S. 1971. **The Birds of Zambia.** London: Collins.

Berkvens D.L. (ed.) 1988. December 1988 species records. **Newsletter Zambian Orn. Soc.** 18 (12): 70-73.

Bingham M.G., Aspinwall D.R. & Jeffery R.C.V. 1995. Zambia: A Biodiversity Profile. (unpublished report to WWF).

BirdLife International 2000. **Threatened birds of the world.** Barcelona, Spain/Cambridge, UK: Lynx Edicions/BirdLife International.

Bisso R. (ed.) 1997. **The World Guide 1997/98.** Oxford, UK: New Internationalist Publications Ltd.

Bolnick D. 1995. **A Guide to the Common Wild Flowers of Zambia and Neighbouring Regions.** Lusaka: Macmillan Zambia.

Broadley D.G. 1971. The reptiles and amphibians of Zambia. **The Puku** 6: 1-143.

Broadley D.G. 1991. The herpetofauna of Northern Mwinilunga District, Northwestern Zambia. **Arnoldia Zimbabwe** 9 (37): 519-538.

Broadley D.G. & Broadley S. 1997. A revision of the African genus Zygaspis Cope (Reptilia: Amphisbaenia). **Syntarsus** 4: 1-23.

Broadley D.G., Doria C. & Wigge J. 2003. **Snakes of Zambia - An Atlas and Field Guide.** Germany: Chimaira.

Brooke R.K. 1966. A preliminary list of the birds of the Kafue National Park. **Puku** 4: 57-86.

Brown H.D. 1957. The breeding of the Lesser

Flamingo in the Mweru wantipa, Northern Rhodesia. **Ibis** 99: 688-692.

Buk K. 1995. African Wild Dog Survey in Zambia. **Canid News** Vol. 3.

Burton M. & Benson C.W. 1961. The Whale-headed Stork or Shoe-bill: legend and fact. **N. Rhod. J.** 4: 411-426.

Buxton L., Slater J. & Brown L.H. 1978. The breeding behaviour of the shoebill or whale-headed stork *Balaeniceps rex* in the Bangweulu Swamps, Zambia. **E. Afr. Wildl. J.** 16: 201-220.

Childes S.L. & Mundy P.J. 1998. Important Bird Areas in Zimbabwe. Pages 355-384 in: Barnes K.N. (ed.) **The Important Bird Areas of southern Africa.** Johannesburg: BirdLife South Africa.

Childes S.L. & Mundy P.J. 2001. Zimbabwe. Pages 1025-1042 in :Fishpool L.D.C. & Evans M.I. (eds.) **Important Bird Areas in Africa and associated islands: Priority sites for conservation.** Newbury and Cambridge, UK: Pisces Publications and BirdLife International (BirdLife Conservation Series No. 11).

Christian S. 1997. Summary of information relating to the waterfowl associated with the Bangweulu Wetlands. (unpublished report to WWF).

Clarke J. & Loe I. 1974. **A guide to the National Parks of Zambia.** Lusaka: Anglo American Corporation (Central Africa) Limited.

Conant R.A. 1980. First breeding record of Whiskered Tern *Chlidonias hybridus* in Zambia. **Bull. Zambian Orn. Soc.** 12: 39-40.

Cotterill F.P.D. 2002a. Notes on mammal collections and biodiversity conservation in the Ikelenge Pedicle, Mwinilunga District, Northwest Zambia. **BFA Occasional Publications in Biodiversity** No. 10.

Cotterill F.P.D. 2002b. A new species of horseshoe bat (Microchiroptera: Rhinolophidae) from south-central Africa: with comments on its affinities and evolution, and the characterization of rhinolophid species. **Journal of Zoology** 256:165-179.

Cottrell C.B. & Loveridge J.P. 1966. Observations on the *Cryptosepalum* forest of the Mwinilunga district of Zambia. **Proc. Trans. Rhod. Sci. Ass.** 51: 79-120.

Critchlow D.P. 2001. Amphibians of the Nyika National Parks of Malawi and Zambia. **Nyala** 21: 49-63.

Dodman T. 1996a. Status and Distribution of the Black-cheeked Lovebird (Agapornis nigrigenis). (unpublished report to RSPB).

Dodman T. 1996b. Present status and distribution of cranes in the Kafue Flats, Zambia with reference to population estimates of the 1980's. Pages 255-259 Beilfuss R., Tarboton W. & Gichuki N. (eds.) **Proceedings of the 1993 African Crane and Wetland Training Workshop.** Baraboo, Wisconsin: International Crane Foundation.

Dodman T., Katanekwa V., Aspinwall D. & Stjernstedt R. 2000. Status and distribution of the Black-cheeked Lovebird, Zambia. **Ostrich** 71: 228-234.

Douthwaite R.J. 1974. An endangered population of Wattled Cranes (Grus carunculatus). **Biol. Conserv.** 6: 134-142.

Douthwaite R.J. 1977. Filter-feeding ducks of the Kafue Flats, Zambia, 1971-1973. **Ibis** 119: 44-66.

Douthwaite R.J. 1978. Geese and Red-knobbed Coot on the Kafue Flats in Zambia, 1970-1974. **E. Afr. Wildl. J.** 16: 29-47.

Dowsett R.J. 1966. A preliminary list of the birds of the Kafue Flats. **Puku** 4: 101-124.

Dowsett R.J. 1973. New Distribution Records from North-western Province. **Bull. Zambian Orn. Soc.** 5: 66-69.

Dowsett R.J. & Stjernstedt R. 1975. The Birds of the Mafinga Mountains. **The Puku** 7: 107-123.

Dowsett R.J., Aspinwall D.R. & Leonard P.M. 1999. Further additions to the avifauna of Zambia. **Bull. B.O.C.** 119 (2): 94-103.

Dowsett R.J., Aspinwall D.R. & Dowsett-Lemaire F. (in prep.) The Birds of Zambia.

Dowsett R.J. & Dowsett-Lemaire F. 1980. The

systematic status of some Zambian birds. **Gerfaut** 70: 151-199.

Dowsett R.J. & Dowsett-Lemaire F. 1993. Comments on the taxonomy of some Afrotropical bird species. **Tauraco Res. Rep.** 5: 323-389.

Dowsett R.J. & Forbes-Watson A.D. 1993. **Checklist of Birds of the Afrotropical and Malagasy Regions.** Volume 1: Species limits and distribution. Liège, Belgium: Tauraco Press.

Dowsett R.J., Berry, P.S.M. & Foot D. 2003. Sharpe's Starling *Cinnyricinclus sharpii* new to Zambia, and its status in eastern Africa. **Bull. A.B.C.** 10 (2): 125-126.

Dowsett-Lemaire F. 1983. Ecological and territorial requirements of montane forest birds on the Nyika Plateau, south-central Africa. **Gerfaut** 73: 345-378.

Dowsett-Lemaire F. 1985. The forest vegetation of the Nyika Plateau (Malawi-Zambia): ecological and phenological studies. **Bull. Jard. Bot. Nat. Belg.** 55: 301-392.

Dowsett-Lemaire F. 1989. Ecological and biogeographical aspects of forest bird communities in Malawi. **Scopus** 13: 1-80.

Dowsett-Lemaire F. & Dowsett R.J. 1998. Parallels between F. White's phytochoria and avian zoochoria in tropical Africa: an analysis of the forest elements. Pages 87-96 in: Huxley C.R., Lock J.M. & Cutler D.F. (eds). **Chorology, Taxonomy and Ecology of the Floras of Africa and Madagascar.** Kew, UK: Royal Botanic Gardens.

Dowsett-Lemaire F., Dowsett R.J. & Dyer M. 2001. Malawi. Pages 539-555 in :Fishpool L.D.C. & Evans M.I. (eds.) **Important Bird Areas in Africa and associated islands: Priority sites for conservation.** Newbury and Cambridge, UK: Pisces Publications and BirdLife International (BirdLife Conservation Series No. 11).

Fanshawe D.B. 1961. Evergreen Forest relics in Northern Rhodesia. **Kirkia** 1: 20-24.

Farmer L. 1992. **A visitor's guide to the Kasanka National Park.** Lusaka: Kasanka Trust.

Ferrar T. 1998. Draft Master Plan for the Development of Zambia's Protected Areas. EDF/NPWS Sustainable Wildlife Management Project.

Fisher M. 1991. **Nswana - The Heir.** Ndola: The Mission Press.

Fishpool L.D.C. & Evans M.I. (eds.) 2001. **Important Bird Areas in Africa and associated islands: Priority sites for conservation.** Newbury and Cambridge, UK: Pisces Publications and BirdLife International (BirdLife Conservation Series No. 11).

FitzPatrick M.J. 1999. Review of the current knowledge on Odonata associated with wetlands and flood plains of the Zambezi Basin. (unpublished report for Biodiversity Foundation for Africa, Bulawayo).

Friis I. 1991. Urticaceae. Pages 79-116 in: Launert E. & Pope G.V. (eds.) **Flora Zambesiaca** 9 (6).

Goodwin D. 1965. Some remarks on the new barbet. **Bull. Brit. Ornithol. Club** 85: 9-10.

Hartley R. 1993. The Batoka Gorge - a haven for birds of prey. **African Wildlife** 47: 74-78.

Hartley R. 2000a. Ecology of Taita, Peregrine and Lanner Falcons in Zimbabwe. Pages 87-105 in Chancellor R.D. & Meyburg B-U. **Raptors at Risk. Proc. of V World Conference on Birds of Prey.**

Hartley R. 2000b. Zimbabwe Falconers' Club Research Report. **Talon** 20: 17.

Harvey D. 1997. Checklist of the birds of Shiwa Ng'andu. (unpublished).

Heath A., Newport M.A. & Hancock D., 2002. **The butterflies of Zambia.** Nairobi: African Butterfly Research Institute/Lepidopterists' Society of Africa. CD-ROM

Howard G.W. 1989. Recent counts of Wattled Cranes *Bugeranus carunculatus* on the Kafue Flats, Zambia - November 1987. **Scopus** 12: 69-72.

Howard G.W. & Aspinwall D.R. 1984. Aerial censuses of Shoebills, Saddlebilled Storks and Wattled Cranes at the Bangweulu Swamps and Kafue Flats, Zambia. **Ostrich** 55: 207-212.

Howard G.W. & Chabwela H.N. 1986. Red

Lechwe of Busanga Plain, 1985. (unpublished report to the Director, National Parks and Wildlife Service, Chilanga, Zambia, January 1986).

Howard P.C., Viskanic P., Davenport T.R.B., Kigenyi F.W., Baltzer M., Dickinson C.J., Lwanga J.S., Matthews R.A. & Balmford A. 1998. Complementarity and the use of indicator groups for reserve selection in Uganda. **Nature** 394: 472-475.

IUCN 1994. **Guidelines for protected area management categories.** Gland, Switzerland/Cambridge, UK: International Union for Conservation of Nature and Natural Resources.

Jachmann H. 2000. **Zambia's Wildlife Resources: A Brief Ecology.** Lusaka: Wildlife Resource Monitoring Unit, Environmental Council of Zambia.

Jeffery R.C.V. 1992. The Kafue Flats of Zambia: a case study. Pages 57-70 in Matiza T. & Chabwela H.N. (eds.) **Proc. of Wetlands Conservation Conference for Southern Africa.**

Jeffery R.C.V., Bell R.H.V. & Ansell W.F.H. 1989. Chapter 4: Zambia. Pages 11-19 in East R. (ed.) **Antelopes Global survey and regional action plans.** Part 2: Southern and South-central Africa. Gland: IUCN.

Jeffery R., Owens D., Owens M. & Dooley B. 1996. Chapter 7: Zambia. Pages 33-56 in East R. (ed.) **Antelope survey update** No. 2. Antelope Specialist Group. Gland: IUCN.

Kamweneshe B. & Beilfuss R. 2002. Population and distribution of Wattled Cranes and other large waterbirds on the Kafue Flats, Zambia. Working Paper #1. Zambia Crane and Wetland Conservation Project, International Crane Foundation, Baraboo, Wisconsin USA. **www.savingcranes.org**

Kamweneshe B. & Beilfuss R. 2002. Wattled Cranes, waterbirds, and large mammals of the Lukanga Swamp, Zambia. Working Paper #7. Zambia Crane and Wetland Conservation Project, International Crane Foundation, Baraboo, Wisconsin USA. **www.savingcranes.org**

Kamweneshe B. & Beilfuss R. 2002. Wattled

Cranes, waterbirds, and large mammals of the Liuwa Plain National Park, Zambia. Working Paper #9. Zambia Crane and Wetland Conservation Project, International Crane Foundation, Baraboo, Wisconsin USA. **www.savingcranes.org**

Kamweneshe B., Beilfuss R. & Simukonda C. 2002. Population and distribution of Kafue lechwe and other large mammals on the Kafue flats, Zambia. Working Paper #6 Zambia Crane and Wetland Conservation Project, International Crane Foundation, Baraboo, Wisconsin USA. **www.savingcranes.org**

Kingdon J. 1997. **The Kingdon Field Guide to African Mammals.** London: Academic Press.

La Croix I.F., La Croix E.A.S. & La Croix T.M. 1991. **Orchids of Malawi.** Rotterdam, The Netherlands: Balkema.

Lamb C. 1999. **The Africa House.** London: Penguin.

Leonard P.M. 1998a. New to Zambia: Greater Spotted Eagle *Aquila clanga.* **Zambia Bird Report** 1997: 3-5.

Leonard P.M. 1998b. Forest birds in Western Zambezi District. **Zambia Bird Report** 1997: 12-22.

Leonard P.M. 1998c. Recent changes to the Zambian list. **Zambia Bird Report** 1997: 50.

Leonard P.M. 1999a. Recent changes to the Zambian list. **Zambia Bird Report** 1998: 106-107.

Leonard P.M. 1999b. Jacobin Cuckoos *Clamator jacobinus* in papyrus swamp. **Zambia Bird Report** 1998: 109.

Leonard P.M. 2001a. Recent changes to the Zambian list. **Zambia Bird Report** 1999: 85.

Leonard P.M. 2001b. Zambia. Pages 1005-1024 in: Fishpool L.D.C. & Evans M.I. (eds.) **Important Bird Areas in Africa and associated islands: Priority sites for conservation.** Newbury and Cambridge, UK: Pisces Publications and BirdLife International (BirdLife Conservation Series No. 11).

Leonard P.M. 2003. Zambian list hits 750! **Newsletter Zam. Orn. Soc.** 33 (11): 2.

Leonard P.M. (in prep.) Birds of Lusenga Plain National Park.

Leonard P.M. & Beel C. 1996a. Lake Lufira Weaver *Ploceus reichardi* - New to Zambia. **Newsletter Zam. Orn. Soc.** 26 (1): 3-5.

Leonard P.M. & Beel C. 1996b. White-winged Warbler *Bradypterus carpalis* - New to Zambia (and the saga of its discovery). **Newsletter Zam. Orn. Soc.** 26 (12): 139-140.

Leonard P.M. & Beel C. 1999. Two new resident birds in northern Zambia. **Bull. A.B.C.** 6(1): 56-58.

Leonard P.M. & Colebrook-Robjent J. F. R. (in prep.) Changes in the status of some birds in Choma District.

Leonard P.M. & Peters W. 1998. 1997 Species Records. **Zambia Bird Report** 1997: 59-139.

Leonard P.M. & Van Daele P. 1999a. Mwinilunga's Marginal Forests. **Zambia Bird Report** 1998: 1-11.

Leonard P.M. & Van Daele P. 1999b. New to Zambia: Shrike-Flycatcher *Megabyas flammulatus*. **Zambia Bird Report** 1998: 89-92.

Leonard P.M. & Van Daele P. 2001. Baglafecht Weavers *Ploceus baglafecht* near Mbala. **Zambia Bird Report** 1999: 98.

Leonard P.M., Van Daele P. & Beel C. 2001a. Birds of the Mafinga Mountains. **Zambia Bird Report** 1999: 6-15.

Leonard P.M., Van Daele P. & Beel C. 2001b. New to Zambia: White-throated Bee-eater *Merops albicollis*. **Zambia Bird Report** 1999: 73-76.

Leonard P.M., Beel C. & Peters W. 2001c. 1999 Species Records. **Zambia Bird Report** 1999: 100-193.

May J. & Lindholm R. 2002. A Report by the WECSZ Sitatunga Project on the status of sitatunga and management options for the Kasonso - Busanga GMA & Kafue National Park. (unpublished report to ZAWA and the local communities).

McIntyre C. 1999. **Zambia - The Bradt Travel Guide.** Chalfont St. Peter, UK: Bradt.

Oatley, T. B. 1969. Bird Ecology in the Evergreen Forests of North-western Zambia. **Puku** 5: 141-180.

Osborne, T. O. 1978. Notes on the birds of Liuwa National Park and Preliminary Checklist. **Bull. Zambian Orn. Soc.** 10: 8-24.

Payne R.B., Hustler K., Stjernstedt R., Sefc K.M. & Sorenson M.D. 2002. Behavioural and genetic evidence of a recent population switch to a novel host species in brood-parasitic indigobirds Vidua chalybeata. **Ibis** 144: 373-383

Phillipson D.W. (ed.) 1975. **Mosi-Oa-Tunya: A handbook to the Victoria Falls region.** London: Longman.

Phillipson D.W. & Katanekwa N.M. 1992. **National Monuments of Zambia.** (4th revised edn.) Livingstone: National Heritage Conservation Commission.

Pinhey E. 1984. A checklist of the Odonata of Zimbabwe and Zambia. **Smithersia** 3: 1 - 64.

Reader J. 1998. **Africa - A Biography of the Continent.** London: Penguin.

Renson G. 1998. Observations sur la reproduction du Bec-en-sabot *Balaeniceps rex* en Zambie de 1992 à 1997. **Alauda** 66: 81-96.

Robinson S, Van Daele P. & Van De Woestijne C. 2001. New to Zambia: Spur-winged Plover *Vanellus spinosus*. **Zambia Bird Report** 1999: 69-72.

Schüle P. 2002. *Prothymidia sibyllae* sp. nov. from Zambia (Coleoptera, Cicindelidae). **Entomologische Zeitschrift** 12 (10): 306-309.

Scott A.J. 1993. A revised and annotated checklist of the birds of the Luangwa Valley National Parks and adjacent areas. **Occ. Paper Zambian Orn. Soc.** 3: 1-52

Smith P.P. 1997. A preliminary checklist of the vascular plants of the North Luangwa National Park, Zambia. **Kirkia** 16 (2): 205-245.

Smith P. 2003. A reconnaissance survey of the vegetation of Mutinondo Wilderness Area. **www.mutinondozambia.com**

Stattersfield A.J., Crosby M.J., Long A.J. & Wege D.C. 1998. **Endemic bird areas of the world: priorities for bird conservation.** Cambridge, UK: BirdLife International (BirdLife Conservation Series 7).

Stjernstedt R. 1998. Brown Firefinch Indigobirds near Livingstone. **Zambia Bird Report** 1997: 51.

Stjernstedt R. 2003. Cloud Cisticola in Sesheke District. **Zambia Orn. Soc. Newsletter** 33 (4): 4.

Storrs A.E.G. 1979. **Know your Trees.** 1995 reprint, Lusaka: Regional Soil Conservation Unit.

Stuart C. & Stuart T. 2003a. Preliminary Checklists of the Vertebrates occurring in the vicinity of Shoebill Camp. **African-Arabian Wildlife Research Centre - Checklist Series** 6: 1-19.

Stuart C. & Stuart T. 2003b. Checklists of the Wildlife of Kasanka National Park. **African-Arabian Wildlife Research Centre - Checklist Series** 8: 1-53.

Timberlake J.R. (ed.) 2000. **Biodiversity of the Zambezi Basin Wetlands.** Consultancy report for IUCN ROSA. Biodiversity Foundation for Africa, Bulawayo/The Zambezi Society, Harare.

Tree A.J. 1966a. Some recent bird observations from the north Kafue basin. **Ostrich** 37(1): 30-36.

Tree A.J. 1966b. Notes on palaearctic migrants in the north Kafue basin, Zambia. **Ostrich** 37(3): 184-190.

Tucker G.M. & Heath M.F. 1994. **Birds in Europe: their conservation status.** BirdLife Conservation Series No. 2 Cambridge, UK: BirdLife International.

Tumbare M.J. 2000. **Management of River Basins and Dams: The Zambezi River Basin.** Rotterdam, Netherlands: A. A. Balkema.

Turner B. 1986. **Lochinvar National Park** (map). Kafue Basin Research Project, University of Zambia. Published by the Surveyor General, Survey Dept. Lusaka, Zambia.

Van Daele P. 1999a. A sight record of Grey Kestrel *Falco ardosiaceus* in Mwinilunga District. **Zambia Bird Report** 1998: 98-102.

Van Daele P. 1999b. An active nest of Woolly-necked Stork *Ciconia episcopus*. **Zambia Bird Report** 1998: 107-108.

Van Daele P. 2001. Presumed breeding of Avocet *Recurvirostra avosetta* on the Zambezi River in Western Province. **Zambia Bird Report** 1999: 91-92.

Van Daele P. & Leonard P.M. 2001. The Status of Great Crested Grebes *Podiceps cristatus* in Zambia. **Zambia Bird Report** 1999: 88-90.

Van Daele P. & Stjernstedt R. 2001. Bird Surveys of the Barotse Floodplains. **Zambia Bird Report** 1999: 58-68.

van Lavieren L.P. 1973. Shoebill Stork (*Balaeniceps rex*) in Lukanga Swamp. **Bull. Zambian Orn. Soc.** 5: 79.

Warburton L. 1999. Black-cheeked Lovebirds in the wild. **PsittaScene** 11 (2): 8-10.

Warburton L. 2002. Black-cheeked Lovebirds: Africa's most threatened Lovebird. **Africa Birds & Birding** 7 (1): 52-59.

Warburton L. 2003. **The Ecology and Conservation Biology of the Black-cheeked Lovebird *Agapornis nigrigenis* in Zambia.** PhD thesis, University of Natal, Pietermaritzburg, South Africa.

Weaver J., Dunkley A. & Hartley R. R. 2002. Taita Falcon Surveys in the 1980s. **Honeyguide** 48 (2): 175-180.

Wetlands International. 2002. **Waterbird Population Estimates** (Third Edition). Wetlands International Global Series No. 12, Wageningen, The Netherlands.

White F. 1983. **The vegetation of Africa: a descriptive memoir to accompany the UNESCO/AETFAT/UNSO vegetation map of Africa.** Paris: UNESCO.

6. Appendices

Appendix 1: IBA checklists

The following table presents bird checklists for every Important Bird Area in Zambia. They are marked against a complete Zambian list, including scientific names. The table merely indicates whether or not a species has been recorded at a site and unfortunately it has not been possible to give any indication of abundance. Species' conservation status is given with columns for the three main threat categories, namely: Globally threatened species, Restricted-range species and Biome-restriced species.

Where sites comprise two or more discrete areas, these have been given separate checklists. For example, IBA 5: West Lunga NP & Lukwakwa GMA has one list for the National Park and another for the Game Management Area.

Two distinctive subspecies have been included on the table: 'Long-tailed' Neddicky *Cisticola fulvicapilla angusticauda* and 'Katanga' Masked Weaver *Ploceus velatus katangae*. These taxa are treated as separate species and Zambezian endemics by Fishpool & Evans (2001) but here they are treated as races of Neddicky *Cisticola fulvicapilla* and African Masked Weaver *Ploceus velatus* respectively. They are therefore not included in the Zambezian biome list totals. However, seeing as both species are represented by other forms within Zambia, it seems prudent to keep the forms separate in the table for the time being.

Although not currently an IBA, Luambe National Park has been added to the table. This is partly for the sake of completeness, as every other Zambian National Park *is* an IBA and included. It is also to encourage fieldworkers to collect data so that in time Luambe may prove to be a suitable IBA.

It is obvious from the totals that some sites have received more fieldwork than others. Furthermore, some sites have been visited frequently, yet comprehensive data have not been kept. This table highlights those areas that require work and all bird records from IBAs should be sent to the Zambian Ornithological Society. Contact details at the back of the book.

■ **Notes and abbreviations**

Globally threatened species

VU Vulnerable
nt   near-threatened
DD data-deficient

Restricted-range species

RR Restricted-range

Biome-restricted Species

A Afromontane endemic
a Afromontane near-endemic
e Eastern near-endemic
g Guineo-Congolian near-endemic
l Lake Victoria Basin near-endemic
s Sub-Afromontane endemic
Z Zambezian endemic
z Zambezian near-endemic

*   The Kafue Flats list (15a) is a combined list covering the entire Kafue Flats IBA and incorporating the lists for Lochinvar NP, Blue Lagoon NP and Mwanachingwala Conservation Area.

** The Bangweulu Swamps list (28a) covers the entire IBA except Isangano NP which is listed separately.

Species	Globally threatened species	Restricted-range species	Biome-restricted species	1 Hillwood	2 Source of the Zambezi	3 Chitunta Plain	4 Jimbe Drainage	5a West Lunga NP	5b Lukwakwa GMA	6 Minyanya Plain	7 Mbulo Forest	8 Liuwa Plain NP	9 Barotse Floodplains	10 Sioma Ngwezi NP	11 Simungoma	12 Machile	13a Mosi-Oa-Tunya NP	13b Batoka Gorge	14 Kafue NP
Little Grebe *Tachybaptus ruficollis*				•		•		•				•	•	•	•		•		•
Great Crested Grebe *Podiceps cristatus*																			
White-breasted Cormorant *Phalacrocorax carbo*													•				•		•
Reed Cormorant *Phalacrocorax africanus*				•		•		•				•	•	•	•	•	•	•	•
Darter *Anhinga rufa*								•				•	•	•	•		•		•
White Pelican *Pelecanus onocrotalus*				•								•	•	•	•				•
Pink-backed Pelican *Pelecanus rufescens*												•	•	•	•				•
Common Bittern *Botaurus stellaris*													•						
Little Bittern *Ixobrychus minutus*								•		•			•	•			•		•
Dwarf Bittern *Ixobrychus sturmii*				•	•			•					•			•	•	•	•
Black-crowned Night Heron *Nycticorax nycticorax*				•				•	•	•		•	•		•		•		•
White-backed Night Heron *Gorsachius leuconotus*								•					•				•		•
Common Squacco Heron *Ardeola ralloides*								•				•	•	•	•	•	•		•
Madagascar Squacco Heron *Ardeola idae*	VU																		
Rufous-bellied Heron *Ardeola rufiventris*				•			•	•	•	•		•	•	•			•		•
Cattle Egret *Bubulcus ibis*				•	•	•	•	•		•		•	•	•			•		•
Green-backed Heron *Butorides striata*				•				•				•	•		•		•		•
Black Egret *Egretta ardesiaca*												•	•	•			•		•
Slaty Egret *Egretta vinaceigula*	VU		Z					•				•	•	•			•		•
Little Egret *Egretta garzetta*								•				•	•	•			•		•
Yellow-billed Egret *Egretta intermedia*								•	•			•	•	•			•		•
Great White Egret *Egretta alba*				•				•	•			•	•	•	•		•		•
Purple Heron *Ardea purpurea*				•				•		•		•	•	•			•		•
Grey Heron *Ardea cinerea*				•				•		•		•	•	•	•		•	•	•
Black-headed Heron *Ardea melanocephala*				•								•	•				•		•
Goliath Heron *Ardea goliath*				•				•				•	•			•	•		•
Hamerkop *Scopus umbretta*				•		•	•	•	•	•		•	•	•	•		•		•
Yellow-billed Stork *Mycteria ibis*				•				•				•	•				•		•
Openbill Stork *Anastomus lamelligerus*				•		•		•				•	•	•	•		•	•	•
Black Stork *Ciconia nigra*																	•	•	•
Abdim's Stork *Ciconia abdimii*				•		•		•				•	•				•		•
Woolly-necked Stork *Ciconia episcopus*				•	•	•	•	•	•	•	•						•		•
White Stork *Ciconia ciconia*				•									•				•		•
Saddle-billed Stork *Ephippiorhynchus senegalensis*				•				•	•	•		•	•	•			•		•
Marabou Stork *Leptoptilos crumeniferus*				•			•	•	•	•		•	•	•	•		•		•
Shoebill *Balaeniceps rex*	nt																		
Sacred Ibis *Threskiornis aethiopicus*												•	•		•	•	•		•
Glossy Ibis *Plegadis falcinellus*												•	•		•		•		•
Hadada *Bostrychia hagedash*				•	•	•		•		•	•	•	•	•			•	•	•
African Spoonbill *Platalea alba*								•				•	•		•	•	•		•
Greater Flamingo *Phoenicopterus ruber*												•	•						
Lesser Flamingo *Phoeniconaias minor*	nt												•				•		•
Fulvous Whistling Duck *Dendrocygna bicolor*								•					•		•		•		•
White-faced Whistling Duck *D. viduata*				•				•				•	•	•	•		•		•
White-backed Duck *Thalassornis leuconotus*								•					•	•	•	•	•		•
Egyptian Goose *Alopochen aegyptiaca*								•				•	•		•	•	•		•
Spur-winged Goose *Plectropterus gambensis*				•				•	•	•		•	•	•	•	•	•		•
Knob-billed Duck *Sarkidiornis melanotos*				•				•				•	•	•	•	•	•		•
African Pygmy Goose *Nettapus auritus*								•				•	•	•		•	•		•
African Black Duck *Anas sparsa*				•			•	•									•		•
Yellow-billed Duck *Anas undulata*				•		•		•	•			•	•				•		•
Cape Teal *Anas capensis*												•	•				•		
Pintail *Anas acuta*																			
Red-billed Teal *Anas erythrorhyncha*								•	•			•	•	•	•	•	•		•

15a Kafue Flats*	15b Lochinvar NP	15c Blue Lagoon NP	15d MCA	16 Nkanga R. Cons. Area	17 Mutulanganga	18 Lower Zambezi NP	19 Chisamba	20 Lukanga Swamp	21 Imanda	22 Chimfunshi W. O.	23 North Swaka	24 Wonder Gorge	25 Kasanka NP	26 Lavushi Manda NP	27 Mutinondo Wilderness	28a Bangweulu Swamps	28b Isangano NP	29 North Luangwa NP	30 Shiwa Ng'andu	31 Luapula Mouth	32 Lusenga Plain NP	33 Kalungwishi	34 Mweru Wantipa NP	35a Sumbu NP	35b Tondwa GMA	36 Saise River	37 Uningi Pans	38 Nyika NP	39 Mafinga Mountains	40 South Luangwa NP	41 Lukususi NP	42 Nyanje Hills	Luambe NP
•	•	•	•	•	•	•	•	•					•		•	•			•	•		•	•		•		•			•			
																											•						
•	•	•	•	•		•	•	•					•			•								•	•					•			
•	•	•	•	•		•	•	•		•			•	•		•	•	•	•	•	•		•	•	•	•	•			•			
•	•	•	•	•		•	•	•		•			•	•		•	•	•	•				•	•	•		•			•			
•	•	•	•	•		•	•	•		•			•			•	•	•	•	•			•	•	•					•			
•	•	•	•	•		•	•	•					•			•		•	•	•			•	•	•		•			•			
•		•						•								•																	
•	•	•	•	•		•	•	•		•			•			•	•		•	•			•		•					•			
•	•	•		•		•	•	•		•			•	•	•	•			•			•								•			
•	•	•	•	•		•	•	•					•			•	•	•	•	•				•	•	•	•			•			
				•		•							•	•	•		•	•					•							•			•
•	•	•	•	•		•	•	•		•			•			•	•	•	•	•			•	•	•		•			•	•		
•	•																		•					•						•			
•	•	•	•	•		•	•	•		•			•			•		•	•	•			•	•	•	•	•			•			
•	•	•	•	•	•	•	•	•	•	•	•		•		•	•	•	•	•	•	•	•		•	•	•	•	•		•	•	•	•
•	•		•	•		•	•	•		•			•	•	•	•	•	•	•	•	•			•						•	•		•
•	•	•	•	•		•	•	•					•			•		•	•						•					•			
•	•	•		•		•	•									•																	
•	•	•	•	•		•	•	•	•	•			•			•	•	•	•	•			•	•	•	•	•			•	•		•
•	•	•	•	•		•	•	•					•			•		•	•	•			•	•	•	•	•			•			
•	•	•	•	•		•	•	•	•	•			•		•	•	•	•	•	•			•	•	•		•			•	•		•
•	•	•	•	•		•	•	•		•			•			•	•	•	•	•	•			•	•	•	•			•			
•	•	•	•	•		•	•	•		•			•			•	•	•	•	•			•	•	•	•	•			•			•
•	•	•	•	•		•	•			•						•		•	•				•	•	•		•			•		•	
•	•	•	•	•		•	•	•		•			•			•	•	•	•				•	•	•		•			•	•		•
•	•	•	•	•	•	•	•	•	•	•		•	•	•	•	•	•	•	•	•	•	•	•	•	•	•	•	•		•	•	•	•
•	•	•	•	•		•	•	•		•			•			•		•	•	•			•	•	•		•			•			•
•	•	•	•	•		•	•	•		•			•			•	•	•	•	•			•	•	•			•		•			•
				•		•	•								•			•	•											•		•	
•	•	•	•	•		•	•	•	•	•	•		•		•	•	•	•	•			•		•	•	•		•		•		•	
•	•	•	•	•		•	•	•	•	•	•		•	•	•	•	•	•	•		•		•	•	•					•			
•	•	•	•	•		•	•	•					•	•	•	•		•										•		•	•		
•	•	•	•	•		•	•	•		•			•			•	•	•	•		•		•	•	•		•			•			•
•	•	•	•	•	•	•	•	•		•			•		•	•	•	•	•	•			•	•	•					•			•
								•					•			•							•	•	•								
•	•	•	•	•		•	•	•		•			•			•		•	•				•	•	•		•			•			•
•	•	•	•	•		•	•	•		•			•			•		•	•	•		•	•		•		•	•		•			
•	•			•	•	•	•	•	•	•	•		•	•		•	•	•	•	•	•	•	•	•	•					•			•
•	•	•	•	•		•	•	•		•			•			•		•	•				•	•	•					•			•
•	•					•										•			•				•							•			
•	•			•												•		•					•	•	•					•			
•	•	•	•	•		•	•	•					•			•		•		•					•					•			
[illegible]	•	•	•	•	•	•	•	•		•			•		•	•		•		•			•	•	•		•			•			
[illegible]	•	•		•			•	•					•			•			•						•		•			•			
[illegible]	•	•	•	•		•	•	•		•			•			•		•	•	•			•	•						•	•		•
[illegible]	•	•	•	•		•	•	•		•	•		•	•	•	•	•	•	•	•	•		•	•	•	•	•			•			
[illegible]	•	•	•	•	•	•	•	•		•			•		•	•	•	•	•	•		•		•	•	•	•			•	•		•
[illegible]	•	•	•	•		•	•	•		•	•		•			•	•	•	•	•					•		•			•			
[illegible]	•			•			•	•			•		•		•																•		
[illegible]	•	•	•	•			•	•		•			•			•	•		•	•	•		•		•	•	•						
[illegible]	•																																
[illegible]	•						•																										
[illegible]	•	•	•	•			•	•					•			•		•	•		•	•			•		•			•			
[illegible]																																	

Species	Globally threatened species	Restricted-range species	Biome-restricted species	1 Hillwood	2 Source of the Zambezi	3 Chitunta Plain	4 Jimbe Drainage	5a West Lunga NP	5b Lukwakwa GMA	6 Mimyanya Plain	7 Mbulo Forest	8 Liuwa Plain NP	9 Barotse Floodplains	10 Sioma Ngwezi NP	11 Simungoma	12 Machile	13a Mosi-Oa-Tunya NP	13b Batoka Gorge	14 Kafue NP
Hottentot Teal *Anas hottentota*								•				•	•	•	•		•		•
Garganey *Anas querquedula*																			
Northern Shoveler *Anas clypeata*																			
Cape Shoveler *Anas smithii*																	•		
Southern Pochard *Netta erythrophthalma*												•	•		•		•		•
African Cuckoo Hawk *Aviceda cuculoides*				•			•	•					•		•		•	•	•
Honey Buzzard *Pernis apivorus*							•	•									•		•
Bat Hawk *Macheiramphus alcinus*				•				•				•	•				•	•	•
Black-shouldered Kite *Elanus caeruleus*				•		•	•	•	•	•	•	•	•	•	•	•	•		•
Black/Yellow-billed Kite *Milvus migrans*				•	•	•	•	•	•	•	•	•	•	•	•	•	•	•	•
African Fish Eagle *Haliaeetus vocifer*				•			•	•	•			•	•	•	•	•	•	•	•
Palm-nut Vulture *Gypohierax angolensis*				•						•		•	•						
Hooded Vulture *Necrosyrtes monachus*				•		•		•				•	•		•	•	•		•
African White-backed Vulture *Gyps africanus*				•				•	•			•	•		•	•	•		•
Rüppell's Vulture *Gyps rueppellii*																			
Cape Vulture *Gyps coprotheres*	VU																		•
Lappet-faced Vulture *Torgos tracheliotus*	VU							•	•			•	•		•	•	•		•
White-headed Vulture *Trigonoceps occipitalis*				•		•	•	•		•	•	•	•		•	•	•		•
Black-breasted Snake Eagle *Circaetus pectoralis*				•			•	•	•	•		•	•		•	•	•		•
Brown Snake Eagle *Circaetus cinereus*				•	•	•	•	•	•	•	•	•	•		•	•	•		•
Western Banded Snake Eagle *Circaetus cinerascens*				•	•	•	•	•	•	•	•	•		•		•	•		•
Bateleur *Terathopius ecaudatus*				•	•	•	•	•	•	•		•	•	•	•	•	•		•
Gymnogene *Polyboroides typus*				•	•	•	•	•	•	•	•	•	•	•		•	•		•
European Marsh Harrier *Circus aeruginosus*						•						•							
African Marsh Harrier *Circus ranivorus*				•		•		•				•	•		•		•		•
Pallid Harrier *Circus macrourus*	nt			•								•	•				•		•
Montagu's Harrier *Circus pygargus*												•	•						•
Dark Chanting Goshawk *Melierax metabates*				•	•	•	•			•	•	•		•	•	•	•		•
Gabar Goshawk *Melierax gabar*				•			•	•				•	•	•	•	•	•	•	•
Black Goshawk *Accipiter melanoleucus*				•	•		•	•									•		•
Ovambo Sparrowhawk *Accipiter ovampensis*				•				•		•									•
Red-breasted Sparrowhawk *Accipiter rufiventris*			a																
Little Sparrowhawk *Accipiter minullus*				•				•	•	•				•		•	•	•	•
African Goshawk *Accipiter tachiro*				•	•		•	•			•		•				•	•	•
Shikra *Accipiter badius*				•	•					•	•	•		•			•		•
Lizard Buzzard *Kaupifalco monogrammicus*				•	•	•	•	•	•		•	•		•	•	•	•		•
Common Buzzard *Buteo buteo*				•	•	•	•	•			•	•	•	•		•	•		•
Augur Buzzard *Buteo augur*																	•	•	
Wahlberg's Eagle *Aquila wahlbergi*				•	•	•	•	•		•	•	•	•	•		•	•		•
Lesser Spotted Eagle *Aquila pomarina*				•				•					•	•	•	•			•
Greater Spotted Eagle *Aquila clanga*	VU																		
Tawny Eagle *Aquila rapax*				•								•	•	•	•	•	•		•
Steppe Eagle *Aquila nipalensis*												•	•	•		•			•
Black Eagle *Aquila verreauxii*																	•	•	
African Hawk Eagle *Hieraaetus spilogaster*				•			•	•	•		•		•	•	•	•	•		•
Booted Eagle *Hieraaetus pennatus*				•									•				•		•
Ayres's Hawk Eagle *Hieraaetus ayresii*				•	•			•		•		•			•	•			•
Long-crested Eagle *Lophaetus occipitalis*				•			•	•	•	•		•	•	•		•	•		•
Crowned Eagle *Stephanoaetus coronatus*								•	•								•	•	•
Martial Eagle *Polemaetus bellicosus*				•			•	•	•	•		•	•	•	•	•	•		•
Osprey *Pandion haliaetus*								•					•				•		•
Secretary Bird *Sagittarius serpentarius*				•		•	•	•	•	•		•	•	•	•				
Lesser Kestrel *Falco naumanni*	VU						•	•				•	•		•		•		•
Common Kestrel *Falco tinnunculus*												•	•						•
Greater Kestrel *Falco rupicoloides*										•		•	•		•				•

15a Kafue Flats*	15b Lochinvar NP	15c Blue Lagoon NP	15d MCA	16 Nkanga R. Cons. Area	17 Mutulanganga	18 Lower Zambezi NP	19 Chisamba	20 Lukanga Swamp	21 Imanda	22 Chimfunshi W. O.	23 North Swaka	24 Wonder Gorge	25 Kasanka NP	26 Lavushi Manda NP	27 Mutinondo Wilderness	28a Bangweulu Swamps	28b Isangano NP	29 North Luangwa NP	30 Shiwa Ng'andu	31 Luapula Mouth	32 Lusenga Plain NP	33 Kalungwishi	34 Mweru Wantipa NP	35a Sumbu NP	35b Tondwa GMA	36 Saise River	37 Uningi Pans	38 Nyika NP	39 Mafinga Mountains	40 South Luangwa NP	41 Lukususi NP	42 Nyanje Hills	Luambe NP
•	•	•	•	•			•	•					•			•				•					•	•	•			•			
•	•	•					•									•														•			
•	•																																
•	•																																
•	•	•	•	•		•	•	•					•	•	•	•		•		•					•		•			•			
•	•	•	•	•	•	•	•		•	•			•		•	•		•	•					•						•		•	•
•	•		•	•	•	•	•				•		•						•											•	•		
•	•			•	•	•		•	•						•			•	•								•			•			•
•	•	•	•	•	•	•	•	•	•	•	•		•		•	•		•	•	•		•			•	•	•	•		•	•	•	•
•	•	•	•	•	•	•	•	•	•	•	•	•	•	•	•	•	•	•	•	•	•		•	•	•	•	•	•	•	•	•	•	•
•	•	•	•	•		•	•	•		•			•	•	•	•	•	•	•	•	•		•	•	•					•	•		•
						•					•			•	•			•	•	•		•	•	•			•			•			
•	•	•	•	•	•	•	•		•	•			•	•	•	•		•	•	•		•	•	•	•	•		•		•		•	•
•	•	•	•	•	•	•	•	•		•	•	•	•	•	•	•		•		•		•		•	•	•	•	•		•	•	•	•
																														•			
•	•		•													•																	
•	•	•	•	•	•	•	•						•		•	•		•	•		•			•				•		•			•
•	•	•	•	•	•	•	•	•	•	•		•	•		•	•		•	•			•		•	•	•		•		•	•	•	•
•	•	•	•	•	•	•	•	•	•	•	•	•	•		•	•		•	•	•		•		•	•	•	•			•	•	•	
•	•	•	•	•	•	•	•	•	•		•		•		•	•		•	•	•		•		•	•	•	•	•		•		•	•
•	•			•	•	•		•	•	•	•		•		•	•		•	•	•	•	•	•	•	•					•			•
•	•	•	•	•	•	•	•	•	•	•	•	•	•	•	•	•	•	•	•	•	•	•	•	•	•	•	•	•		•	•	•	•
•	•	•	•	•	•	•	•	•	•	•	•	•	•		•	•		•	•	•				•	•	•	•	•	•	•	•	•	•
•	•	•	•										•		•	•			•			•					•			•			
•	•	•	•	•		•	•	•	•	•	•		•	•	•	•	•	•	•	•	•	•	•	•	•	•	•	•		•			
•	•	•	•	•		•	•	•					•			•												•		•			
•	•	•	•	•			•						•		•	•		•										•		•			
•	•	•	•	•		•	•	•	•	•	•	•	•	•	•	•		•	•		•	•	•							•	•	•	
•	•	•	•	•	•	•	•	•		•			•	•	•	•	•	•		•										•		•	
•	•			•	•	•	•	•		•			•	•		•	•	•	•									•		•			
•	•	•		•		•	•	•			•		•	•	•			•	•				•							•		•	
																												•					
•	•	•	•	•	•	•	•		•		•		•		•	•		•	•											•	•	•	
•	•	•	•	•	•	•	•	•	•	•			•			•		•	•		•		•	•				•	•	•		•	
•	•	•	•	•	•	•	•	•	•	•	•	•	•		•	•	•	•	•		•	•		•						•	•	•	•
•	•	•	•	•	•	•	•	•	•	•	•	•	•	•	•	•	•	•	•	•		•	•		•	•		•		•	•	•	•
•	•	•	•	•	•	•	•	•	•	•	•	•	•		•	•	•	•	•		•	•	•	•		•	•	•	•	•		•	
						•					•	•		•	•			•	•									•	•	•		•	
•	•	•	•	•	•	•	•	•	•	•	•	•	•	•	•	•	•	•	•	•	•	•	•		•	•	•	•	•	•	•	•	•
•	•	•	•	•	•	•	•	•		•	•		•		•				•				•	•						•			
																		•												•			
•	•	•	•	•		•	•						•			•		•					•							•	•		
•	•		•	•	•	•	•	•			•		•		•	•			•		•									•		•	
						•					•	•		•	•																	•	
•	•		•	•	•	•	•	•	•		•		•		•	•		•	•			•		•		•				•	•	•	•
•	•			•	•		•									•				•				•				•		•			
•	•			•	•	•	•	•	•	•	•		•		•	•		•	•	•	•	•						•		•			•
	•	•	•	•		•	•	•		•	•		•	•	•	•		•	•	•		•	•	•	•	•	•	•		•			•
				•		•	•		•	•			•	•	•				•				•	•				•	•	•	•		
	•	•	•	•		•	•	•		•			•		•	•		•	•	•			•	•			•	•		•	•	•	•
	•		•	•		•	•			•			•			•			•	•				•						•			•
	•	•		•		•	•						•			•							•	•						•	•		
	•	•	•	•	•	•	•	•					•		•	•				•							•	•		•	•	•	
	•	•																										•	•				
	•	•		•																													

	Globally threatened species	Restricted-range species	Biome-restricted species	1 Hillwood	2 Source of the Zambezi	3 Chitunta Plain	4 Jimbe Drainage	5a West Lunga NP	5b Lukwakwa GMA	6 Minyanya Plain	7 Mbulo Forest	8 Liuwa Plain NP	9 Barotse Floodplains	10 Sioma Ngwezi NP	11 Simungoma	12 Machile	13a Mosi-Oa-Tunya NP	13b Batoka Gorge	14 Kafue NP
Dickinson's Kestrel *Falco dickinsoni*			Z	•		•	•	•	•			•	•	•	•	•	•	•	•
Western Red-footed Falcon *Falco vespertinus*				•		•		•				•	•				•		•
Eastern Red-footed Falcon *Falco amurensis*						•		•						•			•		•
Red-necked Falcon *Falco chicquera*										•					•		•	•	•
European Hobby *Falco subbuteo*				•	•	•	•	•	•			•	•				•		•
African Hobby *Falco cuvierii*													•						•
Sooty Falcon *Falco concolor*						•											•	•	
Lanner Falcon *Falco biarmicus*				•				•	•			•	•	•	•		•	•	•
Taita Falcon *Falco fasciinucha*	nt																•	•	
Peregrine Falcon *Falco peregrinus*																	•	•	•
Coqui Francolin *Francolinus coqui*				•	•	•	•	•				•		•			•		•
White-throated Francolin *Francolinus albogularis*										•									
Crested Francolin *Francolinus sephaena*														•	•	•	•		•
Shelley's Francolin *Francolinus shelleyi*																	•	•	•
Red-winged Francolin *Francolinus levaillantii*										•			•						
Red-billed Francolin *Francolinus adspersus*													•	•	•				
Natal Francolin *Francolinus natalensis*																•	•	•	•
Hildebrandt's Francolin *Francolinus hildebrandti*																			
Swainson's Francolin *Francolinus swainsonii*													•	•			•		•
Red-necked Francolin *Francolinus afer*				•	•	•	•	•	•	•	•	•	•						•
Common Quail *Coturnix coturnix*													•						
Harlequin Quail *Coturnix delegorguei*				•		•	•	•		•		•	•	•	•		•		•
Blue Quail *Coturnix chinensis*				•		•	•	•	•				•				•		•
Crested Guineafowl *Guttera pucherani*				•		•	•	•					•		•		•		•
Helmeted Guineafowl *Numida meleagris*				•		•	•	•		•		•	•	•	•	•	•		•
Kurrichane Buttonquail *Turnix sylvaticus*				•		•	•	•				•	•				•		•
Black-rumped Buttonquail *Turnix hottentottus*				•		•		•	•	•		•	•				•		•
White-spotted Flufftail *Sarothrura pulchra*			g	•			•												
Buff-spotted Flufftail *Sarothrura elegans*				•			•	•	•								•		•
Red-chested Flufftail *Sarothrura rufa*								•		•			•	•					•
Long-toed Flufftail *Sarothrura lugens*																			
Streaky-breasted Flufftail *Sarothrura boehmi*																			
Red-tailed Flufftail *Sarothrura affinis*			a																
African Water Rail *Rallus caerulescens*													•		•		•		•
Corn Crake *Crex crex*	VU			•													•		•
African Crake *Crecopsis egregia*				•	•	•		•				•	•	•			•		•
Black Crake *Amaurornis flavirostra*				•			•	•	•	•		•	•	•	•	•	•		•
Baillon's Crake *Porzana pusilla*																	•		
Spotted Crake *Porzana porzana*																	•		•
Striped Crake *Aenigmatolimnas marginalis*				•				•									•		•
Purple Gallinule *Porphyrio porphyrio*													•	•					•
Lesser Gallinule *Porphyrula alleni*				•				•					•	•			•		•
Common Moorhen *Gallinula chloropus*								•				•	•		•				•
Lesser Moorhen *Gallinula angulata*				•									•		•				•
Red-knobbed Coot *Fulica cristata*								•				•	•				•		•
Wattled Crane *Grus carunculatus*	VU			•		•	•	•	•	•		•	•	•	•	•			•
Southern Crowned Crane *Balearica regulorum*						•						•	•	•					
African Finfoot *Podica senegalensis*							•	•					•				•		•
Denham's Bustard *Neotis denhami*	nt			•		•	•	•	•			•	•						•
Kori Bustard *Ardeotis kori*															•	•			
Red-crested Korhaan *Eupodotis ruficrista*												•		•	•				•
White-bellied Bustard *Eupodotis senegalensis*				•			•	•	•	•		•	•		•				•
Black-bellied Bustard *Eupodotis melanogaster*				•		•	•	•		•		•	•	•	•		•		•
African Jacana *Actophilornis africanus*				•		•		•				•	•	•	•		•		•
Lesser Jacana *Microparra capensis*							•					•	•				•	•	•

188

15a Kafue Flats*	15b Lochinvar NP	15c Blue Lagoon NP	15d MCA	16 Nkanga R. Cons. Area	17 Mutulanganga	18 Lower Zambezi NP	19 Chisamba	20 Lukanga Swamp	21 Imanda	22 Chimfunshi W. O.	23 North Swaka	24 Wonder Gorge	25 Kasanka NP	26 Lavushi Manda NP	27 Mutinondo Wilderness	28a Bangweulu Swamps	28b Isangano NP	29 North Luangwa NP	30 Shiwa Ng'andu	31 Luapula Mouth	32 Lusenga Plain NP	33 Kalungwishi	34 Mweru Wantipa NP	35a Sumbu NP	35b Tondwa GMA	36 Saise River	37 Uningi Pans	38 Nyika NP	39 Mafinga Mountains	40 South Luangwa NP	41 Lukususi NP	42 Nyanje Hills	Luambe NP
•	•	•	•	•		•	•	•	•	•	•		•		•	•	•	•	•	•		•				•	•			•	•		•
•	•	•	•	•												•												•					
•	•	•	•	•		•	•	•					•			•											•	•		•		•	
•	•	•	•	•		•	•									•		•		•			•					•		•			•
•	•	•	•	•	•		•	•	•	•	•		•		•	•			•	•		•	•	•	•		•	•	•	•	•	•	
•			•	•			•	•					•		•																		
				•																				•									
•	•	•	•	•		•	•	•		•	•				•	•		•	•	•						•	•	•	•	•		•	
												•																					
•	•	•	•	•		•	•				•	•			•	•								•						•		•	
•	•			•			•	•		•	•	•	•	•	•	•	•	•	•		•	•									•	•	
•	•			•	•	•																											
				•		•	•					•	•	•	•			•	•									•	•	•	•		
																												•					
•	•			•	•	•						•																		•		•	
															•			•					•	•				•	•				
•	•	•	•	•	•	•	•	•										•												•			•
•	•	•		•		•	•	•	•	•	•		•	•	•	•	•	•	•	•	•	•	•	•	•	•	•		•	•	•	•	•
•	•																											•	•				
•	•	•	•	•		•		•	•				•			•		•	•			•				•		•		•			•
•	•	•		•		•		•					•		•	•					•	•								•			
					•	•																		•						•			
•	•	•	•	•	•	•	•	•	•	•	•	•	•	•	•	•	•	•	•		•	•	•	•	•					•	•	•	•
•	•	•	•	•		•	•	•	•		•		•		•	•		•			•	•	•	•		•		•		•	•	•	
•	•	•		•				•								•			•			•											
•	•												•						•														
•	•	•		•			•	•			•		•		•	•			•	•		•	•			•		•		•			
											•		•		•				•			•											
•	•	•		•			•						•									•											
																												•					
•	•	•	•	•			•						•			•			•	•			•		•	•	•			•			
•	•	•		•			•	•					•									•					•	•		•			
•	•	•	•	•	•	•	•	•	•				•			•		•		•			•	•		•	•			•	•	•	
•	•	•	•	•		•	•	•	•	•			•			•	•	•	•	•			•	•	•	•	•			•			
•	•			•				•																•									
•	•		•	•			•																										
•	•	•	•	•		•	•																•							•			
•	•	•	•	•		•	•	•					•			•	•		•	•			•		•	•				•			
•	•	•	•	•		•	•	•					•			•		•		•							•			•			
•	•	•	•	•			•	•					•			•			•	•			•		•	•	•			•			
•	•	•	•	•			•	•		•			•			•				•					•	•	•			•			
•	•	•	•	•			•	•								•			•						•		•			•			•
•	•	•	•	•				•		•			•			•	•				•	•			•			•		•			
•	•	•	•	•												•		•			•		•	•	•					•			•
				•				•		•			•	•	•				•											•			
•	•	•		•						•			•	•		•		•	•			•		•	•			•		•			
•	•	•		•																													
	•	•	•	•		•	•	•		•	•		•	•	•	•	•	•	•					•	•		•	•		•	•		
	•	•	•	•		•	•	•		•			•		•	•	•	•	•	•			•	•	•		•			•			•
	•	•	•	•			•	•		•			•			•			•	•		•			•	•	•			•			

	Globally threatened species	Restricted-range species	Biome-restricted species	1 Hillwood	2 Source of the Zambezi	3 Chitunta Plain	4 Jimbe Drainage	5a West Lunga NP	5b Lukwakwa GMA	6 Minyanya Plain	7 Mbulo Forest	8 Liuwa Plain NP	9 Barotse Floodplains	10 Sioma Ngwezi NP	11 Simungoma	12 Machile	13a Mosi-Oa-Tunya NP	13b Batoka Gorge	14 Kafue NP
Painted Snipe *Rostratula benghalensis*				•		•		•				•	•				•		•
Black-winged Stilt *Himantopus himantopus*								•				•	•		•	•	•		•
Avocet *Recurvirostra avosetta*												•	•		•				•
Water Dikkop *Burhinus vermiculatus*								•				•	•	•	•		•		•
Spotted Dikkop *Burhinus capensis*														•	•	•	•		•
Three-banded Courser *Rhinoptilus cinctus*															•	•	•		•
Bronze-winged Courser *Rhinoptilus chalcopterus*				•	•	•	•	•		•				•	•	•	•	•	•
Temminck's Courser *Cursorius temminckii*				•		•	•			•		•	•		•		•		•
Common Pratincole *Glareola pratincola*												•	•		•	•	•		•
Black-winged Pratincole *Glareola nordmanni*	DD			•		•	•					•	•						
Rock Pratincole *Glareola nuchalis*				•				•									•		•
Little Ringed Plover *Charadrius dubius*																			
Ringed Plover *Charadrius hiaticula*								•				•	•				•		•
Kittlitz's Plover *Charadrius pecuarius*												•	•				•		•
Three-banded Plover *Charadrius tricollaris*				•		•		•				•	•	•	•	•	•		•
Forbes's Plover *Charadrius forbesi*							•			•									
White-fronted Sand Plover *Charadrius marginatus*													•		•		•		
Chestnut-banded Plover *Charadrius pallidus*																	•		
Mongolian Plover *Charadrius mongolus*																			
Greater Sand Plover *Charadrius leschenaultii*																			
Caspian Plover *Charadrius asiaticus*				•								•	•			•			•
Pacific Golden Plover *Pluvialis fulva*																			
Grey Plover *Pluvialis squatarola*													•				•		•
Senegal Wattled Plover *Vanellus senegallus*				•		•	•	•	•	•		•	•	•	•	•	•		•
White-crowned Plover *Vanellus albiceps*												•	•	•	•		•	•	•
Blacksmith Plover *Vanellus armatus*								•				•	•	•	•	•	•		•
Spur-winged Plover *Vanellus spinosus*																			
Brown-chested Wattled Plover *Vanellus superciliosus*																			
Lesser Black-winged Plover *Vanellus lugubris*																			•
Crowned Plover *Vanellus coronatus*								•		•		•	•	•	•	•	•	•	•
Long-toed Plover *Vanellus crassirostris*												•	•		•		•		•
Common Snipe *Gallinago gallinago*																			
Ethiopian Snipe *Gallinago nigripennis*				•		•		•				•	•		•	•	•		•
Great Snipe *Gallinago media*	nt			•		•		•				•	•				•		•
Jack Snipe *Lymnocryptes minimus*																			
Black-tailed Godwit *Limosa limosa*																			
Bar-tailed Godwit *Limosa lapponica*								•									•		
Whimbrel *Numenius phaeopus*																			
Curlew *Numenius arquata*												•	•						•
Spotted Redshank *Tringa erythropus*																			•
Common Redshank *Tringa totanus*																			•
Marsh Sandpiper *Tringa stagnatilis*												•	•			•	•		•
Greenshank *Tringa nebularia*						•		•	•	•		•	•	•	•		•		•
Lesser Yellowlegs *Tringa flavipes*																			
Green Sandpiper *Tringa ochropus*				•		•	•						•	•		•	•		•
Solitary Sandpiper *Tringa solitaria*																			
Wood Sandpiper *Tringa glareola*				•		•	•	•	•	•		•	•	•	•		•	•	•
Terek Sandpiper *Xenus cinereus*													•				•		
Common Sandpiper *Actitis hypoleucos*				•		•		•		•		•	•	•	•		•	•	•
Turnstone *Arenaria interpres*												•	•				•		
Knot *Calidris canutus*																			
Sanderling *Calidris alba*														•			•		•
Little Stint *Calidris minuta*								•						•	•	•	•		•
Temminck's Stint *Calidris temminckii*																	•		
Pectoral Sandpiper *Calidris melanotos*																			

15a Kafue Flats*	15b Lochinvar NP	15c Blue Lagoon NP	15d MCA	16 Nkanga R. Cons. Area	17 Mutulanganga	18 Lower Zambezi NP	19 Chisamba	20 Lukanga Swamp	21 Imanda	22 Chimfunshi W. O.	23 North Swaka	24 Wonder Gorge	25 Kasanka NP	26 Lavushi Manda NP	27 Mutinondo Wilderness	28a Bangweulu Swamps	28b Isangano NP	29 North Luangwa NP	30 Shiwa Ng'andu	31 Luapula Mouth	32 Lusenga Plain NP	33 Kalungwishi	34 Mweru Wantipa NP	35a Sumbu NP	35b Tondwa GMA	36 Saise River	37 Uningi Pans	38 Nyika NP	39 Mafinga Mountains	40 South Luangwa NP	41 Lukususi NP	42 Nyanje Hills	Luambe NP
●	●	●	●	●			●	●	●				●		●	●		●						●		●		●	●	●			●
●	●	●	●	●			●	●					●			●		●	●	●	●			●	●	●		●		●			●
●	●	●		●		●	●	●					●			●		●						●	●	●		●		●	●		
●	●	●		●	●								●			●		●						●	●	●			●	●			
●		●		●	●	●							●					●												●	●		●
●	●	●		●		●	●	●		●			●			●		●	●											●	●		●
●	●	●		●				●	●				●			●	●	●	●		●			●		●				●	●		●
●	●			●									●										●							●			
				●			●						●										●	●						●			
●	●	●		●			●	●	●				●			●								●	●					●			
●	●	●		●			●	●	●				●			●		●	●					●	●					●			
●	●	●		●			●	●	●				●			●		●	●					●	●			●		●	●		●
							●									●								●	●					●			
●				●			●						●					●						●						●			
●	●	●																												●			
●	●	●																												●			
●	●	●		●			●	●	●				●			●		●						●						●			
●	●	●					●	●	●	●			●	●	●	●	●													●			
							●									●														●			●
●	●	●		●			●	●	●	●			●		●	●	●	●	●					●	●					●			●
																●								●									
●	●	●		●	●		●	●	●				●			●		●						●	●	●				●			
●	●	●		●			●	●	●				●			●		●						●	●					●		●	
																●									●	●							
●	●	●	●	●			●	●	●				●			●		●					●	●	●	●				●			
●	●	●					●	●	●				●			●		●			●			●	●	●				●			
●	●	●											●			●								●	●					●			
●	●			●										●				●						●	●					●			
●	●	●					●						●			●		●						●	●					●			
	●	●		●																				●						●			●
●	●	●					●	●	●		●		●			●	●	●	●				●	●	●	●	●			●			●
				●			●	●					●	●	●			●									●			●			
●	●	●	●	●	●	●	●	●		●	●		●	●	●	●		●	●	●	●			●	●	●		●	●	●	●		●
●	●	●		●	●	●	●	●		●	●		●	●	●	●		●	●				●				●			●	●	●	●
●	●						●									●								●		●				●			
	●			●																				●						●			
●	●	●	●		●	●	●	●					●			●		●	●					●	●	●				●			●
		●	●																														
●						●																											

	Globally threatened species	Restricted-range species	Biome-restricted species	1 Hillwood	2 Source of the Zambezi	3 Chitunta Plain	4 Jimbe Drainage	5a West Lunga NP	5b Lukwakwa GMA	6 Minyanya Plain	7 Mbulo Forest	8 Liuwa Plain NP	9 Barotse Floodplains	10 Sioma Ngwezi NP	11 Simungoma	12 Machile	13a Mosi-Oa-Tunya NP	13b Batoka Gorge	14 Kafue NP
Curlew Sandpiper *Calidris ferruginea*												•	•	•	•		•		•
Broad-billed Sandpiper *Limicola falcinellus*																			
Ruff *Philomachus pugnax*						•		•				•	•	•	•	•	•		•
Red-necked Phalarope *Phalaropus lobatus*																			
Lesser Black-backed Gull *Larus fuscus*													•						•
Franklin's Gull *Larus pipixcan*																			
Grey-headed Gull *Larus cirrocephalus*												•	•		•		•		•
Gull-billed Tern *Sterna nilotica*													•						
Caspian Tern *Sterna caspia*													•						
Common Tern *Sterna hirundo*																			
Whiskered Tern *Chlidonias hybrida*								•				•	•		•		•		•
White-winged Black Tern *Chlidonias leucopterus*								•				•	•		•	•	•		•
African Skimmer *Rynchops flavirostris*	nt											•	•				•		•
Double-banded Sandgrouse *Pterocles bicinctus*													•	•	•	•	•		•
Yellow-throated Sandgrouse *Pterocles gutturalis*												•	•	•		•			•
Burchell's Sandgrouse *Pterocles burchelli*															•	•			
Afep Pigeon *Columba unicincta*			g	•	•		•												
Rameron Pigeon *Columba arquatrix*			a	•				•	•										
Bronze-naped Pigeon *Columba delegorguei*				•	•		•	•											
Cinnamon Dove *Aplopelia larvata*			a				•	•		•									
Pink-breasted Turtle Dove *Streptopelia lugens*			A																
Laughing Dove *Streptopelia senegalensis*				•		•		•				•	•	•	•	•	•	•	•
African Mourning Dove *Streptopelia decipiens*												•	•	•	•	•			
Cape Turtle Dove *Streptopelia capicola*				•	•	•	•	•	•	•	•	•	•	•	•	•	•	•	•
Red-eyed Dove *Streptopelia semitorquata*				•	•	•	•	•	•	•	•	•	•	•	•		•		•
Emerald-spotted Wood Dove *Turtur chalcospilos*				•	•	•	•	•	•	•	•	•	•	•	•		•		•
Blue-spotted Wood Dove *Turtur afer*				•	•	•	•	•		•	•								
Tambourine Dove *Turtur tympanistria*				•			•	•											
Namaqua Dove *Oena capensis*						•	•	•				•	•	•	•		•		•
Green Pigeon *Treron calvus*				•	•	•	•	•	•	•		•	•	•	•		•		•
Brown-necked Parrot *Poicephalus robustus*				•	•	•	•	•	•		•		•	•	•		•		•
Meyer's Parrot *Poicephalus meyeri*				•	•	•	•	•	•	•	•	•	•	•	•	•	•	•	•
Lilian's Lovebird *Agapornis lilianae*			Z																
Black-cheeked Lovebird *Agapornis nigrigens*	VU	RR	Z												•				•
Schalow's Turaco *Tauraco schalowi*				•	•	•	•	•	•				•	•	•		•		•
Purple-crested Turaco *Tauraco porphyreolophus*																			
Lady Ross's Turaco *Musophaga rossae*				•	•	•	•	•	•	•	•								•
Grey Lourie *Corythaixoides concolor*								•				•	•	•	•	•	•	•	•
Bare-faced Go-away Bird *Corythaixoides personatus*																			
Great Spotted Cuckoo *Clamator glandarius*				•				•				•	•	•	•	•			•
Jacobin Cuckoo *Clamator jacobinus*				•		•	•	•				•	•	•	•	•	•		•
Striped Crested Cuckoo *Clamator levaillantii*				•	•	•	•	•				•	•	•	•	•			•
Thick-billed Cuckoo *Pachycoccyx audeberti*				•	•		•			•									•
Red-chested Cuckoo *Cuculus solitarius*				•	•	•	•	•	•	•	•		•	•	•		•	•	•
Black Cuckoo *Cuculus clamosus*				•	•	•	•		•	•	•	•		•	•	•		•	•
European Grey Cuckoo *Cuculus canorus*				•			•							•	•		•	•	
African Grey Cuckoo *Cuculus gularis*				•	•	•	•	•	•	•	•	•	•	•	•	•			•
Lesser Cuckoo *Cuculus poliocephalus*																			
Madagascar Lesser Cuckoo *Cuculus rochii*																			
Olive Long-tailed Cuckoo *Cercococcyx olivinus*			g	•	•		•			•									
Barred Long-tailed Cuckoo *Cercococcyx montanus*																			
Emerald Cuckoo *Chrysococcyx cupreus*				•	•		•	•	•			•	•	•			•	•	•
Klaas's Cuckoo *Chrysococcyx klaas*				•	•	•	•	•	•	•	•		•	•	•		•	•	•
Didric Cuckoo *Chrysococcyx caprius*				•		•		•		•		•	•	•	•	•	•		•
Green Coucal *Ceuthmochares aereus*				•			•												

	15a Kafue Flats*	15b Lochinvar NP	15c Blue Lagoon NP	15d MCA	16 Nkanga R. Cons. Area	17 Mutulanganga	18 Lower Zambezi NP	19 Chisamba	20 Lukanga Swamp	21 Imanda	22 Chimfunshi W. O.	23 North Swaka	24 Wonder Gorge	25 Kasanka NP	26 Lavushi Manda NP	27 Mutinondo Wilderness	28a Bangweulu Swamps	28b Isangano NP	29 North Luangwa NP	30 Shiwa Ng'andu	31 Luapula Mouth	32 Lusenga Plain NP	33 Kalungwishi	34 Mweru Wantipa NP	35a Sumbu NP	35b Tondwa GMA	36 Saise River	37 Uningi Pans	38 Nyika NP	39 Mafinga Mountains	40 South Luangwa NP	41 Lukususi NP	42 Nyanje Hills	Luambe NP
	•	•	•	•	•		•	•	•								•		•	•					•	•	•		•			•			•
	•	•	•	•	•		•	•	•		•			•			•		•	•		•			•		•		•			•			
	•	•																			•				•						•			
	•	•																													•			
	•	•	•	•			•	•						•					•	•					•				•			
	•	•	•	•	•			•																										
	•	•	•	•	•			•	•					•			•		•							•								
	•	•	•	•	•			•	•					•			•		•	•	•		•		•						•			•
	•	•	•	•				•	•					•			•		•	•					•						•			•
					•	•		•								•			•												•	•		
	•	•	•	•				•	•										•	•					•	•								
																													•	•				
										•										•									•	•				
																													•					
	•	•	•	•			•	•	•	•	•			•			•		•	•					•			•			•	•	•	•
	•	•	•	•	•		•																			•	•				•			•
	•	•	•	•	•		•	•	•	•	•	•	•	•	•	•	•	•	•	•	•	•	•	•	•	•					•	•	•	•
							•	•	•	•		•		•					•	•		•		•							•	•	•	•
	•													•					•						•				•	•	•	•		•
	•	•	•	•	•	•	•	•	•	•	•	•	•	•	•	•	•	•	•	•	•	•	•	•	•	•	•	•	•	•	•	•	•	•
	•	•	•	•	•	•	•	•	•	•	•	•	•	•	•	•	•	•	•	•	•	•	•	•	•	•	•	•			•	•	•	•
	•	•	•	•	•	•	•	•	•	•	•	•	•	•	•	•	•	•	•	•	•	•	•	•	•	•	•				•	•	•	•
				•	•														•												•			
	•				•				•				•						•	•						•			•	•	•	•		•
								•							•														•		•			
	•	•	•	•	•	•	•	•	•		•			•			•		•	•					•	•					•			•
																													•	•	•			
	•	•	•	•	•	•	•							•			•		•												•			
	•	•	•	•	•	•	•	•	•	•	•	•	•	•	•	•	•	•	•	•		•		•	•				•		•			
	•				•														•						•						•			
																												•			•			
	•	•	•	•	•	•	•	•		•	•		•	•	•	•	•		•	•		•		•	•		•		•		•	•		•
	•	•	•	•	•	•	•	•	•	•	•	•	•	•	•	•	•	•	•	•		•			•	•			•		•	•		•
	•				•	•				•	•			•			•	•		•					•				•	•				
																															•			
	•				•	•	•	•		•		•		•		•			•	•				•	•	•		•		•	•		•	•
	•	•	•	•	•	•	•	•	•	•	•		•	•	•	•	•	•	•	•	•		•	•	•	•		•	•	•	•	•	•	•
	•	•	•	•	•	•								•			•		•	•		•		•	•				•		•	•	•	•
																									•	•								

	Globally threatened species	Restricted-range species	Biome-restricted species	1 Hillwood	2 Source of the Zambezi	3 Chitunta Plain	4 Jimbe Drainage	5a West Lunga NP	5b Lukwakwa GMA	6 Minyanya Plain	7 Mbulo Forest	8 Liuwa Plain NP	9 Barotse Floodplains	10 Sioma Ngwezi NP	11 Simungoma	12 Machile	13a Mosi-Oa-Tunya NP	13b Batoka Gorge	14 Kafue NP
African Black Coucal *Centropus grillii*				•		•		•		•	•	•	•	•	•		•		•
Coppery-tailed Coucal *Centropus cupreicaudus*		Z				•	•	•	•	•		•	•	•	•	•	•		•
Senegal Coucal *Centropus senegalensis*				•		•		•		•		•	•		•		•		•
Burchell's Coucal *Centropus superciliosus*				•	•	•	•	•		•		•	•		•		•		•
Barn Owl *Tyto alba*				•		•	•	•	•		•	•	•	•	•			•	•
Grass Owl *Tyto capensis*				•		•				•									•
African Scops Owl *Otus senegalensis*				•	•	•		•		•	•	•	•	•	•		•		•
White-faced Owl *Otus leucotis*				•	•	•		•		•		•	•		•		•		•
Spotted Eagle Owl *Bubo africanus*				•	•	•	•	•					•	•	•		•	•	•
Giant Eagle Owl *Bubo lacteus*				•	•			•				•	•		•		•		•
Pel's Fishing Owl *Scotopelia peli*								•				•				•	•		•
Pearl-spotted Owlet *Glaucidium perlatum*								•				•	•		•	•	•		•
Barred Owlet *Glaucidium capensis*				•			•	•		•		•	•		•		•		•
Wood Owl *Strix woodfordii*				•	•		•	•			•	•	•		•		•		•
Marsh Owl *Asio capensis*				•				•		•		•	•	•	•		•		•
European Nightjar *Caprimulgus europaeus*												•							•
Rufous-cheeked Nightjar *Caprimulgus rufigena*								•		•	•	•			•		•		
Fiery-necked Nightjar *Caprimulgus pectoralis*				•	•	•	•	•		•	•	•	•		•		•		•
Mountain Nightjar *Caprimulgus poliocephalus*			A																
Natal Nightjar *Caprimulgus natalensis*				•		•	•	•		•	•	•	•		•		•		•
Freckled Rock Nightjar *Caprimulgus tristigma*								•									•	•	•
Gaboon Nightjar *Caprimulgus fossii*				•		•	•	•		•	•	•	•		•		•		•
Pennant-winged Nightjar *Macrodipteryx vexillarius*				•	•		•	•		•		•	•		•		•		•
Scarce Swift *Schoutedenapus myoptilus*			A																
Mottled Spinetail *Telacanthura ussheri*																			
Bat-like Spinetail *Neafrapus boehmi*				•			•	•		•						•			•
African Palm Swift *Cypsiurus parvus*				•	•	•		•			•	•	•	•	•		•	•	•
Alpine Swift *Apus melba*																	•	•	
Mottled Swift *Apus aequatorialis*																	•	•	
Pallid Swift *Apus pallidus*																			
European Swift *Apus apus*				•	•	•		•	•			•	•	•	•		•		•
African Black Swift *Apus barbatus*																	•	•	
Little Swift *Apus affinis*				•				•									•	•	•
Horus Swift *Apus horus*													•		•		•		
African White-rumped Swift *Apus caffer*				•											•		•	•	•
Speckled Mousebird *Colius striatus*				•	•	•													
Red-faced Mousebird *Urocolius indicus*								•					•	•	•		•		•
Narina Trogon *Apaloderma narina*				•	•			•		•	•	•		•					•
Bar-tailed Trogon *Apaloderma vittatum*			A																
Half-collared Kingfisher *Alcedo semitorquata*								•					•				•		•
Shining-blue Kingfisher *Alcedo quadribrachys*																			
Malachite Kingfisher *Alcedo cristata*				•		•		•		•		•							•
White-bellied Kingfisher *Alcedo leucogaster*			g				•												
Pygmy Kingfisher *Ceyx pictus*				•	•	•	•	•		•		•					•	•	•
Brown-headed Kingfisher *Halcyon albiventris*				•	•			•	•	•		•				•	•		•
Chestnut-bellied Kingfisher *Halcyon leucocephala*				•	•	•	•	•	•	•	•	•		•	•	•	•		•
Blue-breasted Kingfisher *Halcyon malimbica*				•	•		•				•	•							
Senegal Kingfisher *Halcyon senegalensis*								•		•		•	•	•	•				•
Striped Kingfisher *Halcyon chelicuti*				•	•	•		•				•	•		•		•		•
Giant Kingfisher *Megaceryle maxima*				•				•		•		•	•		•		•	•	•
Pied Kingfisher *Ceryle rudis*				•		•		•	•				•	•	•		•	•	•
Little Bee-eater *Merops pusillus*				•	•	•		•		•	•		•				•		•
White-cheeked Bee-eater *Merops variegatus*				•		•	•	•	•			•	•				•		•
Swallow-tailed Bee-eater *Merops hirundineus*				•	•	•	•					•	•	•	•		•	•	•
White-fronted Bee-eater *Merops bullockoides*								•				•	•	•	•		•		•

15a Kafue Flats*	15b Lochinvar NP	15c Blue Lagoon NP	15d MCA	16 Nkanga R. Cons. Area	17 Mutulanganga	18 Lower Zambezi NP	19 Chisamba	20 Lukanga Swamp	21 Imanda	22 Chimfunshi W. O.	23 North Swaka	24 Wonder Gorge	25 Kasanka NP	26 Lavushi Manda NP	27 Mutinondo Wilderness	28a Bangweulu Swamps	28b Isangano NP	29 North Luangwa NP	30 Shiwa Ng'andu	31 Luapula Mouth	32 Lusenga Plain NP	33 Kalungwishi	34 Mweru Wantipa NP	35a Sumbu NP	35b Tondwa GMA	36 Saise River	37 Uningi Pans	38 Nyika NP	39 Mafinga Mountains	40 South Luangwa NP	41 Lukususi NP	42 Nyanje Hills	Luambe NP
•	•	•	•	•			•	•	•				•			•	•	•						•	•	•		•		•			
•	•	•	•	•		•	•	•		•	•		•		•	•	•		•			•	•	•	•	•	•	•		•	•	•	•
•	•	•		•		•	•	•		•		•		•		•	•	•		•	•		•		•	•	•	•		•	•	•	
•	•	•	•	•	•		•		•	•	•	•	•			•	•	•			•		•		•			•		•	•		
•	•	•		•									•														•						
•	•	•	•	•		•	•		•				•			•	•	•		•			•		•			•		•	•	•	
•	•	•	•	•		•	•	•		•			•			•	•	•		•			•	•				•		•	•	•	
•	•	•	•	•	•	•	•	•	•				•			•	•	•		•		•						•					
•	•	•	•				•		•				•		•		•						•		•			•					
						•			•				•	•		•		•					•					•					
•	•			•	•								•			•		•					•		•			•		•	•		
			•	•		•		•		•	•	•	•		•		•	•		•		•		•				•		•	•		
•	•	•	•	•		•	•	•	•		•		•	•		•	•	•						•				•	•	•	•		
•	•	•	•	•		•		•					•					•						•				•		•			
•	•		•										•					•						•				•					
•	•																											•					
•	•		•	•		•	•	•	•	•	•	•	•			•			•	•	•	•	•					•		•	•	•	
																												•	•	•			
•	•	•	•			•							•		•	•				•			•		•		•			•		•	
•	•	•	•			•		•					•			•	•	•		•					•			•		•	•	•	
•	•	•	•	•		•	•	•	•				•		•	•	•	•		•								•		•	•	•	
						•		•						•						•		•						•					
						•	•													•								•					
•	•	•	•	•	•	•	•		•							•				•								•		•	•	•	•
						•													•									•	•	•			
								•											•						•			•	•	•	•		
•	•	•	•	•		•						•	•	•	•	•		•					•			•		•	•	•	•	•	•
•	•		•	•		•			•			•	•	•				•										•	•	•	•	•	•
						•										•		•										•					
•	•	•	•	•		•			•				•			•		•					•					•		•	•	•	
									•				•			•		•						•				•		•	•	•	•
													•			•										•		•	•	•	•	•	•
•	•			•		•			•		•	•	•	•	•		•			•		•		•						•	•		
																								•						•		•	
•	•	•	•	•	•	•	•	•	•	•		•	•			•	•	•		•	•					•	•	•		•	•	•	
•	•	•	•	•		•	•	•	•		•	•		•		•		•					•			•	•	•				•	•
•	•	•	•	•		•	•	•	•		•	•	•	•		•	•	•		•			•	•	•			•		•	•		
•	•	•	•	•	•	•	•	•	•		•	•	•	•		•	•	•		•	•		•	•	•		•	•		•	•		
•	•	•	•	•	•	•	•	•	•	•	•	•		•		•	•	•		•	•		•	•	•	•	•	•		•	•	•	
•	•	•	•	•		•	•	•		•	•					•		•						•	•					•	•	•	•
•	•	•	•	•		•	•	•					•			•		•					•			•				•	•	•	•

	Globally threatened species	Restricted-range species	Biome-restricted species	1 Hillwood	2 Source of the Zambezi	3 Chitunta Plain	4 Jimbe Drainage	5a West Lunga NP	5b Lukwakwa GMA	6 Minyanya Plain	7 Mbulo Forest	8 Liuwa Plain NP	9 Barotse Floodplains	10 Sioma Ngwezi NP	11 Simungoma	12 Machile	13a Mosi-Oa-Tunya NP	13b Batoka Gorge	14 Kafue NP
White-throated Bee-eater *Merops albicollis*																			
Böhm's Bee-eater *Merops boehmi*		Z						•											•
Madagascar Bee-eater *Merops superciliosus*																	•		
Blue-cheeked Bee-eater *Merops persicus*				•				•	•		•		•	•	•	•	•		•
European Bee-eater *Merops apiaster*				•	•	•	•	•	•		•		•	•	•	•	•	•	•
Northern Carmine Bee-eater *Merops nubicus*																			
Southern Carmine Bee-eater *Merops nubicoides*				•	•		•	•	•		•		•	•	•	•	•		•
European Roller *Coracias garrulus*				•		•	•	•			•		•		•	•	•		•
Lilac-breasted Roller *Coracias caudatus*				•		•	•	•		•		•	•		•	•	•		•
Racket-tailed Roller *Coracias spatulatus*		z		•	•		•	•	•		•		•		•	•	•		•
Purple Roller *Coracias naevius*				•				•			•	•	•		•	•	•		•
Broad-billed Roller *Eurystomus glaucurus*				•	•	•	•	•	•		•		•		•	•	•		•
Red-billed Wood Hoopoe *Phoeniculus purpureus*				•	•	•	•	•	•	•	•		•		•	•	•	•	•
Scimitarbill *Rhinopomastus cyanomelas*				•	•	•	•	•	•	•	•		•		•	•	•		•
Hoopoe *Upupa epops*				•	•	•	•	•	•		•		•		•	•	•		•
Red-billed Hornbill *Tockus erythrorhynchus*															•	•			•
Southern Yellow-billed Hornbill *Tockus leucomelas*															•	•			•
Crowned Hornbill *Tockus alboterminatus*				•	•	•	•	•	•		•	•			•	•			•
Bradfield's Hornbill *Tockus bradfieldi*		Z													•	•			
Pale-billed Hornbill *Tockus pallidirostris*		Z		•	•	•	•	•	•										
African Grey Hornbill *Tockus nasutus*								•			•		•	•	•	•			•
Trumpeter Hornbill *Bycanistes bucinator*				•	•	•	•	•	•				•		•	•			•
Silvery-cheeked Hornbill *Bycanistes brevis*																			
Southern Ground Hornbill *Bucorvus cafer*				•	•	•	•	•	•	•	•		•		•	•			•
Anchieta's Barbet *Stactolaema anchietae*		Z		•	•						•	•							
Whyte's Barbet *Stactolaema whytii*		Z																	
Moustached Green Tinkerbird *Pogoniulus leucomystax*		A																	
Yellow-fronted Tinkerbird *Pogoniulus chrysoconus*				•	•	•	•	•	•	•	•		•		•	•			•
Golden-rumped Tinkerbird *Pogoniulus bilineatus*				•	•	•		•		•	•								
Spot-flanked Barbet *Tricholaema lacrymosa*																			
Acacia Pied Barbet *Tricholaema leucomelas*															•	•			
Miombo Pied Barbet *Tricholaema frontata*		Z				•	•		•	•									•
Black-collared Barbet *Lybius torquatus*				•				•	•	•	•	•	•		•	•	•	•	•
Chaplin's Barbet *Lybius chaplini*	nt	Z																	•
Black-backed Barbet *Lybius minor*		z		•				•	•	•	•		•						•
Crested Barbet *Trachyphonus vaillantii*															•	•	•		•
Green-backed Honeyguide *Prodotiscus zambesiae*				•	•		•		•										•
Brown-backed Honeyguide *Prodotiscus regulus*				•			•	•	•						•		•		•
Scaly-fronted Honeyguide *Indicator variegatus*				•	•		•	•	•		•								•
Greater Honeyguide *Indicator indicator*				•	•	•	•	•	•	•	•	•			•	•	•	•	•
Lesser Honeyguide *Indicator minor*				•	•		•	•	•		•		•						•
Western Least Honeyguide *Indicator exilis*				•	•			•		•									
Eastern Least Honeyguide *Indicator meliphilus*				•						•									
Red-throated Wryneck *Jynx ruficollis*				•		•	•												
Bennett's Woodpecker *Campethera bennettii*				•	•	•	•	•			•		•		•	•	•		•
Golden-tailed Woodpecker *Campethera abingoni*				•	•	•	•		•	•	•				•	•	•		•
Little Spotted Woodpecker *Campethera cailliautii*				•	•			•		•	•	•							•
Brown-eared Woodpecker *Campethera caroli*			g	•			•												
Cardinal Woodpecker *Dendropicos fuscescens*				•	•	•	•	•	•	•	•		•		•	•	•		•
Bearded Woodpecker *Thripias namaquus*				•		•	•	•	•	•	•				•	•	•		•
Olive Woodpecker *Mesopicos griseocephalus*								•			•			•			•		•
African Broadbill *Smithornis capensis*				•	•		•	•	•		•				•				•
African Pitta *Pitta angolensis*				•															
Monotonous Lark *Mirafra passerina*															•		•	•	
Rufous-naped Lark *Mirafra africana*				•		•	•				•		•	•	•	•			•

	15a Kafue Flats*	15b Lochinvar NP	15c Blue Lagoon NP	15d MCA	16 Nkanga R. Cons. Area	17 Mutulanganga	18 Lower Zambezi NP	19 Chisamba	20 Lukanga Swamp	21 Imanda	22 Chimfunshi W. O.	23 North Swaka	24 Wonder Gorge	25 Kasanka NP	26 Lavushi Manda NP	27 Mutinondo Wilderness	28a Bangweulu Swamps	28b Isangano NP	29 North Luangwa NP	30 Shiwa Ng'andu	31 Luapula Mouth	32 Lusenga Plain NP	33 Kalungwishi	34 Mweru Wantipa NP	35a Sumbu NP	35b Tondwa GMA	36 Saise River	37 Uningi Pans	38 Nyika NP	39 Mafinga Mountains	40 South Luangwa NP	41 Lukususi NP	42 Nyanje Hills	Luambe NP
														•	•															•					
														•	•	•			•	•	•				•	•				•	•	•	•	•
	•	•	•	•	•		•	•	•		•			•	•	•		•	•	•	•			•	•	•	•	•	•		•		•	
	•	•	•	•	•	•	•	•	•	•	•	•	•	•	•	•	•	•	•	•	•	•	•	•	•	•	•	•	•	•	•	•	•	•
																														•				
	•	•	•	•	•		•	•	•		•			•	•				•	•				•	•	•				•	•	•	•	
	•	•	•	•	•		•	•	•		•			•	•				•	•				•	•					•	•	•	•	
	•	•	•	•		•	•	•	•	•				•	•	•			•	•	•				•	•				•	•	•	•	•
	•	•	•		•		•	•			•	•	•	•					•	•			•		•					•	•	•	•	
	•	•			•		•	•			•						•													•				
	•	•			•	•		•						•	•				•	•	•		•	•	•				•	•	•	•	•
	•	•	•		•		•	•	•	•	•	•	•	•	•	•	•	•	•	•	•	•	•	•	•	•		•	•	•	•	•	•	•
	•	•			•	•	•	•	•	•	•	•	•	•					•	•		•	•	•	•				•	•	•	•	•
	•	•	•	•	•	•	•	•	•	•		•	•						•	•				•	•	•				•	•	•	•	•
																												•	•					
	•	•		•	•		•	•			•	•		•	•	•	•	•	•	•	•	•	•	•		•				•	•	•	•	•
										•				•	•	•						•				•				•				
																										•								
	•	•	•		•		•			•		•	•	•	•				•	•		•	•	•			•			•		•		
	•	•	•	•	•	•	•	•	•	•	•	•	•	•					•	•	•	•	•		•	•			•		•	•	•	
	•		•		•						•								•										•		•	•	•	•
	•	•	•	•	•	•	•	•	•	•	•	•	•	•					•	•	•	•	•		•	•		•	•		•	•	•	•
																													•					
																																•		
	•	•	•	•	•	•	•	•	•	•	•	•	•	•					•	•		•			•						•	•	•	•
	•	•		•	•	•	•	•	•	•	•	•	•	•	•	•			•	•	•	•		•	•	•				•	•	•	•	•
			•	•	•	•	•	•			•			•	•					•	•	•	•	•	•			•			•	•		
	•			•	•		•	•			•	•		•	•	•	•	•	•	•		•	•	•		•				•	•	•	•	•
			•						•						•					•	•							•	•	•				
	•	•		•	•	•	•			•	•		•	•	•	•		•	•		•	•		•	•				•	•	•	•	•
				•	•	•				•				•	•				•		•			•	•				•	•			
		•	•	•	•			•	•										•	•									•					

Species	Globally threatened species	Restricted-range species	Biome-restricted species	1 Hillwood	2 Source of the Zambezi	3 Chitunta Plain	4 Jimbe Drainage	5a West Lunga NP	5b Lukwakwa GMA	6 Minyanya Plain	7 Mbulo Forest	8 Liuwa Plain NP	9 Barotse Floodplains	10 Sioma Ngwezi NP	11 Simungoma	12 Machile	13a Mosi-Oa-Tunya NP	13b Batoka Gorge	14 Kafue NP
Angola Lark *Mirafra angolensis*			Z	•		•	•			•									
Flappet Lark *Mirafra rufocinnamomea*				•	•	•	•	•	•	•		•	•	•	•	•	•	•	•
Clapper Lark *Mirafra apiata*												•	•						
Fawn-coloured Lark *Mirafra africanoides*										•		•	•	•					
Dusky Lark *Pinarocorys nigricans*				•		•	•	•				•		•			•		•
Red-capped Lark *Calandrella cinerea*				•		•	•	•	•			•	•	•			•	•	•
Pink-billed Lark *Spizocorys conirostris*												•	•						
Chestnut-backed Sparrow-Lark *Eremopterix leucotis*													•			•	•		•
Grey-backed Sparrow-Lark *Eremopterix verticalis*												•	•	•		•			•
Fischer's Sparrow-Lark *Eremopterix leucopareia*																			
Black Saw-wing *Psalidoprocne pristoptera*				•	•	•	•	•	•										•
White-headed Saw-wing *Psalidoprocne albiceps*			a																
European Sand Martin *Riparia riparia*				•	•	•	•		•			•							•
African Sand Martin *Riparia paludicola*								•				•	•	•		•			•
Banded Martin *Riparia cincta*				•		•	•	•	•	•		•	•	•		•			•
Grey-rumped Swallow *Pseudhirundo griseopyga*				•		•	•	•	•	•		•	•	•		•			•
Red-breasted Swallow *Hirundo semirufa*				•		•	•	•	•			•				•	•		•
Mosque Swallow *Hirundo senegalensis*				•	•	•					•	•	•		•		•		•
Lesser Striped Swallow *Hirundo abyssinica*				•	•	•	•	•	•			•	•	•		•	•	•	•
Greater Striped Swallow *Hirundo cucullata*							•			•		•	•			•	•		•
Red-rumped Swallow *Hirundo daurica*																			
South African Cliff Swallow *Hirundo spilodera*						•						•	•						
Red-throated Cliff Swallow *Hirundo rufigula*			z	•		•													
African Rock Martin *Hirundo fuligula*																	•	•	
Blue Swallow *Hirundo atrocaerulea*	VU	A																	
Black-and-rufous Swallow *Hirundo nigrorufa*			Z	•		•	•												
Wire-tailed Swallow *Hirundo smithii*								•				•	•		•		•	•	•
Pearl-breasted Swallow *Hirundo dimidiata*				•		•	•	•	•	•			•			•	•		•
White-throated Swallow *Hirundo albigularis*				•				•	•			•	•			•			•
European Swallow *Hirundo rustica*				•	•	•	•	•	•	•		•	•	•	•	•	•	•	•
Angola Swallow *Hirundo angolensis*				•		•													
House Martin *Delichon urbicum*				•	•	•	•	•				•	•	•	•	•	•	•	•
Yellow Wagtail *Motacilla flava*				•		•		•				•	•	•	•		•		•
Cape Wagtail *Motacilla capensis*				•		•		•	•			•	•	•	•		•		•
Grey Wagtail *Motacilla cinerea*																			
Mountain Wagtail *Motacilla clara*																	•	•	
African Pied Wagtail *Motacilla aguimp*				•		•		•				•		•	•	•	•	•	•
Richard's Pipit *Anthus richardi*				•		•	•	•	•	•		•	•						•
Long-billed Pipit *Anthus similis*				•	•	•		•	•	•	•	•	•	•					•
Plain-backed Pipit *Anthus leucophrys*				•		•		•	•	•	•	•	•	•	•	•			•
Buffy Pipit *Anthus vaalensis*				•		•	•		•		•	•	•	•	•				•
Short-tailed Pipit *Anthus brachyurus*				•		•	•												
Little Tawny Pipit *Anthus cafer*																			•
Tree Pipit *Anthus trivialis*				•	•	•													•
Red-throated Pipit *Anthus cervinus*																			
Striped Pipit *Anthus lineiventris*							•										•		•
Yellow-throated Longclaw *Macronyx croceus*																			
Fülleborn's Longclaw *Macronyx fuellebornii*			z	•		•	•	•	•	•		•	•						•
Rosy-breasted Longclaw *Macronyx ameliae*				•		•	•	•	•	•									•
Grimwood's Longclaw *Macronyx grimwoodi*	DD		Z			•					•								
Black Cuckoo-shrike *Campephaga flava*				•	•	•	•	•	•		•	•	•	•		•	•	•	•
Purple-throated Cuckoo-shrike *Campephaga quiscalina*					•		•	•	•										•
White-breasted Cuckoo-shrike *Coracina pectoralis*				•	•	•	•	•	•	•	•		•		•				•
Eastern Mountain Greenbul *Andropadus nigriceps*			A																
Little Greenbul *Andropadus virens*				•	•	•	•												

15a Kafue Flats*	15b Lochinvar NP	15c Blue Lagoon NP	15d MCA	16 Nkanga R. Cons. Area	17 Mutulanganga	18 Lower Zambezi NP	19 Chisamba	20 Lukanga Swamp	21 Imanda	22 Chimfunshi W. O.	23 North Swaka	24 Wonder Gorge	25 Kasanka NP	26 Lavushi Manda NP	27 Mutinondo Wilderness	28a Bangweulu Swamps	28b Isangano NP	29 North Luangwa NP	30 Shiwa Ng'andu	31 Luapula Mouth	32 Lusenga Plain NP	33 Kalungwishi	34 Mweru Wantipa NP	35a Sumbu NP	35b Tondwa GMA	36 Saise River	37 Uningi Pans	38 Nyika NP	39 Mafinga Mountains	40 South Luangwa NP	41 Lukususi NP	42 Nyanje Hills	Luambe NP

	Globally threatened species	Restricted-range species	Biome-restricted species	1 Hillwood	2 Source of the Zambezi	3 Chitunta Plain	4 Jimbe Drainage	5a West Lunga NP	5b Lukwakwa GMA	6 Minyanya Plain	7 Mbulo Forest	8 Liuwa Plain NP	9 Barotse Floodplains	10 Sioma Ngwezi NP	11 Simungoma	12 Machile	13a Mosi-Oa-Tunya NP	13b Batoka Gorge	14 Kafue NP
Sombre Bulbul *Andropadus importunus*			e																
Honeyguide Greenbul *Baeopogon indicator*			g	●	●		●												
Joyful Greenbul *Chlorocichla laetissima*			a																
Yellow-bellied Greenbul *Chlorocichla flaviventris*								●	●					●	●	●	●	●	●
Yellow-throated Leaflove *Chlorocichla flavicollis*				●	●		●	●	●	●	●	●							
Terrestrial Bulbul *Phyllastrephus terrestris*															●	●			●
Grey-olive Bulbul *Phyllastrephus cerviniventris*			e			●		●											●
Cabanis's Greenbul *Phyllastrephus cabanisi*			a	●	●		●			●		●							
Yellow-streaked Bulbul *Phyllastrephus flavostriatus*																			
Bristlebill *Bleda syndactylus*			g	●	●		●												
Common Bulbul *Pycnonotus barbatus*				●	●	●	●	●	●	●	●	●	●	●	●	●	●	●	●
Red-eyed Bulbul *Pycnonotus nigricans*															●	●	●		
Black-collared Bulbul *Neolestes torquatus*				●			●												
White-throated Nicator *Nicator gularis*			e												●	●			
Rufous Ant Thrush *Stizorhina fraseri*			g	●	●		●												
European Rock Thrush *Monticola saxatilis*																			
Miombo Rock Thrush *Monticola angolensis*			z	●	●	●	●	●	●								●		●
Olive Thrush *Turdus olivaceus*			a																
West African Thrush *Turdus pelios*				●	●		●	●			●								
Kurrichane Thrush *Turdus libonyana*			z	●	●	●	●	●	●		●				●	●		●	●
Groundscraper Thrush *Psophocichla litsitsirupa*				●	●	●	●	●	●	●	●	●			●	●			●
Orange Thrush *Zoothera gurneyi*			A																
White-chested Alethe *Alethe fuelleborni*			A																
Starred Robin *Pogonocichla stellata*			A																
Bocage's Robin *Sheppardia bocagei*			s						●										
Sharpe's Akalat *Sheppardia sharpei*		RR	A																
Thrush-Nightingale *Luscinia luscinia*															●	●		●	●
Olive-flanked Robin *Cossypha anomala*			A																
Grey-winged Robin *Cossypha polioptera*				●	●		●												
Cape Robin *Cossypha caffra*			a																
Heuglin's Robin *Cossypha heuglini*				●	●	●	●	●	●	●	●	●	●	●	●	●	●	●	●
Red-capped Robin *Cossypha natalensis*				●	●		●		●	●	●	●							●
Boulder Chat *Pinarornis plumosus*			Z																
Collared Palm Thrush *Cichladusa arquata*			z								●				●				●
Central Bearded Scrub Robin *Erythropygia barbata*			Z	●	●	●	●	●	●		●								●
Eastern Bearded Scrub Robin *Erythropygia quadrivirgata*			e												●	●	●	●	●
White-browed Scrub Robin *Erythropygia leucophrys*				●	●	●	●	●	●	●	●	●	●	●	●	●	●	●	●
Stonechat *Saxicola torquatus*				●	●	●	●	●	●	●	●	●	●		●				
Whinchat *Saxicola rubetra*																			
European Wheatear *Oenanthe oenanthe*												●							●
Capped Wheatear *Oenanthe pileata*				●			●	●		●			●		●	●			
Isabelline Wheatear *Oenanthe isabellina*																			
Familiar Chat *Cercomela familiaris*																	●	●	●
Sooty Chat *Myrmecocichla nigra*				●		●	●	●	●	●		●	●			●			
Arnot's Chat *Myrmecocichla arnotti*			Z	●	●		●	●	●						●		●	●	●
Mocking Chat *Myrmecocichla cinnamomeiventris*																	●	●	●
Broad-tailed Warbler *Schoenicola platyurus*				●		●	●	●											●
Little Rush Warbler *Bradypterus baboecala*								●	●	●			●	●	●		●		
White-winged Warbler *Bradypterus carpalis*			l																
Cinnamon Bracken Warbler *Bradypterus cinnamomeus*			A																
Evergreen Forest Warbler *Bradypterus lopezi*			a	●	●														
Bamboo Warbler *Bradypterus alfredi*			s	●	●		●												
African Moustached Warbler *Melocichla mentalis*				●	●	●	●	●	●										
River Warbler *Locustella fluviatilis*															●		●		
Sedge Warbler *Acrocephalus schoenobaenus*				●			●								●				●

15a Kafue Flats*	15b Lochinvar NP	15c Blue Lagoon NP	15d MCA	16 Nkanga R. Cons. Area	17 Mutulanganga	18 Lower Zambezi NP	19 Chisamba	20 Lukanga Swamp	21 Imanda	22 Chimfunshi W. O.	23 North Swaka	24 Wonder Gorge	25 Kasanka NP	26 Lavushi Manda NP	27 Mutinondo Wilderness	28a Bangweulu Swamps	28b Isangano NP	29 North Luangwa NP	30 Shiwa Ng'andu	31 Luapula Mouth	32 Lusenga Plain NP	33 Kalungwishi	34 Mweru Wantipa NP	35a Sumbu NP	35b Tondwa GMA	36 Saise River	37 Uningi Pans	38 Nyika NP	39 Mafinga Mountains	40 South Luangwa NP	41 Lukususi NP	42 Nyanje Hills	Luambe NP
•			•		•	•																											
•	•		•	•	•	•	•	•					•					•		•			•	•	•				•		•	•	
•	•		•	•	•			•			•		•					•					•	•					•		•	•	
							•	•	•		•		•		•			•		•									•	•			
							•	•	•				•					•		•		•		•					•				
																												•	•				
•	•		•	•	•	•	•	•	•	•	•	•	•	•	•	•	•	•	•	•	•	•	•	•	•	•	•	•	•	•	•	•	•
				•	•													•					•	•	•				•				
																												•					
			•				•		•	•	•	•	•	•				•		•	•							•	•	•	•	•	
							•	•	•				•					•		•	•							•	•				
•	•	•	•		•		•	•	•	•	•	•	•	•	•	•		•		•	•	•		•	•	•		•	•	•	•	•	
•	•		•	•			•	•					•					•		•		•							•			•	
																												•	•				
																												•	•				
																												•	•				
•	•	•	•		•	•	•																				•	•	•				
			•																				•					•					
•	•	•	•	•	•	•	•	•	•	•	•	•	•	•	•	•	•	•	•	•	•	•	•	•	•	•	•	•	•	•	•	•	•
•	•		•	•	•	•	•	•	•	•	•	•	•					•		•		•		•				•	•	•	•		•
•	•	•	•	•	•		•	•	•				•					•		•								•	•	•		•	
							•	•		•	•	•	•	•	•	•	•	•	•	•								•		•		•	
•	•		•	•	•	•	•						•					•		•	•					•		•	•	•	•	•	
•	•	•	•	•	•	•	•	•	•	•	•	•	•					•		•	•		•	•	•			•	•	•	•	•	•
			•														•			•			•			•	•	•					
•	•	•	•	•	•		•	•					•			•		•		•			•					•	•	•		•	
•	•	•	•	•		•	•						•		•	•		•		•			•			•		•	•	•			
	•	•	•			•												•		•	•							•	•	•			
•	•	•	•	•		•	•						•				•	•		•		•						•	•	•		•	•
•	•		•			•	•					•	•			•	•	•	•	•		•								•		•	
•		•				•	•					•	•	•	•			•		•		•							•	•		•	
			•									•	•			•		•		•		•							•	•	•	•	•
								•	•	•	•		•		•			•		•	•							•	•	•			
•	•	•	•	•		•	•		•	•			•			•		•		•		•			•	•		•	•	•			
																			•														
								•	•	•			•					•		•	•							•		•			
								•	•	•	•		•					•		•	•					•		•	•		•	•	•
•	•	•	•	•	•	•			•	•	•		•							•		•			•	•		•	•		•		•

	Globally threatened species	Restricted-range species	Biome-restricted species	1 Hillwood	2 Source of the Zambezi	3 Chitunta Plain	4 Jimbe Drainage	5a West Lunga NP	5b Lukwakwa GMA	6 Minyanya Plain	7 Mbulo Forest	8 Liuwa Plain NP	9 Barotse Floodplains	10 Sioma Ngwezi NP	11 Simungoma	12 Machile	13a Mosi-Oa-Tunya NP	13b Batoka Gorge	14 Kafue NP
Reed Warbler *Acrocephalus scirpaceus*													•	•	•	•	•		•
Marsh Warbler *Acrocephalus palustris*														•			•		•
Great Reed Warbler *Acrocephalus arundinaceus*													•	•	•	•	•		•
Lesser Swamp Warbler *Acrocephalus gracilirostris*									•	•			•	•	•	•	•		•
Greater Swamp Warbler *Acrocephalus rufescens*									•	•			•	•	•	•	•		•
Olive-tree Warbler *Hippolais olivetorum*																			
Icterine Warbler *Hippolais icterina*										•			•	•	•	•	•		•
Papyrus Yellow Warbler *Chloropeta gracilirostris*	VU	I																	
African Yellow Warbler *Chloropeta natalensis*				•	•		•			•									•
Mountain Yellow Warbler *Chloropeta similis*			A																
Green-capped Eremomela *Eremomela scotops*				•	•	•	•	•	•	•	•	•		•			•		•
Black-collared Eremomela *Eremomela atricollis*			Z	•	•	•	•												•
Burnt-necked Eremomela *Eremomela usticollis*													•	•	•	•	•		•
Yellow-bellied Eremomela *Eremomela icteropygialis*				•	•	•	•	•	•	•		•	•	•	•	•			•
Red-capped Crombec *Sylvietta ruficapilla*			z	•	•	•	•	•	•	•	•	•							•
Long-billed Crombec *Sylvietta rufescens*										•		•	•	•	•	•	•	•	•
Willow Warbler *Phylloscopus trochilus*				•	•	•	•	•	•	•	•	•	•	•	•	•	•		•
Yellow-throated Warbler *Phylloscopus ruficapilla*			A																
Laura's Warbler *Phylloscopus laurae*			Z	•			•												
Yellow-bellied Hyliota *Hyliota flavigaster*				•	•	•	•	•	•	•		•							•
Southern Hyliota *Hyliota australis*				•	•		•	•	•	•									•
Garden Warbler *Sylvia borin*				•	•	•		•					•	•			•		•
Blackcap *Sylvia atricapilla*				•															
Common Whitethroat *Sylvia communis*													•	•	•	•	•		•
Tit-babbler *Sylvia subcaerulea*													•	•					
Brown Parisoma *Sylvia lugens*			A																
Cloud Cisticola *Cisticola textrix*										•									
Pale-crowned Cisticola *Cisticola cinnamomeus*				•			•			•	•		•	•					•
Wing-snapping Cisticola *Cisticola ayresii*			a	•			•	•											
Black-tailed Cisticola *Cisticola dambo*			z	•			•	•		•									
Fan-tailed Cisticola *Cisticola juncidis*								•	•	•		•	•	•	•	•	•		•
Desert Cisticola *Cisticola aridulus*								•	•			•	•	•	•				•
Croaking Cisticola *Cisticola natalensis*				•			•	•	•	•		•	•			•			•
Stout Cisticola *Cisticola robustus*				•			•	•	•	•									
Wailing Cisticola *Cisticola lais*			A																
Tinkling Cisticola *Cisticola rufilatus*			z	•			•	•	•	•		•		•		•			•
Rattling Cisticola *Cisticola chiniana*								•	•	•		•	•	•	•	•	•		•
Churring Cisticola *Cisticola njombe*		RR	A																
Short-winged Cisticola *Cisticola brachypterus*				•	•	•	•	•				•	•						•
Neddicky *Cisticola fulvicapilla*										•	•			•		•	•		
~ 'Long-tailed' Neddicky *Cisticola f. angusticauda*			Z	•	•	•	•	•	•										
Rock-loving Cisticola *Cisticola aberrans*																	•	•	
Whistling Cisticola *Cisticola lateralis*				•	•		•												
Trilling Cisticola *Cisticola woosnami*				•		•	•	•	•										•
Red-faced Cisticola *Cisticola erythrops*				•			•	•	•								•		•
Singing Cisticola *Cisticola cantans*																			
Black-lored Cisticola *Cisticola nigriloris*		RR	A																
Greater Black-backed Cisticola *Cisticola galactotes*										•		•	•	•	•	•	•		•
Chirping Cisticola *Cisticola pipiens*			Z			•		•	•	•		•	•	•					•
Lesser Black-backed Cisticola *Cisticola tinniens*						•	•		•		•								•
Tawny-flanked Prinia *Prinia subflava*				•	•	•	•	•	•	•		•	•	•	•	•	•	•	•
Black-chested Prinia *Prinia flavicans*										•		•		•					
White-chinned Prinia *Prinia leucopogon*			g	•	•		•												
Red-winged Warbler *Heliolais erythropterus*																			
Yellow-breasted Apalis *Apalis flavida*				•	•	•	•	•	•	•	•		•	•	•	•	•	•	•

15a Kafue Flats*	15b Lochinvar NP	15c Blue Lagoon NP	15d MCA	16 Nkanga R. Cons. Area	17 Mutulanganga	18 Lower Zambezi NP	19 Chisamba	20 Lukanga Swamp	21 Imanda	22 Chimfunshi W. O.	23 North Swaka	24 Wonder Gorge	25 Kasanka NP	26 Lavushi Manda NP	27 Mutinondo Wilderness	28a Bangweulu Swamps	28b Isangano NP	29 North Luangwa NP	30 Shiwa Ng'andu	31 Luapula Mouth	32 Lusenga Plain NP	33 Kalungwishi	34 Mweru Wantipa NP	35a Sumbu NP	35b Tondwa GMA	36 Saise River	37 Uningi Pans	38 Nyika NP	39 Mafinga Mountains	40 South Luangwa NP	41 Lukususi NP	42 Nyanje Hills	Luambe NP
•	•		•	•	•			•	•				•			•	•			•							•	•		•			
•	•	•	•	•	•	•	•	•	•				•			•				•							•			•		•	
•	•	•	•			•	•	•					•			•	•		•					•	•	•	•	•		•			
•	•	•	•					•								•	•		•					•	•		•			•			
•	•							•																	•					•			
•	•	•	•	•	•			•																						•			
•			•			•	•			•	•	•		•				•		•	•		•			•	•	•	•				
			•			•	•			•	•	•	•	•	•	•	•	•		•			•	•	•	•	•	•		•	•	•	•
								•	•			•	•	•	•	•	•			•			•	•	•					•			
•	•	•	•	•		•		•																						•			
•	•	•	•	•		•		•		•	•	•	•		•	•		•		•						•	•			•			
			•			•	•	•		•	•	•	•	•	•	•	•	•		•			•	•		•	•			•	•	•	
•	•	•	•	•		•	•		•				•		•	•		•		•			•	•	•	•		•	•	•		•	
•	•	•	•			•	•	•	•	•	•	•	•	•		•		•		•			•	•	•	•	•	•	•	•		•	
			•																									•					
						•	•			•			•					•		•			•	•				•		•			
			•			•	•			•	•	•	•	•		•				•			•	•				•		•	•	•	•
•		•		•		•	•			•		•	•			•				•							•			•			
•	•	•	•	•		•		•	•	•	•	•	•		•			•		•		•	•	•	•	•	•	•	•	•		•	
•	•	•	•	•		•	•	•	•			•						•		•		•	•	•	•	•	•	•	•	•		•	
																												•	•				
•	•	•	•	•				•					•			•				•							•						
																												•					
•	•	•	•	•		•	•			•	•					•	•	•		•			•	•	•	•	•			•	•		
•	•	•	•	•		•	•	•		•						•											•			•			
•	•	•	•	•		•	•	•	•			•						•					•	•			•			•		•	
								•												•			•	•		•				•			
•			•							•																•							
																												•					
•	•	•	•	•		•	•	•		•	•	•		•		•	•	•	•	•	•	•	•	•	•	•	•	•		•	•	•	
•	•		•			•	•	•										•								•				•	•	•	
								•	•			•		•	•	•				•		•								•		•	
												•	•	•	•	•			•										•				
•			•	•				•			•	•		•			•	•		•	•	•	•	•	•	•				•	•		
																												•	•				
•	•	•	•	•			•	•								•						•									•		
•	•	•	•	•		•	•	•		•	•		•			•	•	•	•	•	•	•	•	•	•		•	•	•		•		
												•																		•	•		•
•	•	•	•	•		•	•	•	•	•	•		•			•		•		•						•				•		•	•

	Globally threatened species	Restricted-range species	Biome-restricted species	1 Hillwood	2 Source of the Zambezi	3 Chitunta Plain	4 Jimbe Drainage	5a West Lunga NP	5b Lukwakwa GMA	6 Minyanya Plain	7 Mbulo Forest	8 Liuwa Plain NP	9 Barotse Floodplains	10 Sioma Ngwezi NP	11 Simungoma	12 Machile	13a Mosi-Oa-Tunya NP	13b Batoka Gorge	14 Kafue NP
Bar-throated Apalis *Apalis thoracica*			a																
Grey Apalis *Apalis cinerea*			a	•	•		•				•								
Buff-throated Apalis *Apalis rufogularis*			g	•	•		•												
Chestnut-headed Apalis *Apalis chapini*		RR	A																
Bleating Bush Warbler *Camaroptera brachyura*				•	•	•	•	•	•	•	•	•		•	•	•	•	•	•
Miombo Barred Warbler *Camaroptera undosa*			z	•		•	•		•					•					•
Marico Flycatcher *Bradornis mariquensis*															•	•	•		
Pallid Flycatcher *Bradornis pallidus*				•		•	•	•	•	•		•			•	•	•		•
Slaty Flycatcher *Melaenornis chocolatinus*			A																
Southern Black Flycatcher *Melaenornis pammelaina*				•	•	•		•		•	•	•		•	•	•	•		•
Collared Flycatcher *Ficedula albicollis*				•				•											•
Spotted Flycatcher *Muscicapa striata*				•	•	•	•	•	•	•	•	•	•	•	•	•	•	•	•
Dusky Flycatcher *Muscicapa adusta*				•	•		•		•										•
Swamp Flycatcher *Muscicapa aquatica*																			
Cassin's Grey Flycatcher *Muscicapa cassini*			g																
Ashy Flycatcher *Muscicapa caerulescens*				•	•	•	•	•	•					•	•	•	•		•
Sooty Flycatcher *Muscicapa infuscata*			g	•	•		•												
Böhm's Flycatcher *Muscicapa boehmi*			Z	•	•		•		•										•
Lead-coloured Flycatcher *Myioparus plumbeus*				•	•	•	•	•			•			•	•	•	•		•
Shrike-Flycatcher *Megabyas flammulatus*			g				•												
Cape Batis *Batis capensis*			a																
Margaret's Batis *Batis margaritae*			Z					•	•	•									
Chinspot Batis *Batis molitor*				•	•	•	•	•	•	•		•		•	•	•	•	•	•
Chestnut Wattle-eye *Dyaphorophyia castanea*			g				•												
Black-throated Wattle-eye *Platysteira peltata*				•	•		•	•		•	•	•							•
Livingstone's Flycatcher *Erythrocercus livingstonei*			e																
White-tailed Blue Flycatcher *Elminia albicauda*			z	•	•	•	•	•	•	•		•							•
White-tailed Crested Flycatcher *Elminia albonotata*			A																
Blue-mantled Flycatcher *Trochocercus cyanomelas*			e	•	•					•		•							
Paradise Flycatcher *Terpsiphone viridis*				•	•	•	•	•		•	•	•	•	•	•	•	•	•	•
Red-bellied Paradise Flycatcher *Terpsiphone rufiventer*			g	•	•		•												
African Hill Babbler *Pseudoalcippe abyssinica*			A																
Spotted Thrush-Babbler *Ptyrticus turdinus*							•												
Arrow-marked Babbler *Turdoides jardineii*				•	•	•	•	•	•			•		•	•	•	•		•
White-rumped Babbler *Turdoides leucopygia*				•				•	•	•		•		•	•	•			•
Miombo Grey Tit *Parus griseiventris*			Z	•	•		•	•		•	•			•					•
Southern Black Tit *Parus niger*														•	•	•	•	•	•
White-winged Black Tit *Parus leucomelas*				•	•	•	•	•		•									•
Rufous-bellied Tit *Parus rufiventris*			z	•	•	•	•	•	•	•	•	•		•					•
Grey Penduline Tit *Anthoscopus caroli*				•	•	•	•		•			•			•	•		•	•
Spotted Creeper *Salpornis spilonotus*				•	•		•	•	•	•									•
Red-and-blue Sunbird *Anthreptes anchietae*			Z	•			•												•
Violet-backed Sunbird *Anthreptes longuemarei*				•	•	•	•	•	•	•		•			•	•	•		•
Collared Sunbird *Anthreptes collaris*				•	•	•	•	•	•	•						•			•
Bates's Sunbird *Nectarinia batesi*			g	•	•		•												
Olive Sunbird *Nectarinia olivacea*				•	•		•		•		•								•
Green-headed Sunbird *Nectarinia verticalis*																			
Bannerman's Sunbird *Nectarinia bannermani*			Z	•	•		•					•							
Green-throated Sunbird *Nectarinia rubescens*			g	•			•												
Amethyst Sunbird *Nectarinia amethystina*				•			•	•	•	•	•	•			•	•	•		•
Scarlet-chested Sunbird *Nectarinia senegalensis*				•			•	•	•	•	•	•			•	•	•	•	•
Yellow-bellied Sunbird *Nectarinia venusta*				•	•		•	•	•		•			•			•		•
White-bellied Sunbird *Nectarinia talatala*			z	•				•	•	•		•		•	•	•		•	•
Oustalet's White-bellied Sunbird *Nectarinia oustaleti*			Z																
Greater Double-collared Sunbird *Nectarinia afra*			a																

15a Kafue Flats*	15b Lochinvar NP	15c Blue Lagoon NP	15d MCA	16 Nkanga R. Cons. Area	17 Mutulanganga	18 Lower Zambezi NP	19 Chisamba	20 Lukanga Swamp	21 Imanda	22 Chimfunshi W. O.	23 North Swaka	24 Wonder Gorge	25 Kasanka NP	26 Lavushi Manda NP	27 Mutinondo Wilderness	28a Bangweulu Swamps	28b Isangano NP	29 North Luangwa NP	30 Shiwa Ng'andu	31 Luapula Mouth	32 Lusenga Plain NP	33 Kalungwishi	34 Mweru Wantipa NP	35a Sumbu NP	35b Tondwa GMA	36 Saise River	37 Uningi Pans	38 Nyika NP	39 Mafinga Mountains	40 South Luangwa NP	41 Lukususi NP	42 Nyanje Hills	Luambe NP
														•	•				•									•	•				
									•	•	•		•			•			•		•	•						•	•				
																												•	•				
•	•	•	•	•	•		•	•	•	•								•	•		•			•	•	•			•	•		•	•
•	•		•	•			•	•		•	•		•	•	•	•		•	•		•	•				•			•	•			
•	•		•	•			•	•	•	•			•	•	•	•	•	•	•		•	•		•				•	•		•	•	•
•	•	•	•	•						•	•			•				•	•		•	•		•				•	•	•	•	•	
•	•	•		•										•				•	•										•				
•	•	•	•	•	•	•		•	•	•			•	•				•	•	•		•	•					•	•	•		•	
										•	•			•	•		•	•	•		•	•	•		•			•	•				
•	•	•		•				•							•			•	•			•			•								
•	•		•	•	•	•		•		•	•		•	•				•	•		•	•	•	•	•		•		•	•		•	•
•	•	•	•				•			•	•		•	•				•	•		•	•			•	•			•	•		•	•
																												•	•				
•	•	•	•	•	•	•		•					•	•		•	•	•	•		•	•		•	•	•		•	•	•	•	•	•
				•	•		•	•																						•			•
				•	•																											•	
													•		•	•			•		•							•	•				
																•			•		•							•	•				
								•	•	•		•		•																			
•	•	•	•	•	•	•		•		•		•	•	•		•		•	•		•	•	•	•	•	•	•	•	•	•	•	•	•
																												•					
•	•	•		•	•	•	•	•		•	•		•		•		•	•	•		•	•	•					•	•	•	•	•	•
•	•			•		•	•	•		•	•		•		•		•	•	•		•	•						•	•	•	•	•	•
		•		•		•	•	•			•	•	•		•			•												•	•		
•	•	•		•	•	•	•	•		•			•		•		•			•										•	•	•	
•		•		•		•	•	•		•	•		•		•		•	•	•		•	•	•							•	•	•	
			•			•		•		•		•		•					•		•	•							•	•	•	•	•
•	•		•	•		•		•		•	•	•	•	•		•		•	•				•		•				•	•	•	•	•
												•		•	•		•				•				•				•	•	•	•	•
•	•			•			•			•			•				•		•		•	•							•	•	•	•	•
									•		•	•		•				•	•		•	•	•					•	•				
													•		•				•		•							•	•				
•	•	•		•	•	•	•	•		•		•	•		•		•	•	•		•	•	•	•	•	•	•	•	•	•	•	•	•
•	•	•	•	•	•	•	•	•		•		•	•		•		•	•	•	•	•	•	•	•	•	•	•	•	•	•	•	•	•
•	•	•	•	•	•	•	•	•		•		•	•		•		•	•	•	•	•	•	•	•	•		•	•	•	•	•	•	•
•	•	•	•	•	•	•	•	•		•		•	•		•		•	•	•		•	•							•	•	•	•	•
																					•				•	•							
																													•				

	Globally threatened species	Restricted-range species	Biome-restricted species	1 Hillwood	2 Source of the Zambezi	3 Chitunta Plain	4 Jimbe Drainage	5a West Lunga NP	5b Lukwakwa GMA	6 Minyanya Plain	7 Mbulo Forest	8 Liuwa Plain NP	9 Barotse Floodplains	10 Sioma Ngwezi NP	11 Simungoma	12 Machile	13a Mosi-Oa-Tunya NP	13b Batoka Gorge	14 Kafue NP
Miombo Double-collared Sunbird *N. manoensis*			Z	•	•	•	•			•									•
Eastern Double-collared Sunbird *N. mediocris*			A																
Shelley's Sunbird *Nectarinia shelleyi*			Z					•											•
Marico Sunbird *Nectarinia mariquensis*													•	•	•	•	•		
Orange-tufted Sunbird *Nectarinia bouvieri*				•			•												
Purple-banded Sunbird *Nectarinia bifasciata*				•			•	•		•	•		•	•	•	•	•		•
Coppery Sunbird *Nectarinia cuprea*				•	•	•	•	•		•		•	•	•	•	•	•		•
Yellow-tufted Malachite Sunbird *N. famosa*			a																
Scarlet-tufted Malachite Sunbird *N. johnstoni*			A																
Bronze Sunbird *Nectarinia kilimensis*			A																
Yellow White-eye *Zosterops senegalensis*				•	•	•	•	•		•	•	•	•	•		•			•
European Golden Oriole *Oriolus oriolus*				•			•	•				•	•	•		•			•
African Golden Oriole *Oriolus auratus*				•	•	•	•	•	•	•	•	•		•	•	•	•		•
Eastern Black-headed Oriole *Oriolus larvatus*				•	•	•	•	•	•	•	•	•		•	•	•	•		•
Sousa's Shrike *Lanius souzae*			z	•	•	•	•	•	•	•		•							•
Red-backed Shrike *Lanius collurio*				•		•	•	•				•	•	•	•	•	•		•
Lesser Grey Shrike *Lanius minor*				•		•	•	•				•	•	•	•	•	•		•
Fiscal Shrike *Lanius collaris*				•		•	•	•	•	•	•	•		•	•	•	•		•
Magpie Shrike *Urolestes melanoleucus*														•	•	•			•
Brubru *Nilaus afer*				•	•	•	•	•	•	•	•	•		•	•	•	•	•	•
Southern Puffback *Dryoscopus cubla*				•	•	•	•	•	•	•	•	•	•	•	•	•	•	•	•
Marsh Tchagra *Tchagra minutus*				•			•	•	•										
Brown-headed Tchagra *Tchagra australis*				•	•	•	•	•	•	•		•		•	•	•	•		•
Black-crowned Tchagra *Tchagra senegalus*				•	•	•	•	•	•	•		•		•	•	•	•		•
Tropical Boubou *Laniarius aethiopicus*				•	•	•	•	•	•		•	•		•		•			•
Swamp Boubou *Laniarius bicolor*													•	•	•				
Crimson-breasted Shrike *Laniarius atrococcineus*														•	•	•			
Fülleborn's Black Boubou *Laniarius fuelleborni*		RR	A																
Orange-breasted Bush Shrike *Malaconotus sulphureopectus*				•	•	•	•	•	•	•	•	•	•	•	•	•	•		•
Many-coloured Bush Shrike *Malaconotus multicolor*				•	•				•	•		•							
Gorgeous Bush Shrike *Malaconotus viridis*							•	•											
Grey-headed Bush Shrike *Malaconotus blanchoti*				•	•	•	•	•	•	•	•	•		•	•	•	•		•
White Helmet Shrike *Prionops plumatus*				•	•	•	•	•	•	•	•	•		•	•	•	•		•
Retz's Red-billed Helmet Shrike *Prionops retzii*				•	•		•	•	•		•			•	•	•	•		•
Square-tailed Drongo *Dicrurus ludwigii*							•		•		•								
Fork-tailed Drongo *Dicrurus adsimilis*				•	•	•	•	•	•	•	•	•		•	•	•	•		•
Pied Crow *Corvus albus*				•				•		•				•	•	•	•		•
Black Crow *Corvus capensis*										•	•								
White-necked Raven *Corvus albicollis*																			
Waller's Red-winged Starling *Onychognathus walleri*			A																
Red-winged Starling *Onychognathus morio*																	•	•	
Slender-billed Chestnut-winged Starling *O. tenuirostris*			A																
Cape Glossy Starling *Lamprotornis nitens*															•	•			
Greater Blue-eared Starling *L. chalybaeus*										•			•	•	•				•
Lesser Blue-eared Starling *L. chloropterus*								•									•		•
Sharp-tailed Starling *Lamprotornis acuticaudus*			Z				•	•	•	•		•		•					
Splendid Glossy Starling *L. splendidus*				•	•	•	•	•			•								
Burchell's Starling *Lamprotornis australis*														•	•	•	•		
Southern Long-tailed Starling *L. mevesii*			Z												•	•		•	•
Violet-backed Starling *Cinnyricinclus leucogaster*				•	•	•	•	•		•	•	•		•	•	•	•		•
Sharpe's Starling *Cinnyricinclus sharpii*			A																
White-winged Starling *Neocichla gutturalis*			Z																
Wattled Starling *Creatophora cinerea*				•		•	•	•			•		•	•		•			•
Yellow-billed Oxpecker *Buphagus africanus*								•					•	•			•		•
Red-billed Oxpecker *Buphagus erythrorhynchus*								•					•	•			•	•	•

15a Kafue Flats*	15b Lochinvar NP	15c Blue Lagoon NP	15d MCA	16 Nkanga R. Cons. Area	17 Mutulanganga	18 Lower Zambezi NP	19 Chisamba	20 Lukanga Swamp	21 Imanda	22 Chimfunshi W. O.	23 North Swaka	24 Wonder Gorge	25 Kasanka NP	26 Lavushi Manda NP	27 Mutinondo Wilderness	28a Bangweulu Swamps	28b Isangano NP	29 North Luangwa NP	30 Shiwa Ng'andu	31 Luapula Mouth	32 Lusenga Plain NP	33 Kalungwishi	34 Mweru Wantipa NP	35a Sumbu NP	35b Tondwa GMA	36 Saise River	37 Uningi Pans	38 Nyika NP	39 Mafinga Mountains	40 South Luangwa NP	41 Lukususi NP	42 Nyanje Hills	Luambe NP

Species	Globally threatened species	Restricted-range species	Biome-restricted species	1 Hillwood	2 Source of the Zambezi	3 Chitunta Plain	4 Jimbe Drainage	5a West Lunga NP	5b Lukwakwa GMA	6 Minyanya Plain	7 Mbulo Forest	8 Liuwa Plain NP	9 Barotse Floodplains	10 Sioma Ngwezi NP	11 Simungoma	12 Machile	13a Mosi-Oa-Tunya NP	13b Batoka Gorge	14 Kafue NP
House Sparrow *Passer domesticus*				•													•		•
Grey-headed Sparrow *Passer griseus*				•				•				•	•				•		•
Southern Grey-headed Sparrow *Passer diffusus*														•	•	•	•	•	•
Yellow-throated Petronia *Petronia superciliaris*				•	•	•	•	•	•	•	•	•		•	•	•	•	•	•
Red-billed Buffalo Weaver *Bubalornis niger*														•	•	•	•		•
Scaly-feathered Finch *Sporopipes squamifrons*															•	•			
White-browed Sparrow-weaver *Plocepasser mahali*														•	•	•	•	•	•
Chestnut-mantled Sparrow-weaver *P. rufoscapulatus*			Z							•									
Baglafecht Weaver *Ploceus baglafecht*			a																
Bertram's Weaver *Ploceus bertrandi*			A																
Slender-billed Weaver *Ploceus pelzelni*																			
Spectacled Weaver *Ploceus ocularis*				•	•	•		•	•	•	•		•	•		•	•		•
Bocage's Weaver *Ploceus temporalis*			Z	•		•													
Large Golden Weaver *Ploceus xanthops*				•		•	•	•	•	•	•	•	•		•	•	•	•	•
Southern Brown-throated Weaver *P. xanthopterus*														•	•				
Lesser Masked Weaver *Ploceus intermedius*								•		•				•	•	•	•		•
African Masked Weaver *Ploceus velatus*										•			•	•	•	•	•	•	•
~ 'Katanga' Masked Weaver *Ploceus v. katangae*			Z																
Lake Tanganyika Weaver *Ploceus reichardi*		RR	Z																
Village Weaver *Ploceus cucullatus*				•		•		•	•	•	•		•		•	•	•		•
Yellow-backed Weaver *Ploceus melanocephalus*																			
Compact Weaver *Ploceus superciliosus*							•												
Dark-backed Weaver *Ploceus bicolor*				•	•		•	•	•		•								
Bar-winged Weaver *Ploceus angolensis*			Z							•									
Olive-headed Weaver *Ploceus olivaceiceps*	nt		Z																
Red-headed Weaver *Anaplectes melanotis*				•		•		•	•	•	•		•		•	•	•		•
Cardinal Quelea *Quelea cardinalis*																			
Red-headed Quelea *Quelea erythrops*				•		•	•	•	•	•			•						•
Red-billed Quelea *Quelea quelea*				•		•		•		•	•		•	•	•	•	•	•	•
Yellow-crowned Bishop *Euplectes afer*													•	•	•	•	•		•
Black-winged Red Bishop *Euplectes hordeaceus*								•											•
Red Bishop *Euplectes orix*													•	•	•	•	•		•
Yellow Bishop *Euplectes capensis*						•	•		•								•	•	•
Red-shouldered Whydah *Euplectes axillaris*								•	•	•			•	•	•	•			•
Yellow-mantled Whydah *Euplectes macrourus*				•		•	•	•		•	•						•	•	•
White-winged Whydah *Euplectes albonotatus*																•	•	•	•
Red-collared Whydah *Euplectes ardens*				•		•	•	•											•
Long-tailed Whydah *Euplectes progne*											•	•							
Marsh Whydah *Euplectes hartlaubi*				•		•		•		•									
Mountain Marsh Whydah *E. psammocromius*		RR	A																
Thick-billed Weaver *Amblyospiza albifrons*										•				•	•		•		•
Melba Finch *Pytilia melba*							•	•					•	•	•	•	•	•	•
Orange-winged Pytilia *Pytilia afra*				•	•	•	•	•	•						•	•			
Red-faced Crimsonwing *Cryptospiza reichenovii*			A																
Black-bellied Seed-cracker *Pyrenestes ostrinus*				•			•												
Red-throated Twinspot *Hypargos niveoguttatus*			z	•			•	•	•								•	•	•
Green Twinspot *Mandingoa nitidula*				•			•	•											
Brown Firefinch *Lagonosticta rufopicta*								•	•		•		•	•	•	•		•	
Red-billed Firefinch *Lagonosticta senegala*														•	•	•	•	•	•
Blue-billed Firefinch *Lagonosticta rubricata*				•	•	•	•												•
Jameson's Firefinch *Lagonosticta rhodopareia*														•	•	•	•	•	•
Black-tailed Grey Waxbill *Estrilda perreini*				•	•		•	•		•									
Swee Waxbill *Estrilda melanotis*			a																
Fawn-breasted Waxbill *Estrilda paludicola*				•	•	•	•	•	•										•
Orange-cheeked Waxbill *Estrilda melpoda*																			

15a Kafue Flats*	15b Lochinvar NP	15c Blue Lagoon NP	15d MCA	16 Nkanga R. Cons. Area	17 Mutulanganga	18 Lower Zambezi NP	19 Chisamba	20 Lukanga Swamp	21 Imanda	22 Chimfunshi W. O.	23 North Swaka	24 Wonder Gorge	25 Kasanka NP	26 Lavushi Manda NP	27 Mutinondo Wilderness	28a Bangweulu Swamps	28b Isangano NP	29 North Luangwa NP	30 Shiwa Ng'andu	31 Luapula Mouth	32 Lusenga Plain NP	33 Kalungwishi	34 Mweru Wantipa NP	35a Sumbu NP	35b Tondwa GMA	36 Saise River	37 Uningi Pans	38 Nyika NP	39 Mafinga Mountains	40 South Luangwa NP	41 Lukususi NP	42 Nyanje Hills	Luambe NP

	Globally threatened species	Restricted-range species	Biome-restricted species	1 Hillwood	2 Source of the Zambezi	3 Chitunta Plain	4 Jimbe Drainage	5a West Lunga NP	5b Lukwakwa GMA	6 Minyanya Plain	7 Mbulo Forest	8 Liuwa Plain NP	9 Barotse Floodplains	10 Sioma Ngwezi NP	11 Simungoma	12 Machile	13a Mosi-Oa-Tunya NP	13b Batoka Gorge	14 Kafue NP
Common Waxbill *Estrilda astrild*				•	•	•	•	•		•	•	•	•	•	•	•	•	•	•
Black-cheeked Waxbill *Estrilda erythronotos*															•	•	•		
Blue Waxbill *Uraeginthus angolensis*														•	•	•	•	•	•
Red-cheeked Cordon-bleu *Uraeginthus bengalus*				•			•	•	•										
Violet-eared Waxbill *Uraeginthus granatinus*				•				•		•					•	•	•		•
Zebra Waxbill *Amandava subflava*				•		•	•	•	•	•	•		•		•		•		•
Locust Finch *Paludipasser locustella*				•		•	•		•		•	•							•
Quailfinch *Ortygospiza atricollis*										•		•	•	•		•	•		•
Black-chinned Quailfinch *Ortygospiza gabonensis*				•		•	•	•	•										
Bronze Mannikin *Spermestes cucullata*				•		•	•	•	•	•	•	•	•	•	•		•		•
Red-backed Mannikin *Spermestes bicolor*				•			•	•											•
Magpie Mannikin *Spermestes fringilloides*								•											
Cut-throat Finch *Amadina fasciata*															•	•	•	•	•
Village Indigobird *Vidua chalybeata*													•		•	•	•		•
Dusky Indigobird *Vidua purpurascens*															•	•	•		•
Variable Indigobird *Vidua funerea*				•			•												•
Green Indigobird *Vidua codringtoni*			Z																
Pin-tailed Widow *Vidua macroura*				•		•	•	•		•		•	•	•	•	•	•		•
Shaft-tailed Widow *Vidua regia*								•					•		•	•	•		
Long-tailed Paradise Widow *Vidua paradisaea*							•								•	•	•		•
Broad-tailed Paradise Widow *Vidua obtusa*		z		•	•	•	•	•	•	•					•		•		
Parasitic Weaver *Anomalospiza imberbis*				•		•	•		•		•		•			•	•		•
Cape Canary *Serinus canicollis*		a																	
African Citril *Serinus citrinelloides*		a																	
Black-faced Canary *Serinus capistratus*		z		•	•		•		•										
Black-throated Canary *Serinus atrogularis*				•			•	•	•	•		•	•	•	•	•	•		•
Yellow-fronted Canary *Serinus mozambicus*				•			•	•	•	•	•	•	•	•	•	•	•	•	•
Yellow Canary *Serinus flaviventris*															•				
Bully Canary *Serinus sulphuratus*				•		•	•	•	•				•		•				•
Black-eared Seed-eater *Serinus mennelli*		Z		•	•	•		•		•									•
Streaky-headed Seed-eater *Serinus gularis*																			
Stripe-breasted Seed-eater *Serinus reichardi*				•	•					•				•					•
Streaky Seed-eater *Serinus striolatus*		A																	
Lark-like Bunting *Emberiza impetuani*																			
Cinnamon-breasted Rock Bunting *E. tahapisi*				•			•	•	•	•		•	•			•	•	•	•
Cape Bunting *Emberiza capensis*																			
Golden-breasted Bunting *Emberiza flaviventris*				•	•	•	•	•	•	•	•	•		•	•	•	•	•	•
Cabanis's Bunting *Emberiza cabanisi*				•	•	•	•	•		•		•	•						•
Site Totals				388	194	256	310	368	249	242	151	328	333	324	321	302	381	154	492

15a Kafue Flats*	15b Lochinvar NP	15c Blue Lagoon NP	15d MCA	16 Nkanga R. Cons. Area	17 Mutulanganga	18 Lower Zambezi NP	19 Chisamba	20 Lukanga Swamp	21 Imanda	22 Chimfunshi W. O.	23 North Swaka	24 Wonder Gorge	25 Kasanka NP	26 Lavushi Manda NP	27 Mutinondo Wilderness	28a Bangweulu Swamps	28b Isangano NP	29 North Luangwa NP	30 Shiwa Ng'andu	31 Luapula Mouth	32 Lusenga Plain NP	33 Kalungwishi	34 Mweru Wantipa NP	35a Sumbu NP	35b Tondwa GMA	36 Saise River	37 Uningi Pans	38 Nyika NP	39 Mafinga Mountains	40 South Luangwa NP	41 Lukususi NP	42 Nyanje Hills	Luambe NP
•	•	•	•	•			•	•	•	•	•	•		•		•	•	•		•			•		•			•	•	•		•	•	•	•
•	•	•	•	•	•	•	•	•	•		•	•				•	•	•										•		•		•	•	•	•	•
																						•			•	•	•								
•	•	•	•	•	•			•	•	•	•	•		•	•		•		•	•	•		•	•		•	•	•			•	•	•		
•	•	•	•	•						•		•		•	•	•		•			•		•			•								
•	•	•	•	•				•	•																								
										•	•			•	•			•															
•	•	•	•	•	•	•	•	•		•	•	•	•	•	•	•		•		•			•	•	•	•		•	•	•		•	•	•	
				•		•	•	•		•	•	•	•	•	•					•	•		•		•								•	
•	•			•							•			•		•						•												
•	•			•		•	•	•																						•				
•	•	•	•	•	•	•	•	•					•							•	•									•		•		
•	•	•	•	•		•	•	•			•		•							•			•							•		•		
•	•	•	•			•	•	•					•			•				•	•					•	•			•				
								•																					•	•				
																													•	•				
										•		•			•					•														
•	•	•	•	•			•	•						•						•	•		•				•							
•	•	•	•	•		•	•	•		•	•		•	•		•	•	•	•			•		•						•	•	•	•	
				•		•	•			•	•	•	•	•	•				•			•								•	•	•	•	
							•	•		•	•	•	•	•	•		•			•										•				
				•		•		•		•	•	•	•	•	•			•			•						•			•	•	•	•	•
				•		•	•			•	•	•	•	•	•			•			•									•		•	•	
																														•	•	•		
•	•		•					•																						•				
•	•	•	•	•		•	•	•		•	•	•	•	•	•			•		•			•		•			•		•		•	•	•
•	•	•	•	•		•	•	•		•	•	•	•	•	•	•		•		•			•		•			•		•	•	•	•	•
				•		•	•			•	•	•	•	•	•			•			•						•			•		•	•	
				•		•				•	•	•	•	•	•			•			•						•			•	•	•	•	
•	•		•					•						•				•			•		•			•				•		•	•	•
•	•	•		•	•	•	•	•					•		•		•			•	•	•	•	•	•			•		•	•	•	•	•

| 463 | 447 | 337 | 365 | 437 | 198 | 378 | 404 | 338 | 221 | 291 | 280 | 134 | 417 | 203 | 298 | 380 | 166 | 345 | 373 | 212 | 214 | 231 | 283 | 295 | 217 | 192 | 215 | 224 | 144 | 458 | 210 | 222 | 201 |

Appendix 2: Biome-restricted species

The following appendices list the species in each biome that occur in Zambia and whether they are endemic or near-endemic to that biome.

2.1 Afromontane (including Sub-Afromontane)

34 Endemics (A)
20 Near-endemics (a)
2   Sub-Afromontane endemics (s)

a   Red-breasted Sparrowhawk
a   Red-tailed Flufftail
a   Rameron Pigeon
a   Cinnamon Dove
A   Pink-breasted Turtle Dove
A   Mountain Nightjar
A   Scarce Swift
A   Bar-tailed Trogon
A   Moustached Green Tinkerbird
a   White-headed Saw-wing
A   Blue Swallow
A   Eastern Mountain Greenbul
a   Joyful Greenbul
a   Cabanis's Greenbul
a   Olive Thrush
A   Orange Thrush
A   White-chested Alethe
A   Starred Robin
s   Bocage's Robin
A   Sharpe's Akalat
A   Olive-flanked Robin
a   Cape Robin
A   Cinnamon Bracken Warbler
a   Evergreen Forest Warbler
s   Bamboo Warbler
A   Mountain Yellow Warbler
A   Yellow-throated Warbler
A   Brown Parisoma
a   Wing-snapping Cisticola
A   Wailing Cisticola
A   Churring Cisticola
A   Black-lored Cisticola
a   Bar-throated Apalis
a   Grey Apalis
A   Chestnut-headed Apalis
A   Slaty Flycatcher
a   Cape Batis
A   White-tailed Crested Flycatcher
A   African Hill Babbler
a   Greater Double-collared Sunbird
A   Eastern Double-collared Sunbird

a   Yellow-tufted Malachite Sunbird
A   Scarlet-tufted Malachite Sunbird
A   Bronze Sunbird
A   Fülleborn's Black Boubou
A   Waller's Red-winged Starling
A   Slender-billed Chestnut-winged Starling
A   Sharpe's Starling
a   Baglafecht Weaver
A   Bertram's Weaver
A   Mountain Marsh Whydah
A   Red-faced Crimsonwing
a   Swee Waxbill
a   Cape Canary
a   African Citril
A   Streaky Seed-eater

2.2 Eastern

6   Near-endemics (e)

e   Sombre Bulbul
e   Grey-olive Bulbul
e   White-throated Nicator
e   Eastern Bearded Scrub Robin
e   Livingstone's Flycatcher
e   Blue-mantled Flycatcher

2.3 Guineo-Congolian

17 Near-endemics (g)

g   White-spotted Flufftail
g   Afep Pigeon
g   Olive Long-tailed Cuckoo
g   White-bellied Kingfisher
g   Brown-eared Woodpecker
g   Honeyguide Greenbul
g   Bristlebill
g   Rufous Ant Thrush
g   White-chinned Prinia
g   Buff-throated Apalis
g   Cassin's Grey Flycatcher
g   Sooty Flycatcher
g   Shrike-Flycatcher
g   Chestnut Wattle-eye
g   Red-bellied Paradise Flycatcher
g   Bates's Sunbird
g   Green-throated Sunbird

2.4 Lake Victoria Basin

2   Near-endemics (l)

l   White-winged Warbler
l   Papyrus Yellow Warbler

2.5 Zambezian

39   Endemics (Z)
18   Near -endemics (z)

Z   Slaty Egret
Z   Dickinson's Kestrel
Z   Lilian's Lovebird
Z   Black-cheeked Lovebird
Z   Coppery-tailed Coucal
Z   Böhm's Bee-eater
z   Racket-tailed Roller
Z   Bradfield's Hornbill
Z   Pale-billed Hornbill
Z   Anchieta's Barbet
Z   Whyte's Barbet
Z   Miombo Pied Barbet
Z   Chaplin's Barbet
z   Black-backed Barbet
Z   Angola Lark
z   Red-throated Cliff Swallow
Z   Black-and-rufous Swallow
z   Fülleborn's Longclaw
Z   Grimwood's Longclaw
z   Miombo Rock Thrush
z   Kurrichane Thrush
Z   Boulder Chat
z   Collared Palm Thrush

Z   Central Bearded Scrub Robin
Z   Arnot's Chat
Z   Black-collared Eremomela
z   Red-capped Crombec
Z   Laura's Warbler
z   Black-tailed Cisticola
z   Tinkling Cisticola
Z   Chirping Cisticola
z   Miombo Barred Warbler
Z   Böhm's Flycatcher
Z   Margaret's Batis
z   White-tailed Blue Flycatcher
Z   Miombo Grey Tit
z   Rufous-bellied Tit
Z   Red-and-blue Sunbird
Z   Bannerman's Sunbird
z   White-bellied Sunbird
Z   Oustalet's White-bellied Sunbird
Z   Miombo Double-collared Sunbird
Z   Shelley's Sunbird
z   Sousa's Shrike
Z   Sharp-tailed Starling
Z   Southern Long-tailed Starling
Z   White-winged Starling
Z   Chestnut-mantled Sparrow-weaver
Z   Bocage's Weaver
Z   Lake Tanganyika Weaver
Z   Bar-winged Weaver
Z   Olive-headed Weaver
z   Red-throated Twinspot
Z   Green Indigobird
z   Broad-tailed Paradise Widow
z   Black-faced Canary
Z   Black-eared Seed-eater

Waterbirds in the Bangweulu Swamps (IBA 28). (Edmund Farmer)

Appendix 3: Globally important congregations – qualifying sites

	1% threshold	8 Liuwa Plain NP	9 Barotse Floodplains	12 Machile	14 Kafue NP	15 Kafue Flats	20 Lukanga Swamp	28 Bangweulu Swamps	31 Luapula Mouth	34 Mweru Wantipa NP	35.2 Tondwa GMA	37 Uningi Pans	40 South Luangwa NP
(i) >1% of biogeographic population of congregatory waterbird													
Great Crested Grebe	10											●	
Reed Cormorant	10,000					●		●					
White Pelican	1,500					●		●		●			
Rufous-bellied Heron	1,000							●					
Black Egret	1,000	●				●							
Slaty Egret	40	●											
Yellow-billed Egret	1,000												
Openbill Stork	4,000					●	●	●					
African Spoonbill	1,000					●							
Fulvous Whistling Duck	2,500					●							
White-faced Whistling Duck	10,000					●							
White-backed Duck	180					●						●	
Egyptian Goose	3,500					●							
Spur-winged Goose	2,500					●		●					
Knob-billed Duck	3,000					●							
African Pygmy Goose	1,750					●							
Yellow-billed Duck	1,000												
Red-billed Teal	7,500					●							
Hottentot Teal	1,000					●							
Southern Pochard	500					●			●				
Wattled Crane	80	●	●			●		●					
Southern Crowned Crane	580												
Common Pratincole	2,000	●				●							
Black-winged Pratincole	370	●											
Kittlitz's Plover	1,000					●							
Caspian Plover	480					●		●					
Long-toed Plover	380					●							
Black-tailed Godwit	1,000					●							
Marsh Sandpiper	750												
Little Stint	10,000					●							
Curlew Sandpiper	3,300					●							
Ruff	20,000					●							
Grey-headed Gull	3,000												
Whiskered Tern	100					●							
African Skimmer	100					●							
(ii) >1% global population of terrestrial sp.													
Black-cheeked Lovebird	100			●	●								
Southern Carmine Bee-eater	6,000												●
(iii) regularly holds >20,000 waterbirds													
		●				●		●					

Appendix 4: Taxonomic notes

The taxonomy followed in this book is based largely on Dowsett & Forbes-Watson (1993) with a few minor changes made to keep in line with the forthcoming Zambian avifauna (Dowsett, Aspinwall & Dowsett-Lemaire in prep., Leonard 1998c, 1999a, 2001). This treatment differs in a few ways to that used by Fishpool & Evans (2001). These differences and a few other points are outlined below. It should be noted that in some cases the differing treatment affects the placement of a species within both the Restricted-range and the Biome-restricted categories.

Green-backed Heron *Butorides striata* - genus is feminine, note new spelling.

Egyptian Goose *Alopochen aegyptiaca* - genus is feminine, note new spelling.

Black-breasted Snake Eagle *Circaetus pectoralis* - treated as a race of Short-toed Eagle by Fishpool & Evans but split here.

Kurrichane *Turnix sylvaticus* Black-rumped Buttonquails *T. hottentottus* - genus is masculine, note new spellings.

Bronze-naped Pigeon *Columba delegorguei* - treated as two species by Fishpool & Evans: Western *C. iriditorques* and Eastern Bronze-naped Pigeons *C. delegorguei,* with the former included in the Guineo-Congolian biome.

Green Pigeon *Treron calvus* - genus is masculine, note new spelling.

Lilac-breasted *Coracias caudatus*, Racket-tailed *C. spatulatus* and Purple Rollers *C. naevius* - genus is masculine, note new spellings.

White-chested Tinkerbird *Pogoniulus makawai* - treated as a species by Fishpool & Evans and listed as a restricted-range species (s052) and included in the Zambezian biome. Listed by BirdLife International (2000) as data deficient. Not treated as a valid species in this book.

House Martin *Delichon urbicum* - genus is neuter, note new spelling.

Yellow-streaked Bulbul *Phyllastrephus flavostriatus* - treated as two species by Fishpool & Evans with Zambian form known as Sharpe's Greenbul *P. alfredi* and listed as a restricted-range species (EBA 105) and included in the Afromontane biome.

Bristlebill *Bleda syndactylus* - genus is masculine, note new spelling.

Rufous Ant Thrush *Stizorhina fraseri* - Fishpool & Evans place this species in the genus *Neocossyphus*.

Stonechat *Saxicola torquatus* - genus is masculine, note new spelling.

Mocking Chat *Myrmecocichla cinnamomeiventris* - Fishpool & Evans place this species in the genus *Thamnolaea*.

Broad-tailed Warbler *Schoenicola platyurus* - Fishpool & Evans use *S. brevirostris* but here it is lumped with the Indian taxa.

Tit-babbler *Sylvia subcaerulea* - genus is feminine, note new spelling.

Neddicky *Cisticola fulvicapilla* - treated as two species by Fishpool & Evans: Piping Cisticola *C. fulvicapilla* and Tabora Cisticola (or Long-tailed Neddicky) *C. angusticaudus*, the latter included in the Zambezian biome. Here the two are considered conspecific and the correct spelling of the long-tailed race is *C. f. angusticauda*.

Red-winged Warbler *Heliolais erythropterus* - genus is masculine, note new spelling.

Slaty Flycatcher *Melaenornis chocolatinus* - treated as three species by Fishpool & Evans, the Zambian form known as White-eyed Slaty Flycatcher *Dioptrornis fischeri.*

White-tailed Crested Flycatcher *Elminia albonotata* - Fishpool & Evans place this species in the genus *Trochocercus*.

White-rumped Babbler *Turdoides leucopygia* - treated as two species by Fishpool & Evans with the Zambian form known as Angola Babbler *T. hartlaubii* and included in the Zambezian biome. Genus is feminine, note new spelling.

Greater Double-collared Sunbird *Nectarinia afra* - the various forms across eastern and southern Africa are treated as several species by Fishpool & Evans, in which Zambian birds are called *N. prigoginei* in error for *N. graueri*, which in turn is the name given to the same birds in the Malawi chapter of the same book. All forms are treated as races of *N. afra* here.

Marsh *Tchagra minutus* and Black-crowned Tchagras *T. senegalus* - genus is masculine, note new spellings.

Gorgeous Bush Shrike *Malaconotus viridis* - Fishpool & Evans place this species in the genus *Telophorus*.

African Masked Weaver *Ploceus velatus* - treated as two species by Fishpool & Evans: African Masked Weaver *P. velatus* and Katanga Masked Weaver *P. katangae*, the latter included in the Zambezian biome.

Red-headed Weaver *Anaplectes melanotis* - *melanotis* replaces *rubriceps* as it is the earliest name.

Brown Firefinch *Lagonosticta rufopicta* - treated as two species by Fishpool & Evans: Brown *L. nitidula* and Bar-breasted Firefinches *L. rufopicta*, with the former included in the Zambezian biome.

Locust Finch *Paludipasser locustella* - now considered to be in monotypic genus. Fishpool & Evans used the genus *Ortygospiza*.

mannikins *Spermestes spp.* - Fishpool & Evans used the genus *Lonchura*.

Parasitic Weaver *Anomalospiza imberbis* - now considered to be a member of the *Viduidae* so is placed at the end of that family.

African Citril *Serinus citrinelloides* - treated as three species by Fishpool & Evans: African *S. citrinelloides*, Western *S. frontalis* and Eastern Citrils *S. hypostictus*.

Streaky Seed-eater *Serinus striolatus* - treated as two species by Fishpool & Evans: Streaky *S. striolatus* and Yellow-browed Seed-eaters *S. whytii*, the latter listed as a restricted-range species (EBA 105).

Little Bittern

7. Useful Information

Travel Tips

■ Maps and navigation

Excellent, detailed maps (both 1:250,000 and 1:50,000) covering the whole of Zambia can be bought cheaply from the main government map office at the Ministry of Lands in Lusaka. This is in the basement of Mulungushi House by the corner of Independence Avenue and Nationalist Road. These maps are highly recommended, particularly if you intend to visit some of the more remote sites in this book. In a few areas, driving off-road is inevitable and in such situations a GPS (Global Positioning System) can be very useful.

■ Transport

Zambian public transport services connect most of the main regional towns and taxis are often a reasonably cheap way of reaching areas nearby. Hitch-hiking is acceptable, though lifts are normally paid for.

■ Driving

Reaching many of the sites listed in this book will require you to use your own vehicle. Zambia's road network is not well developed. Tarred roads, in varying states of repair, connect many District headquarters (Bomas) to Provincial headquarters, all of which are linked by tarred road to Lusaka. Most other roads are gravel or dirt. Getting to most sites will involve driving on such roads and therefore high-clearance vehicles are important. Four-wheel drive is less important, though it is necessary when driving on Kalahari sand in the west and occasionally during the rains when driving conditions can become difficult. Note that some roads become impassable at this time. Driving at night is not recommended. Although supplies are reasonably widespread, it is worth carrying some extra fuel and a selection of spares and tools (including a tyre mending kit and pump), particularly when visiting more remote areas. Gravel roads can be deceptive and the smoother they are, the faster you are tempted to drive and the greater the chance of skidding, so avoid driving faster than 60kph on gravel roads. In sand, four-wheel drive is important. To avoid getting stuck, keep your revs high, maintain your momentum, avoid braking suddenly and lower your tyre pressures if necessary. A common problem in the early dry season when the grass is tall is engine overheating due to the radiator filling up with grass seeds. In such situations, ensure you remove seeds at regular intervals. If you are exploring distant, remote and unfamiliar areas, it is advisable to travel with two vehicles.

■ Camping

Outside National Parks, it is generally possible to camp anywhere and Zambia abounds in beautiful, wild and remote areas that are perfect for camping. However, where appropriate, it is advisable and polite to seek the permission of the local landowner or village head before doing so. A courteous explanation of the reasons for your visit will invariably grant you a warm welcome. If you intend to leave a camp or vehicle whilst you explore on foot, it is wise to leave somebody to act as a guard. Employing a full-time guard and helper on a trip into the bush is highly recommended. Furthermore, local villagers are often keen to act as guides or porters if you choose to travel any distance on foot. Suitable payment should be negotiated, but not issued, before departure.

■ Health and safety

Guidebooks and travel companies provide all the advice one needs regarding health and safety matters when travelling in Zambia, but three points warrant repetition here. Firstly, be aware of the risk of malaria, seek current advice, sleep in a sealed tent or under a net and take prophylaxis as recommended. Secondly, always ensure you have sufficient water and some method of purification (even if this comprises a pot and a campfire for boiling). Thirdly, do not under-estimate the danger of being in the sun too long. Ensure you use sun-block and drink plenty of water.

Lions on the Busanga Plains, Kafue NP (IBA 14)
(Heather Tyrrell/Sunvil Africa)

The Zambian Ornithological Society

The Zambian Ornithological Society (ZOS) was formed in 1969 and its object is to stimulate interest in and to further the study and conservation of wild birds in Zambia. In addition to publishing information on Zambian birds, the Society is engaged in a number of ornithological projects, environmental education, conservation and recreational activities. Any interested person can become a member of ZOS.

ZOS is the affiliate of BirdLife International in Zambia and ZOS co-ordinates the Zambian Important Bird Area programme.

All Zambian bird records are gratefully received and data from IBAs concerning all flora and fauna are especially welcome.

For more information contact:

The Zambian Ornithological Society, P.O. Box 33944, Lusaka, Zambia

zos@zamnet.zm

BirdLife International

Over 1200 bird species across the world are currently under threat of extinction in some way - over 12% of the world's birds. BirdLife International is a worldwide Partnership of conservation organisations that seeks to conserve all wild bird species and their habitats. Through this work, BirdLife strives to protect the world's biological diversity and supports the sustainable use by humans of the world's natural resources. BirdLife is present in 103 territories worldwide.

Birdlife's long-term aims are to:
- prevent the extinction of any bird species
- maintain and where possible improve the conservation status of all bird species
- conserve and where appropriate improve and enlarge sites and habitats important for birds
- help, through birds, to conserve biodiversity and to improve the quality of people's lives
- integrate bird conservation into sustaining people's livelihoods.

The Partnership works towards these aims by:
- identifying priorities for bird and biodiversity conservation through scientific research and data collection
- promoting conservation action for birds, using the Partnership to create a strong voice for birds to governments and other decision makers - the Partnership can save many more birds than any one organisation can in isolation
- carrying out national programmes of actions for birds, including managing species, sites and habitats, education and enlisting public support.

BirdLife is now the world's leading authority on the status of the world's birds, their habitats and the urgent problems that face them.

The Partnership is co-ordinated by staff in Cambridge (UK), Wageningen (The Netherlands), Nairobi (Kenya), Quito (Ecuador), Tokyo (Japan), Brussels (Belgium) and Amman (Jordan).

For more information contact:

BirdLife International　　　　Tel: +44 1223 277318
Wellbrook Court　　　　　　Fax +44 1223 277200
Girton Road　　　　　　　　Email: birdlife@birdlife.org.uk
Cambridge　　　　　　　　　www.birdlife.net
CB3 0NA
United Kingdom